Plumbing

Revision Guide

John Thompson

www.harcourt.co.uk

✓ Free online support
✓ Useful weblinks
✓ 24 hour online ordering

01865 888058

Heinemann

From Harcourt

Heinemann Educational Publishers
Halley Court, Jordan Hill, Oxford OX2 8EJ
Part of Harcourt Education

Heinemann is the registered trademark of
Harcourt Education Limited

© Harcourt Education Ltd 2007

First published 2007

10 09 08 07
10 9 8 7 6 5 4 3 2 1

British Library Cataloguing in Publication Data is available
from the British Library on request.

ISBN: 978 0 435 402 14 3

Copyright notice

Edited by Jane Anson & Bridget Lawless

Produced by HL Studios, Long Hanborough, Oxford

Original illustrations © Harcourt Education Limited, 2007

Illustrated by HL Studios, Long Hanborough, Oxford

Cover design by GD Associates

Printed in the UK by Scotprint

Cover photo © Harcourt Education Limited/Gareth Boden; Getty Images/PhotoDisc

Every effort has been made to contact copyright holders of material reproduced in
this book. Any errors or omissions will be rectified in subsequent printings if notice
is given to the publishers.

Contents

Acknowledgements

The author and publisher would like to thank the following individuals and organisations for permission to reproduce photographs:

All pictures **Harcourt Education Ltd/Gareth Boden** apart from the following:

Alamy Images/Sciencephoto p 40 middle; **ARCO** p 11; **Construction Photography** pp147 top left, 147 top right, 149; **Dreamstime/Chris Green** p 7; **Dreamstime** p148 top right; **Ginny Stroud-Lewis** pp 10, 126 left, 127 top left; **Harcourt Education Ltd/Jules Selmes** p 20; **Kevan Thomas/JTL** pp 274 bottom, 305; **Lead Sheet Association** p189; **MorgueFile/Ronnie Bergeron** p 39; **Photos.com** pp 12, 13; **Science Photo Library** p147 bottom left; **Topfoto** p148 top left

Introduction

The aim of the Guide is to –

- complement *Plumbing NVQ and Technical Certificate Level 2* and *Plumbing NVQ and Technical Certificate Level 3*
- provide essential revision support and preparation to plumbing students who are taking the multiple choice examinations as part of the Level 2 & 3 Certificates in Plumbing and the Plumbing NVQs at Level 2 & 3.

The guide is structured in a chapter based format that mirrors the units from the Level 2 and 3 certificates. Each chapter contains the essential job knowledge requirements of the particular subject in a condensed yet easy to read format. As you progress through the Guide you will notice some duplication of content from chapter to chapter e.g. key information sources. This ensures that each chapter can be used on a stand alone basis, largely without reference to other chapters, so easing the revision process for you. The end of each chapter contains a number of short answer and multiple choice type questions covering the key points of learning. You are encouraged to complete these as a check on your progress and to confirm your understanding of the content of the chapter.

The last section of the Guide contains answers to the revision questions together with an explanation of the answer, in order to assist with points that you may not fully understand.

More in-depth feedback on particular subjects can be made by referring to *Plumbing NVQ and Technical Certificate Level 2* and *Plumbing NVQ and Technical Certificate Level 3* .

Good luck with your examination preparations.

01 Health and safety

By the end of this chapter you should be able to demonstrate understanding of the following health and safety topics. This will assist you in completing the knowledge assessment in the Safety in Plumbing Activities Unit of the Level 2 Certificate in Basic Plumbing Studies:

- Health and safety legislation
  - Health and safety policy
  - The Health and Safety at Work Act
  - The Construction, Design and Management Regulations
  - Construction (Health, Safety and Welfare Regulations)
  - The Reporting of Injuries, Diseases and Dangerous Occurrences Regulations
  - The Electricity at Work Regulations
  - The Fire Precautions Act
  - The Safety Signs and Signals Regulations
  - The Provision and Use of Work Equipment Regulations
  - The Manual Handling Operations Regulations
  - The Personal Protective Equipment at Work Regulations
  - The Lifting Operations and Lifting Equipment Regulations
  - The Work at Height Regulations
  - The Control of Substances Hazardous to Health Regulations
  - The Control of Asbestos at Work Regulations
  - The Control of Lead at Work Regulations.
- Personal safety and the safety of others
  - Using personal protective equipment
  - Electrical power tools
  - Work at heights
  - Work in excavations
  - Work with hazardous substances
  - Work with LPG gas heating equipment
  - Fire safety
  - First-aid arrangements.

Main items of health and safety legislation in plumbing

Health and safety policy

There are two main organisations that deal with health and safety:

- the Health and Safety Commission (HSC) – responsible for health and safety regulation in the UK, i.e. setting policy
- the Health and Safety Executive – responsible for enforcement of the health and safety regulations.

The Health and Safety at Work Act (HASAWA)

The Health and Safety at Work Act (HASAWA) 1974 lays down responsibilities for employers, the self-employed, manufacturers or suppliers of materials and employees in carrying out work safely.

Main employer responsibilities under the regulations are:

- the provision and maintenance of plant and systems of work that are safe and without risk to health (this includes the supply of all necessary personal protective equipment)
- safety in the use, handling, storage and transport of articles and substances
- the provision of information, instruction, training and supervision as necessary to ensure the health and safety at work of employees
- the provision of access to and exit from the workplace that is safe and without risk
- the provision of adequate facilities and arrangements for welfare at work.

Main employee responsibilities under the regulations are:

- take reasonable care at work of your own health and safety and that of others who may be affected by what you do or do not do
- do not intentionally or recklessly interfere with or misuse anything provided for your health and safety
- co-operate with your employer on health and safety matters. Assist your employer in meeting their statutory obligations
- bring to your employer's attention any situation you think presents a serious and imminent danger
- bring to your employer's attention any weakness you might spot in their health and safety arrangements.

HASAWA in addition requires that employers:

- produce a health and safety policy statement when employing five or more operatives
- undertake risk assessments associated with the work activities carried out, identify safety control measures necessary to minimise the risks,

Did you know?

HASAWA also provides protection for members of the public against unsafe work activities.

Did you know?

Young or inexperienced workers are particularly at risk when carrying out plumbing work. That's why health and safety regulations place emphasis on employers providing sufficient information, instruction and training before the work begins.

inform employees of the risk and train them in the effective application of the control measures and periodically review the risk assessments
- the risk assessments must be in writing if more than five persons are employed by the firm.

Types of safety controls used by firms

There are a variety of control systems that can be used by plumbing companies:

- risk assessments – an identification of the work activities carried out by the plumbing firm that could cause harm to staff or others. In undertaking the risk assessment, safety control measures are then identified that will minimise the risk to the lowest practicable level; the firm's employees are then advised of the results of the risk assessment, including the safety controls that have to be applied when carrying out the work
- method statements – firms produce method statements for high-risk activities such as working at height to line a flue system. The method statement draws together the findings/control measures of all the risk assessments associated with the activity, such as working at heights, working with flue-liner materials, working with mortar mixes, etc. into one simple document which is provided to employees, co-contractors, etc. to provide guidance on how the work activity will be carried out
- permit-to-work systems – a permit-to-work system is used as a safety control for very high-risk or potentially fatal activities. The permit-to-work is essentially a fixed checklist of tasks that must be completed before an activity is carried out. The permit-to-work will usually be counter-signed by a supervisory level company official. A permit-to-work system could apply to high-risk activities such as working with gas heating equipment in potential fire-risk areas, working on electrical equipment and working in confined spaces such as sewers.

The Construction Design and Management Regulations

The main objectives are:

- the CDM Regulations are aimed at improving the overall management and co-ordination of health, safety and welfare throughout all stages of a construction project to reduce the large numbers of serious and fatal accidents and cases of ill health that occur every year in the construction industry
- the CDM Regulations place duties on all those who can contribute to the health and safety of a construction project. The Regulations place duties upon clients, designers, contractors and planning supervisors, and require the production of certain documents – the health and safety plan and the health and safety file.

Did you know?

Risk assessment should be carried out before the work is started.

Did you know?

CDM Regulations
These apply to large construction projects, requiring all those involved in the project to safely work together.

Construction (Health, Safety and Welfare Regulations)

These regulations lay down key requirements for the safety of construction sites:

- generally ensuring a safe place of work
- precautions against falls from height or into excavations
- protection against falling objects
- protection against structural collapse (while work is taking place), i.e. the building falling down!
- safeguards when working in excavations
- prevention of drowning (falling into water)
- provision of safe traffic routes (on sites)
- prevention and control of emergencies (site emergency evacuation procedures, etc.)
- provision of welfare facilities – WCs, washing facilities, canteens/rest areas, shower facilities (if required)
- provision of site-wide issues – clean and tidy sites, adequate lighting, constant and fresh air supply, etc.
- training, inspection and reports – proper training of staff, use of properly trained staff to do the work, proper supervision of staff and monitoring the work carried out by staff to ensure it is carried out in a safe manner.

The Reporting of Injuries, Diseases and Dangerous Occurrences Regulations (RIDDOR)

RIDDOR lays down the requirements for the employer reporting the following to the Health and Safety Executive:

- injuries – fatalities (including members of the public) or injuries resulting in three days off work
- diseases – if a doctor advises that an employee is suffering from a work-related disease listed under RIDDOR
- dangerous occurrences – something that happened that could have resulted in a reportable injury, e.g. the collapse of an excavation.

Detail of reportable accidents should be forwarded by the employer to the HSE on form F2508. If a fatality is being reported then this must take place within ten days.

The HSE will make a decision based on the report form forwarded regarding the level of investigation and subsequent action required, which may include legal action for breaches of health and safety regulations.

A firm should maintain an accident book for recording detail of all types of injury that occur while carrying out work, however minor. The accident book is used by the employing firm to monitor the level of accidents that occur and establish whether any additional safety controls are required to do the work.

Definition

Accident book – a document where detail of all accidents is recorded, no matter how minor.

If an accident occurs (whether it is RIDDOR reportable or not), an employee may be required to complete an accident report form; this should preferably be completed by the injured employee as soon after the accident as possible. If it is completed by a third party, then the employee must carefully check that the details are a clear identification of the events that took place, as once signed, an accident report could be used in legal proceedings!

The Electricity at Work Regulations

These regulations lay down requirements for safe working with electricity:

- duties of those involved in undertaking the electrical work
- systems, work activities and protective equipment
- strength and capability of electrical equipment
- insulation, protection and placing of conductors
- earthing and other suitable precautions
- integrity of reference conductors
- making connections
- means for protecting from excess current
- means of cutting off the supply and isolation
- precautions for work on equipment made dead
- work on or near live conductors
- working space, access and lighting
- competence to prevent danger and injury.

Did you know?

Many of the requirements of the Electricity at Work Regulations are absolute: failure to comply could lead to legal action.

The Fire Precautions Act

Employers' duties include safety in relation to fire hazards, both from the work processes and activities carried out, and general fire safety in the workplace. Employers must carry out a fire-risk assessment. The risk assessment is to enable employers to identify and then take steps to eliminate, reduce or control safety risks (including risks from fire) to make sure that no one gets hurt or becomes ill. Where more than 20 people are employed at a property, the property will require a fire certificate from the local enforcing authority.

General fire precautions that an employer may provide include:

- means of detecting and giving warning in case of fire
- escape routes
- fire-fighting equipment
- training of staff in fire safety.

The Safety Signs and Signals Regulations

The Safety Signs and Signals Regulations provide a standardised approach for displaying safety signs in the workplace.

	Prohibition signs	Mandatory signs	Warning signs	Information or safe condition signs
Shape:	Circular	Circular	Triangular	Square or rectangular
Colour:	Red borders and cross bar. Black symbols on white background	White symbol on blue background	Yellow background with black border and symbol	White symbols on green background
Meaning:	Shows what must NOT be done	Shows what must be done	Warns of hazard or danger	Indicates or gives information on safety provision
Example:	No smoking	Wear eye protection	Danger electric shock risk	First-aid facilities

Figure 1.1 Safety signs

The Provision and Use of Work Equipment Regulations (PUWER)

The Regulations require risks to persons' health and safety from equipment that they use at work, to be prevented or controlled. Work equipment includes all tools (power or hand) and work equipment such as threading machines and bending machines. In general terms, the Regulations require that equipment provided for use at work is:

- suitable for the intended use
- safe for use, maintained in a safe condition and, in certain circumstances, inspected to ensure this remains the case
- used only by people who have received adequate information, instruction and training
- accompanied by suitable safety measures, e.g. protective devices, markings, warnings.

The Manual Handling Operations Regulations

These Regulations lay down requirements for moving loads by hand; this could involve pushing, pulling, lowering the load, etc. The following control measures are identified in the Regulations:

- avoid hazardous manual handling operations so far as is reasonably practicable, for example by using a mechanical lifting aid such as a sack trolley to move the load
- make a suitable and sufficient risk assessment of any hazardous manual handling operations that cannot be avoided
- reduce the risk of injury from those operations so far as is reasonably practicable, providing such controls as training staff in safe or kinetic lifting techniques.

Did you know?

The safe condition of hand tools such as hammers and spanners is covered by PUWER.

Did you know?

The use of abrasive wheels is now covered by PUWER; all staff using such equipment need to be properly trained, informed and supervised.

Did you know?

Cartridge-fixing devices

PUWER has laid down new requirements for the use of cartridge-fixing devices, based on a risk assessment of the work and proper training of staff; any age restriction detailed in previous legislation has been removed.

A risk assessment for manual handling will include taking into account the following five factors:

- the task
- the load
- the working environment
- individual capability (of the person carrying out the lifting)
- other factors, for example use of protective clothing.

The Personal Protective Equipment at Work Regulations (PPE)

PPE is defined in the Regulations as 'all equipment (including clothing affording protection against the weather) which is intended to be worn or held by a person at work and which protects him against one or more risks to his health or safety', e.g. safety helmets, gloves, eye protection, high-visibility clothing, safety footwear and safety harnesses. The provision of respiratory and hearing protection is the subject of separate legislation.

The main requirement of the PPE at Work Regulations is that personal protective equipment is to be supplied and used at work wherever there are risks to health and safety that cannot be adequately controlled in other ways.

The Regulations also require that PPE:

- is properly assessed before use to ensure it is suitable
- is maintained and stored properly
- is provided with instructions on how to use it safely
- is used correctly by employees.

Under the Regulations, PPE must be supplied by the employer on a free-of-charge basis to the employee.

Figure 1.2 Example of a mechanical lifting device (sack trolley)

The Lifting Operations and Lifting Equipment Regulations

The Regulations aim to reduce risks to people's health and safety from lifting equipment (such as cranes, pulleys, ropes, slings, etc.) provided for use at work. Generally, the Regulations require that lifting equipment provided for use at work is:

- strong and stable enough for the particular use and marked to indicate safe working loads
- positioned and installed to minimise any risks
- used safely, i.e. the work is planned, organised and performed by competent people
- subject to ongoing thorough examination and where appropriate, inspection by competent people.

The Work at Height Regulations

The Work at Height Regulations apply to all work at heights where there is a risk of a fall liable to cause personal injury. They place duties on employers, the self-employed, and any person who controls the work of others. The Regulations require duty holders to ensure that:

- all work at height is properly planned and organised
- all work at height takes account of weather conditions that could endanger health and safety
- those involved in work at height are trained and competent
- the place where work at height is done is safe
- equipment for work at height is appropriately inspected
- the risks from fragile surfaces are properly controlled
- the risks from falling objects are properly controlled.

The Control of Substances Hazardous to Health Regulations (COSHH)

The Regulations require employers to control exposure to hazardous substances to prevent ill health. They have to protect both employees and others who may be exposed by complying with the Control of Substances Hazardous to Health Regulations. To comply with the COSHH regulations an employer must:

- assess the risks
- decide what precautions are needed
- prevent or adequately control exposure
- ensure that control measures are used and maintained
- monitor the level of exposure to the substance
- carry out appropriate health surveillance where required
- prepare procedures to deal with accidents and emergencies
- ensure employees are adequately informed, trained and supervised.

The Control of Asbestos at Work Regulations

Key requirements of the Regulations are:

- asbestos insulating materials or linings of white, blue and brown asbestos must only be removed/worked on by licensed contractors
- on identifying high-risk white, blue or brown asbestos materials, work must be stopped in order that a risk assessment may be conducted in relation to working with/or working in the proximity of the asbestos material
- work with asbestos material must be the subject of a risk assessment with appropriate control measures provided, e.g. on-site washing facilities
- asbestos materials must be properly disposed of in approved packaging (preventing the spread of any fibres) and asbestos materials must be properly disposed of at approved waste sites
- operatives undertaking work in the proximity of asbestos or in the removal of asbestos materials must be properly informed, instructed and trained.

Work with asbestos cement-based materials does not present as high a risk and this may be carried out by non-licensed contractors provided a risk assessment is undertaken and effective control measures are used to prevent the spread of any material and to protect workers, e.g. the use of effective protective clothing and respiratory protective equipment.

The Control of Lead at Work Regulations

The regulations require the following to be put in place:

- duties – employers and employees alike are responsible for protecting themselves and others on premises where leadwork is being carried out or who are likely to be exposed to lead from that work
- training – operatives should be provided with proper information, instruction and training on the safe use of lead
- assessment of risk of exposure – if there is a risk of exposure to lead in a form that may be inhaled or ingested, the level of risk must be assessed and the findings properly recorded. Correct working practices and proper controls should be established and appropriate protective and safety equipment provided before the work proceeds
- control measures – the employer and employee must ensure, as far as is reasonably practical, that all measures are taken to restrict and control exposure
- protective clothing – each employee should be provided with and should wear adequate protective clothing
- respiratory equipment and ventilation – suitable masks or respiratory equipment must be provided and used where there is a risk of exposure to airborne lead dust or fumes.

Did you know?

There are three types of asbestos, commonly known as chrysotile, amosite and crocidolite (white, blue and brown respectively).

Safety tip

Asbestos can be deadly!
Breathing in asbestos dust can lead to chronic (long-term) fatal diseases such as mesothelioma (cancer of the inner chest lining), lung cancer or asbestosis (scarring of the lung).

Did you know?

Asbestos is more likely to be found in properties built before 1980.

Did you know?

Use of lead
Plumbers may encounter old lead pipe in buildings or sheet lead used as weatherproofing on the outside of buildings.

- washing facilities and canteen areas – adequate washing and changing facilities should be provided. Washing of the hands is essential before eating, drinking or smoking and before leaving the workplace. Food and drink should not be consumed in any area where leadwork is being carried out. Washing of hands and face and changing of contaminated clothes should take place before entering canteen areas
- spread of contamination – both employer and employee should take such steps as are reasonably practicable to prevent lead contamination from spreading beyond the workplace or storage area
- waste and scrap – old lead sheet being replaced should be removed with care. Scrap and dust should be taken to approved collectors to facilitate recycling. Vehicles transporting scrap and dust should be thoroughly washed and cleaned after use
- lifting lead – lead is heavy. Proper lifting equipment and additional staff should be available and always used to ensure the safety of operatives lifting and moving lead sheet
- medical surveillance – the blood lead level of operatives regularly working with lead should be monitored at regular intervals
- maintenance records – it is the duty of the employer to provide and maintain adequate records that show details of risk assessments, information and training provided, precautionary measures taken, medical surveillance and ventilation and respiratory equipment provided.

Personal safety and the safety of others

Using personal protective equipment

Eye protection

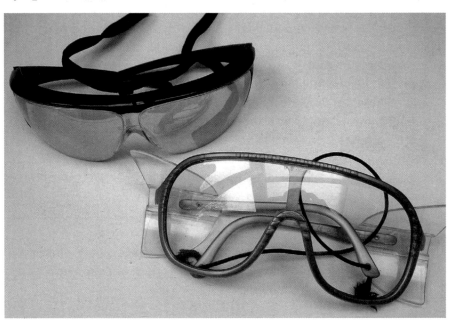

Figure 1.3 Example of eye protection (safety glasses)

Eye protection comes in the form of:

- safety glasses – a typical application could be lead welding
- safety goggles – these provide a higher level of protection than safety glasses, as they should fit closely to the face
- welding goggles – these include specialist coloured lenses.

Eye protection that is used to guard against the threat created by flying objects should include lenses that are of the high-impact resistant type.

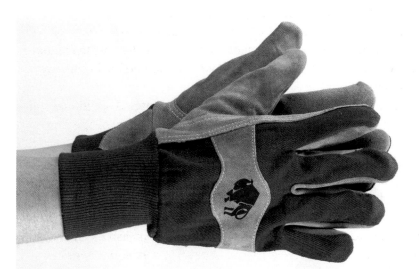

Figure 1.4 General-purpose gloves

Hand protection

Hand protection that is normally used in plumbing includes:

- general-purpose gloves – these help protect against cutting or puncture wounds; an example of their use could be lifting concrete blocks or lifting steel tube
- specialist gloves – these are typically used to deal with hazardous substances such as dry ice used in pipe-freezing applications
- rubber gloves – these help protect against contact with used soil and waste systems and sanitary appliances.

Gloves also provide protection against a disease known as dermatitis, which is caused by the hands coming into contact with materials classed as irritants.

Head protection

It is a mandatory requirement to wear a safety helmet on new-build and major construction sites. In addition a safety helmet will need to be worn when work is taking place at heights or above the point where you are working – that could be in a trench. A safety helmet must:

- be properly adjusted to fit you
- be replaced if it becomes defective or damaged.

Did you know?
Rubber gloves help protect against a very serious disease primarily spread by rats, known as Weil's Disease (Leptospirosis).

Remember
Barrier creams
These are often used as a form of hand protection to prevent substances entering through cuts in the skin. A typical application is when handling sheet lead.

Foot protection

It is important to wear adequate foot protection for the majority of plumbing installation work carried out, owing to the weight of the components used. Adequate foot protection (which can be in the form of a safety shoe) usually includes:

- metal toe protection
- strong rubber soles and sturdy uppers.

In addition, some forms of safety footwear can provide additional protection against electric shock.

Knee protection

Figure 1.5 Knee pads

Plumbing work can include a certain amount of kneeling, which can lead to painful conditions such as Housemaid's Knee. Knee protection should therefore be considered which can be in the form of:

- external fasten-on knee pads, or
- knee pads built into workwear.

Protective overalls

Protective overalls, alternatively known as workwear, will need to be worn for most plumbing activities. Protective overalls are available in many styles, they essentially:

- protect the worker's clothing
- assist in preventing the removal of hazardous or contaminated substances from the work-site.

Disposable overalls are available and tend to be used for more specialist activities such as work on drains or sewers, or working with asbestos.

Did you know?

When working on many construction sites you will be required to wear a high-visibility jacket or vest to guard against site traffic dangers.

Ear protection

Ear protection should be worn when working in noisy areas or with equipment that generates high levels of noise. Ear protection is usually in the form of:

- ear defenders, or
- ear plugs.

The need to wear ear protection may be indicated by safety signs or through risk assessments carried out by construction or plumbing companies.

Respiratory protection

There are many forms of respiratory protection:

- simple dust mask – an example of its use could be working with loft insulation
- cartridge-type respirator – these can guard against a range of substances such as high levels of dust or fumes; different disposable cartridges are required to protect against different types of substances
- full breathing apparatus – usually used in specialist work in confined spaces such as drains or sewers.

Electrical power tools

The Electricity at Work Regulations lay down the requirements for electrical power tool safety. Here are some of the key requirements:

- low-voltage (cordless) power tools tend to be preferred to their mains-fed counterparts, as they are safer to use
- on construction sites in particular, 110-volt power tools tend to be used as an alternative to the standard 240 volts found in domestic properties – lower voltage is again safer by design
- all power tools should be visually checked for signs of damage before they are used – damaged cables, plugs and casings, etc. Damaged tools must be taken out of service until disposed of or repaired
- all power tools should be subject to a Portable Appliance Test (PAT), this is a periodic check for electrical safety by a competent trained person, the recommended frequency of test for construction applications is three-monthly; all tested appliances should include a test label showing that the appliance has passed the test and the date of the next test should be displayed
- a Residual Current Device (RCD) is a type of electrical protection device that can be used in the electrical circuit supplying the power tool in order to provide added protection to the user
- power tools, e.g. circular saws, may also be supplied with adjustable guards. The tool must always be used with the guard firmly in place – it's there to protect the user! On no circumstances must it be removed to make the job easier.

> **Safety tip**
> Ear protection will normally be required when using a large hammer drill, or possibly a circular saw.

> **Safety tip**
> Full breathing apparatus must only be used by operatives who have been fully trained in its use and application.

> **Did you know?**
> In order to provide a 110-volt power supply, a transformer will be required to change the voltage of the circuit – 110-volt supplies are colour coded yellow.

Work at heights

Ladders

Falls from ladders account for a high proportion of accidents in the construction industry. Here are some of the key points of ladder safety:

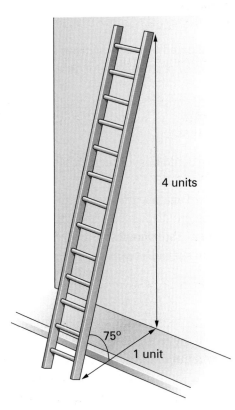

4 units

75°

1 unit

Figure 1.6 Angle of ladder from the building

- a ladder should only be used to gain access to a work platform such as a scaffold, or for short-term work of usually less than 30 minutes' duration. Work at heights for longer periods should be carried out using safer access equipment such as a mobile tower scaffold
- there are a number of classes of ladder – Class 1 (industrial ladders) should normally be used for construction activities
- the ladder should be checked for safety and for visible signs of damage each time it is used – if in any doubt the ladder should not be used
- care must be taken when transporting the ladder around site and when erecting it
- the ladder must only be used on firm, level ground.
- if the ladder is to be used on or near a public footpath or road, there should be barriers around its base
- the angle of the ladder to the building should be 75°, or 4 up to 1 out
- the ladder should preferably be secured at the top and bottom, footing by a co-worker is an alternative method of securing at the bottom
- the top of the ladder should project 1m or approximately five rungs above a working platform or roof access point.

Roof ladders

Roof ladders are only suitable for short-term working, e.g. limited work on chimney stacks. Here are the key points of roof ladder safety:

- the ladder should be properly manufactured and tested for safety, home-made roof ladders are not acceptable
- carry out a visual inspection of the roof ladder each time it is used, to make sure it is in a safe condition
- the supports under the ladder must rest fully on the roof when fitted
- the ladder should be the correct length for the roof
- the ladder gaining access to the roof ladder must be securely fixed at the top and be sited next to the roof ladder
- the use of roof ladders usually requires two people, one to work on the roof, the other to safely provide tools and equipment.

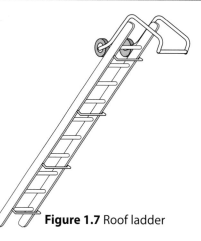

Figure 1.7 Roof ladder

Step ladders

Step ladders are commonly used by plumbers; the following covers the key points related to their use:

- the step ladder should be visually checked for any signs of damage before use
- the step ladder should only be used on firm, level ground so that it may fit squarely on the ground
- the step ladder must be properly extended at all times and be of the correct height for the job, working off the top step is not permitted as it is unsafe
- step ladders are only suitable for relatively short-term working, for longer-term working a safer alternative would be to use access equipment such as a mobile elevated work platform (scissor lift).

Did you know?

A full chimney scaffold system is required to carry out more long-term work activities such as the installation of sheet lead weatherings to a chimney.

Mobile tower scaffolds

Mobile tower scaffolds provide a safer solution to gaining access for plumbers working at heights. Here are the main points associated with their use:

- they should only be erected by those who have been properly trained
- a tower scaffold over 2m from floor height must be fitted with toeboards and guard rails. A guardrail must be fitted between 0.4m and 0.7m above the working platform. The hand rail should be no more than 910mm above the working platform
- when in use, the scaffold wheels must be locked
- the platform should not be moved whilst holding people or materials
- the tower must be stable, there should normally be a 1:3 base to height ratio
- outriggers may be used to increase the height of the tower and its stability
- towers above 9m in height should be firmly secured to the building
- towers should not normally be used above 12m in height
- the tower should include a purpose-designed ladder securely fixed inside the structure to gain access to the working platform.

Safety tip

Harnesses

It is common practice for employers to require those working long-term at height to wear a harness, anchored whilst working to a point such as the scaffold, to protect against falls.

Work in excavations

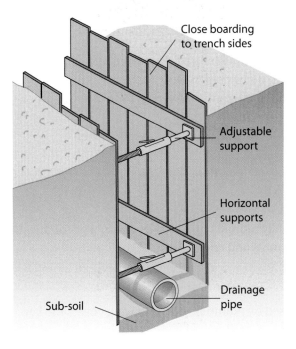

Figure 1.8 Shoring of trenches

Work in excavations can be particularly hazardous and therefore a risk assessment must be conducted before the work is commenced to ensure that proper control measures are applied to safely do the work. The following are typical measures:

- an assessment of the ground material type must be undertaken to determine the need for shoring
- only properly trained plumbers must work in excavations
- any work carried out should be in pairs, one plumber carrying out the work in the trench, the other passing tools and materials
- fencing must be erected around trenches over 2m in depth to prevent persons falling into the trench
- material removed from the trench should be safely stored so that it may not fall back into the trench
- barriers such as vehicle stop-blocks may need to be used where dump trucks are being used in the vicinity of the trench, this is to prevent the vehicle falling into it.

Work with hazardous substances

Work with hazardous substances falls under the COSHH Regulations, requiring an assessment of the risk of using the substance to be carried out before the work begins. Manufacturers of substances in support of the risk assessment process are required to adequately package the product,

TOXIC

HARMFUL

CORROSIVE

IRRITANT

OXIDISING

EXTREMELY FLAMMABLE

Figure 1.9 Categories of hazardous substance

showing the dangers that the substance presents, and provide instruction on its use. Hazardous substances tend to fall into the following categories:

- toxic – poisonous liquids and gases
- harmful – a general term that is used as a classification for many hazardous substances
- corrosive – products that may corrode such as bleach
- irritant – products, such as loft insulation, that may cause irritation to parts of the body
- extremely flammable – substances that may lead to fire, e.g. LPG
- oxidising – these are substances that remove oxygen from the surrounding air, e.g. ABS cement for jointing plastic pipework.

Work with LPG gas heating equipment

Work with gas heating equipment can be a particularly dangerous activity as it can lead to:

- risk of fire through the ignition of combustible substances in the vicinity of the work area. Many insurance companies, in order to provide insurance to plumbing companies, require them to cease using LPG gas heating equipment at least 1 hour before leaving a site, so that any burning material is seen to be properly extinguished, and on high-risk jobs plumbing contractors may be asked to use a permit-to-work system.

- Risk of gas leakage:
  - gas heating equipment must be properly assembled and checked for leaks using soap solution
  - leaking gas, as it is heavier than air, will sink to the lowest points in a room, with the ability to form an explosive concentration
  - storage of cylinders should preferably take place in an open-air secure compound, all cylinder valves should be fully closed and protective dust caps should be in place, cylinders should be kept in an upright position.

Transportation of LPG

Transportation of LPG falls under the Packaged Goods Regulations. Specific measures required to be in place include:

- labels on vehicles to identify hazardous LPG contents
- two dry-powder fire extinguishers must be carried on the vehicle
- it is preferable that the storage cabin of the vehicle is ventilated, this is essential if large quantities are carried
- if significant quantities are being transported the driver will need to undertake special training in order to receive a TREMCARD, necessary for moving significant quantities of LPG.

Fire safety

Plumbers need to be aware of the fire risk that may be associated with their work. Some of the dangers are:

- igniting combustible materials in the location of hot working
- faults caused by electrical work.

In order for a fire to occur the following need to be present:

- fuel – combustible material
- oxygen – air supply
- heat – ignition source.

Figure 1.10 The fire triangle

Remove any of these three items and fire will not take place.

Classes of fire

Fires are classed into groups according to the fuel type:

- Class A – fires involving solid materials, extinguished by water
- Class B – fires involving flammable liquids, extinguished by foam or carbon dioxide
- Class C – fires involving flammable gases, extinguished by dry powder
- Class D – fires involving flammable metals, extinguished by dry powder.

Fire-fighting equipment

There are a variety of different types of fire-fighting equipment. In undertaking plumbing work you are more likely to come across the fire extinguisher as the main source of protection; here are some points to its use:

- an extinguisher should be kept in the immediate work area when hot working, e.g. using LPG gas heating equipment
- a fire extinguisher should only be used when it is safe to do so, personal safety must come before attempts to contain a fire
- fire extinguishers should only be used by those trained in their use
- the following shows the colour coding for extinguishers for dealing with the different types of fire.

Remember

Keeping the workplace tidy of combustible materials or protecting combustible materials when using a blow torch will remove a component from the fire triangle and fire will not start.

Type of extinguisher	Colour code	Main use
Water	Red	Wood, paper or fabrics
Foam	Cream	Petrol, oil, fats and paints
Carbon dioxide	Black	Electrical equipment
Dry powder	Blue	Liquids, gases, electrical equipment

Figure 1.11 Fire extinguisher colour code

Action in the event of a fire

Your employer will normally have procedures for actions in the event of a fire; if it's a larger site then the client or main contractor will have their own procedures. Whatever the case, you must be familiar with those procedures, which will include:

- the various fire escape routes from the building
- the location of designated safe fire assembly points, which you must go to in the event of an emergency
- if you discover the fire
  - raise the alarm immediately
  - leave by the nearest exit
  - ensure that the emergency service is summoned.

Summoning the emergency services

These procedures apply to a range of different type of emergencies including fire:

1. find a telephone in a safe environment, well away from the emergency
2. dial the emergency service number: 999

3. keep calm, and when asked by the operator, give the name of the emergency service required, e.g. fire

4. when you get through, provide the location of the emergency first and then the nature of the emergency, e.g. fire in cellar; also provide details of any specialist hazards that the emergency service may encounter, e.g. storage of flammable liquids

5. when the call has been completed, ensure that someone is available to meet the emergency service and to show them the location of the incident.

First-aid arrangements

The requirements for providing first aid are laid down in the First Aid at Work Regulations, which require the employer to conduct a risk assessment of first-aid arrangements for the company, this will include establishing the need for first-aid kits and trained first-aiders.

The following shows the typical contents of a first-aid kit.

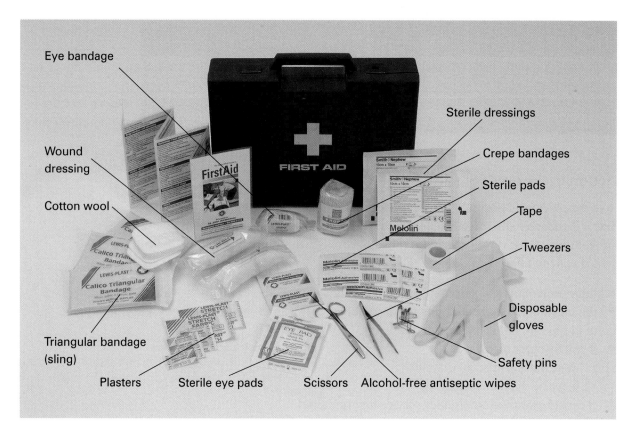

Figure 1.12 First-aid kit

The kit should only contain items for first aid, no other medicines must be stored in the kit (this includes headache tablets). Where plumbers are working in domestic properties it is normal practice for a first-aid kit to be provided on each company vehicle and for each plumber to receive a basic level of first-aid training.

Typical areas for first-aid training

A typical first-aid course for a plumber will cover:

- electric shock – removing the casualty from a live supply using an insulating material such as wood; Cardio Pulmonary Resuscitation (CPR); dealing with unconsciousness (no sign of breathing)
- placing the injured person in the recovery position (so long as they do not bear signs of a damaged back), and keeping them warm until the emergency services arrive
- treatment for burns – flood the injury with cold clean water
- dealing with broken bones – prevention of movement at the site of the injury until it is properly secured and supported
- substance in the eye – bathing the eye in eye-wash (clean water).

Short answer questions

1. Under the Health and Safety at Work Act, an employer must prepare a health and safety policy statement when employing how many operatives?
2. When should a risk assessment of a work activity be carried out?
3. What type of stringent safety control system may be required when 'hot working' indoors with LPG gas heating equipment?
4. Under RIDDOR, what type of injuries must be reported to the HSE?
5. What type of device may be used as a safer alternative to manual handling?
6. What action must be taken on finding white asbestos insulating material on site?
7. What type of safety equipment may be required in order to carry out lead welding indoors for prolonged periods of time?
8. What type of safety glasses are required when working with a percussion drill?
9. What action should be taken if a safety helmet is found to be cracked?
10. What is the safest type of power tool to use on construction sites?

Multiple-choice test

1. Who is responsible for providing PPE to plumbers?
   a) *The plumber*   c) *The employer*
   b) *The site agent* d) *The architect*

2. The Health and Safety at Work Act applies to which of the following working on construction sites?
   a) *All operatives*   c) *Site visitors only*
   b) *Management staff only*   d) *Full-time staff only*

3. The organisation responsible for the enforcement of health and safety legislation is called the:
   a) *Health & Safety Enforcer*
   b) *Health & Safety Commission*
   c) *Health & Safety Directorate*
   d) *Health & Safety Executive*

4. Blue asbestos material found on construction sites must be removed by:
   a) *Licensed contractors*
   b) *Any operative finding it*
   c) *Any operative finding it who has the correct PPE*
   d) *Supervisory staff who have the correct PPE*

5. The provision of which of the following is a requirement of the Construction (Health, Safety and Welfare) Regulations?
   a) *First-aid equipment*
   b) *Personal protective equipment*
   c) *Canteen facilities*
   d) *Accident book*

6. What type of PPE is essential when lead welding outdoors for short periods of time?
   a) *Full breathing apparatus*
   b) *Dust mask*
   c) *Safety glasses*
   d) *Welding mask*

7. What type of hand protection will provide the highest level of protection when working on used soil pipework?
   a) *Barrier cream*
   b) *Rubber gloves*
   c) *General-purpose gloves*
   d) *Leather gloves*

8. Which disease can be spread by rats via the drainage system?
   a) *Hodgkin's disease*
   b) *Parkinson's disease*
   c) *Weil's disease*
   d) *Smithson's disease*

9. What is the minimum level of respiratory protection required when removing a solid fuel fire back boiler?
   a) *No protection is required*
   b) *Full breathing apparatus*
   c) *Half-face respirator*
   d) *Dust mask*

10. A 110-volt transformer for use on a construction site is colour coded:
    a) *Blue*   c) *Green*
    b) *Red*   d) *Yellow*

11. What is the recommended interval for a Portable Appliance Test (PAT) on a circular saw used on a construction site?
a) 1 month   c) 6 months
b) 3 months   d) 12 months

12. Before working with a mains-fed power tool:
a) It should be visually inspected for signs of damage
b) It should be stripped down and serviced
c) It must only be used if operating at 440V
d) All guards must be removed so the tool can be used properly

13. What type of ladder should normally be used for construction work?
a) Domestic class   c) Class 2
b) Class 1   d) Class 3

14. The approximate angle that a ladder should be set to a building is:
a) 45°   c) 75°
b) 60°   d) 90°

15. What is the approximate height that a ladder should project above a working platform?
a) 500mm   c) 1000mm
b) 750mm   d) 1200mm

16. What item of equipment must be fitted to a mobile tower scaffold that is 2m or more above floor level?
a) Rails   c) Shoring
b) Outriggers   d) Pulley system

17. The COSHH regulations control the use of:
a) Personal protective equipment
b) Electricity at work
c) First aid at work
d) Hazardous substances

18. Propane is classified as what type of substance?
a) Toxic
b) Corrosive
c) Extremely flammable
d) Irritant

19. What type of injury may occur when coming into contact with an LPG cylinder where gas is being drawn from it at too high a rate?
a) Freeze burns
b) Dermatitis
c) Broken bones
d) Cuts through flying metal

20. The following safety sign (white symbol on a blue background) is an example of a:

a) Prohibition sign c) Warning sign
b) Mandatory sign   d) Information sign

21. The safety sign below identifies which of the following hazards:

a) Hard hats must be worn
b) Danger electric shock
c) Wear eye protection
d) No smoking

22. Burning wood is classed as which type of fire?
a) Class A   c) Class C
b) Class B   d) Class D

23. What type of fire extinguisher is marked with a cream panel?
a) Water   c) Dry powder
b) Carbon dioxide d) Foam

24. What is the first item of information to provide to the emergency service when reporting an emergency?
a) The location of the incident
b) The number of people involved
c) Nature of any injuries
d) The caller's name

25. On finding a fire in a building a plumber's first action should be to:
a) Raise the alarm   c) Leave the building
b) Fight the fire   d) Carry on working

26. Which of the following should not be kept in a
first-aid kit?
a) Sterile dressings   c) Eye dressing
b) Plasters   d) Headache tablets

27. A first-aider should treat a severe burn by:
a) Washing it with cold water
b) Washing it with hot water
c) Coating the burn with antiseptic cream
d) Coating the burn with after-sun lotion

28. A person being electrocuted should be removed
from the live supply by means of:
a) A length of metal pipe
b) Length of dry timber
c) Length of wet timber
d) Scaffold pole

29. The danger from 'mushrooming' on cold
chisels is:
a) Damage to the hammer head
b) Flying splinters
c) Hearing damage
d) Respiratory damage

30. Abrasive wheels may only be used by plumbers:
a) Who are over 18 years of age
b) Who are over 21 years of age
c) Who have been properly trained and
instructed in their use
d) Who are deemed to be registered abrasive
wheel contractors

By the end of this chapter you should be able to demonstrate understanding of the following working relationships topics which will assist you in completing knowledge assessment in the Effective Working Relationships Unit of the Level 2 Certificate in Basic Plumbing Studies:

- Sources of information:
  - Technical standards
  - Site information sources.
- Company structure:
  - Sole trader
  - Partnerships
  - Limited companies (Private)
  - Public Limited Companies (PLCs)
- The construction management team
- Other occupations involved in the construction process
  - Architect
  - Project manager/clerk of works
  - Structural engineer
  - Building surveyor
  - Building control officer
  - Water regulations inspector
  - Facilities manager
  - Building services engineer
- Communicating with customers/co-contractors:
  - Methods of communication
  - Communication and job responsibilities of plumbing staff
  - Resolving disputes.

Sources of Information

There are a number of information sources that plumbers may have to use to obtain the necessary detail to undertake their work.

Technical Standards

- Building Regulations – these lay down the statutory requirements that must be followed when carrying out installation, commissioning and maintenance work on a variety of plumbing systems. The responsibility for monitoring compliance with the Building Regulations is that of the Local Authority. Guidance on the Building Regulations is produced in the form of a series of Approved Documents, these may be freely downloaded from the DCLG website at www.communities.gov.uk.
- Water Regulations – these lay down the statutory requirements that must be carried out when installing, commissioning and maintaining water systems. Responsibility for monitoring compliance with the Water

Did you know?

Building Regulations cover the key safety requirements for the installation of most systems that a plumber installs.

Did you know?

British Standards

These are produced by the British Standards Institution.

Regulations is given to the local water undertakers. Water Regulations documentation can be freely downloaded from www.defra.gov.uk.

- British Standards – these support statutory documentation such as the Building Regulations, providing greater detail on installation requirements. Although British Standards are not statutory (legal) documents, they can be used in potential legal action relating to defective systems installation.
- Manufacturer instructions – these are provided by appliance or component manufacturers to outline the installation, commissioning and maintenance requirements of their products. Manufacturer instructions usually take precedent over British Standards but should not conflict with Building or Water Regulations, which are statutory (legal) requirements.

Site information sources

The following outlines the range of site information sources that are commonly used:

- site plans – site or location plans show the location of the building or site to adjacent roads, properties or services
- building plans – these are the detailed plans for the property, showing key building details such as location of doors/windows, room sizes, boiler position, etc
- services layout plans – these are detailed drawings of the building services, such as pipe runs, position and layout
- job specification – a job specification is often provided as support to building plans; it details items such as the type, size and position of key components such as boilers
- work programme – a work programme details the point at which various aspects of plumbing work fit into the overall construction programme, e.g. first fix hot and cold water system
- bill of quantities – a bill of quantities details the quantities of components and materials used on a job.

Company structure

There are a number of different types of structure that companies may adopt in the plumbing industry.

Sole trader

One person looks after the business and typically will deal with all the management jobs including pricing the work, arranging the jobs, organising materials, managing any staff and dealing with the paperwork including the accounts. Despite the name, a sole trader may employ staff.

Did you know?

A delivery note is usually provided by a merchant when delivering materials and an advice note is usually provided when payment of an invoice has been received.

Did you know?

Approximately 80% of businesses in the plumbing industry employ between 1 and 4 people.

The sole trader is entitled to all the profits from the business, however he/she is personally responsible for all the debts of the business should it fail. A sole trader type of company is more suited to businesses with low numbers of staff.

Partnerships

Two or more people own the business and share the management workload. Partnerships are particularly suited to two or more different tradespeople working together, e.g. a builder and a joiner. Similar to the sole trader, the partners are entitled to all the profits from the business, however they are also responsible for all the debts of the business should it fail. Again, a partnership is more suited to businesses with low numbers of staff.

Limited Companies (Private)

A limited company must be registered with Companies House. A number of directors are appointed (essentially the owners of the business), they each have shares in the company. The owners are not personally liable for business debts should the business fail (other than the assets that they have put into the business), there is however more complexity involved in the running of the business. Limited company status is more suited to medium to larger plumbing businesses.

Public Limited Companies (PLCs)

These are the largest plumbing companies. They trade their shares on the stock market, provided they have a share capital above £50,000.

The construction management team

The following chart details a range of construction management people that may be encountered in the running of plumbing jobs.

Job	Main responsibilities	Other aspects
Contracts manager	• Responsible for running several contracts • Works closely with construction management team • Link between the other sections of the business and the MD/CEO • Makes sure the job is running to cost and programme	• Office-based • Some site visits

Figure 2.1 Construction management role (*continues overleaf*)

Job	Main responsibilities	Other aspects
Construction manager (Site manager, site agent or building manager)	• Responsible for running a construction site or a section of a large project • Develops strategy for the project • Plans ahead to solve problems before they happen • Makes sure site and construction processes are carried out safely • Communicates with clients to report progress and seek further information • Motivates workforce	• On larger contracts, the construction manager could have the support of supervisory staff
Site supervisor (Foreman)	• Responsible for the trade supervisor and trade operatives • Supervises the day-to-day running of the job	• Reports to the construction manager
Trade supervisor (Charge hand)	• Supervises operatives from a specific trade (e.g. bricklayers)	• Reports to the site supervisor • This role is usually only needed on very large jobs
Planner	• Ensures the project is completed on time and within budget • Reschedules projects as necessary • Works closely with estimators to establish working methods and costs • Plans the most effective use of time, people, plant and equipment • Schedules events in a logical sequence • Visits sites to monitor progress	• Works with construction manager
Site engineer	• Ensures the technical aspects of the construction projects are correct • Sets out the site so that things are in the right place • Interprets original plans, documents and drawings • Liaises with workforce and subcontractors on practical matters • Checks quality • Refers queries to the relevant people • Provides 'as built' details	• Key role in ensuring things are built correctly and to the right quality • May supervise parts of the construction

Figure 2.1 Construction management role (*continued*)

Job	Main responsibilities	Other aspects
Quantity surveyor – contractor (Commercial manager, Cost consultant)	• Advises on and monitors the costs of a project • Allocates cost effectively, including work to specialist subcontractors • Manages costs • Negotiates with client's quantity surveyor on payments and final account • Arranges payments to subcontractors	
Buyer (Procurement officer)	• Identifies suppliers of materials • Obtains quotations from suppliers • Purchases all the construction materials needed for a job • Negotiates on prices and delivery • Resolves quality or delivery problems	• Liaises with other members of the construction team
Estimator	• Calculates how much a project will cost including plant, materials and labour • Identifies the most cost-effective construction methods • Establishes costs for labour, plant, equipment and materials • Calculates cash flows and margins • Seeks clarification on contract issues affecting costs	• This information is used as the basis of the tender the contractor submits to a client prior to getting the contract
Accounts department	• Invoices for work carried out • Pays staff, suppliers and subcontractors • Produces financial reports and budget forecasts • Deals with Inland Revenue and Customs and Excise (VAT)	• Works with Construction manager
Administration department	• Works closely with accounts to keep financial records • Deals with customers and other enquiries • Records and files work records, time sheets etc.	• Most systems are electronic, but companies often keep hard-copy records

Figure 2.1 Construction management role (*continues overleaf*)

Job	Main responsibilities	Other aspects
Human resources department	• Oversees employees' training and development needs • Assists with the recruitment and selection of new staff • Deals with industrial relations matters.	• Some businesses will also employ a human resources officer, who looks after Health and Safety matters. (Otherwise, Health and Safety would be the responsibility of the Construction or Contracts manager)

Figure 2.1 Construction management role (*continued*)

Other occupations involved in the construction process

Architect

Architects carry out the planning and designing of buildings. The architect's primary work includes:

- meeting and negotiating with clients/customers
- creating building designs
- preparing detailed drawings and specifications
- obtaining planning permission and preparing legal documents
- choosing building materials
- inspecting work on site
- advising the client on their choice of a contractor.

Project manager/clerk of works

Did you know?

On larger jobs the clerk of works will issue a variation order for additional work not in the original contract.

The project manager (sometimes called clerk of works) is responsible for the planning, management, co-ordination and financial control of a project. He/she is regarded primarily as the client's/customer's representative on-site and may be contracted to work for the client directly, the architect or a specialist consultant. The clerk of works primarily deals with job progress.

Structural engineer

Structural engineers are involved in the design of buildings and structures such as bridges. Their main role is to ensure that the structure functions safely and will not be subject to potential collapse.

Building surveyor

The building surveyor's work includes:

- organising and carrying out structural surveys
- legal work, including negotiating with local authorities
- preparing plans and specifications
- advising people on building matters such as conservation and insulation.

Building control officer

The building control officer usually works for the local authority, ensuring that the erection of new buildings and modifications to existing buildings are carried out to the requirements laid down in key technical standards including the Building Regulations and supporting British Standards. A building control officer's work includes:

- checking applications for the erection of new buildings and modifications to existing buildings
- checking plans and keeping records of how each project is progressing
- carrying out inspections of foundations, drainage and other major building elements
- issuing a completion certificate when a project is finished.

Water Regulations inspector

Water Regulations inspectors usually work for the local water company. Their role is similar to the building control officer, they:

- review notifications of work provided by plumbing contractors and provide approval to undertake the work
- check plumbing work for compliance with the water regulations
- issue a completion certificate when a project is finished.

Did you know?

The proper name for the water company is the water undertaker.

Facilities manager

A facilities manager deals with the ongoing maintenance/management of the property once it has been built and occupied. The job role includes:

- planning how the inside of the building should be organised for the people occupying it
- managing renovation works
- managing routine maintenance
- managing the building's security
- managing the cleaning and general upkeep of the building.

Building services engineer

Building services engineers carry out the following work related to the essential services in a building: water systems, sanitation systems, heating and ventilation systems, electrical and lighting systems, communication and security systems and lifts/escalators. Their work includes:

- designing the services
- planning, installing, maintaining and repairing services
- making detailed calculations and drawings.

Communicating with customers/ co-contractors

Effectively dealing with customers or co-contractors onsite is essential to the smooth running of a job. Here are a few pointers to effective communication:

- always be polite – many problems onsite arise from a failure to communicate properly or in a proper manner
- always deal with a query if it is raised – the vast majority of complaints raised by customers in the plumbing industry relate to failure to provide information or failure to respond to a query while the work is being carried out
- if a query is raised, remember to take all the details, only deal with queries that are regarded as your normal responsibilities and if the query needs to be passed on to someone else for action, arrange for it to be passed on and try and set a timescale for the response
- a good plumbing company will see good communication skills as a key part of their staff recruitment requirements. It will want to ensure that effective communication takes place between its staff and customers/co-contractors, as well as effective communication between its management/supervisory staff and its plumbers through activities like toolbox talks, designed to deal with better carrying out of the work.

Methods of communication

The following are the main methods of communication used in plumbing activities:

- letter – used for quotations, complaints, job information
- phone – for providing advice, guidance, quick instructions
- fax – a faster method of communicating written information such as quotations, etc.
- e-mail – the fastest method of communicating written information such as quotations, etc.

The phone is regarded as an informal method of communicating information, i.e. there is no permanent record of the discussion and therefore no evidence that could be used should a future problem arise. This type of communication is only suitable for use in dealing with subjects of relatively low importance.

Definition

Toolbox talk – a briefing given by supervisory/management staff on subjects such as safety, customer care, etc.

Letter, fax and e-mail are formal methods of communication where there is a permanent record of the communication that took place. The contents of these types of communication can therefore be used in legal action should a dispute arise, as they are written evidence of the communication that took place.

Communication and job responsibilities of plumbing staff

A great deal of plumbing work involves communication and problem-solving. As your career progresses you'll constantly need to understand the level of responsibility that you have in your company; this will lay down how you deal with problem-solving/communication issues. How companies deal with this can vary, but let's take a look at some typical examples:

- apprentice plumber – works directly with a qualified member of staff who provides the necessary level of work instruction and supervision to undertake the work. A plumbing apprentice would not usually be involved in direct communications with customers/co-contractors related to work problems/issues, and would usually pass these on to the plumber to handle
- Level 2 (or equivalent) qualified plumber – usually does not take full responsibility for the job; generally responds to queries for information from customer/co-contractors, requests for additional work or major changes to the work are usually forwarded to the supervisor for action
- Level 3 (or equivalent) qualified plumber – usually takes full responsibility for the job, including dealing with queries from customers and co-contractors, a Level 3 plumber may be given the responsibility for dealing with requests for additional work, including the confirmation of the work and pricing information.

So essentially an apprentice or a Level 2 qualified plumber will more than likely have to forward requests for work or complaint issues to other staff in the business to deal with.

Resolving disputes

This subject links with the last, in that the extent of the action to be taken is based on the extent of the job holder's responsibility in the business. Here are a few key points:

- customer complaints should be actioned as soon as possible – if left they have a tendency to 'spiral out of control'. Ensuring that the right person gets the information to deal with the complaint is essential if you don't have the authority to deal with it yourself

Remember

It's good practice to maintain regular communication with your employer on the extent of your job responsibilities as your career progresses.

Definition

Arbitration – Guidance on resolving employment disputes and the arbitration process is provided by the Arbitration, Conciliation and Advisory Service (ACAS).

- plumbers can sometimes see quite serious problems between work colleagues onsite, if this occurs most businesses usually require their operatives to report the matter – again it's an item of good practice, disputes such as this need urgent resolution as they have a tendency to affect the work carried out and may leave a bad impression of the company on customers and co-contractors

- most companies encourage staff to raise personnel issues such as pay and conditions with them direct rather than through chatting with work colleagues

- formal disputes between staff and management of a company may be dealt with via the Trade Union if key personnel involved in the dispute are members. Dispute resolution may require formal meetings between management and affected personnel, these meetings are usually well structured, with a formal agenda and purpose for the meeting

- in the event that disputes between the union and management of large companies cannot be resolved, the matter is usually handed over to independent arbitration – this is where a third party reviews the case and recommends solutions to overcome the problem.

Short answer questions

1. The requirements for the energy efficiency of heating appliances are detailed in which document?
2. The position of sanitaryware in a new-build property can be determined by using which site document?
3. What does the term PLC stand for?
4. What is the role of a quantity surveyor?
5. What is the role of a trade supervisor?
6. What is the role of a structural engineer in the construction team?
7. What is the role of a Water Regulations inspector?
8. Which method of communication is regarded as being the fastest formal communication method?
9. What plumbing qualifications are normally required to fully co-ordinate a job?
10. What action is necessary when witnessing a fight between two operatives of a plumbing company onsite?

Multiple-choice test

1. Statutory requirements for the installation of cold water systems are laid down in:
   a) BS 6700
   b) Building Regulations
   c) Water Regulations
   d) Gas Safety Regulations

2. Approximately what percentage of plumbing businesses in the UK employ between one and four operatives?
   a) 50%   c) 70%
   b) 60%   d) 80%

3. A small business in which the shareholders are not personally liable for the debts of the business should it fail is said to be a:
   a) Limited company
   b) Public limited company
   c) Partnership
   d) Sole trader

4. Which of the following is responsible for creating building designs?
   a) Clerk of works
   b) Buyer
   c) Architect
   d) Building control officer

5. Which of the following works for the client, ensuring that the work is to standard, on time and within budget?
   a) Site manager
   b) Clerk of works
   c) Buyer
   d) Building control officer

6. Which of the following is not part of the Building Services Engineering Sector:
   a) Electrical installation
   b) Plumbing
   c) Heating and ventilation installation
   d) Construction

7. Who is responsible for an apprentice plumber whilst onsite?
   a) Training centre
   b) Training provider
   c) Supervising plumber
   d) Project manager

8. Work instructions to a trainee onsite will usually be provided by what means?
   a) Fax   c) Letter
   b) E-mail   d) Verbal instruction

9. A plumbing operative receives a request from a clerk of works to move a boiler onsite from its originally agreed position. What action should be taken:
   a) Get on with the work as quickly as possible
   b) Refuse to carry out the work
   c) Advise that the matter will have to be referred to the supervisor
   d) Immediately leave the site

10. When communicating with co-workers onsite they are more likely to respond positively when you are displaying which of the following?
    a) Rudeness   c) Politeness
    b) Aggressiveness   d) A lack of concern

Key plumbing principles

By the end of this chapter you should be able to demonstrate understanding of the following range of plumbing scientific principles which will assist you in completing knowledge assessment in the Key Plumbing Principles Unit of the Level 2 Certificate in Basic Plumbing Studies:

- Properties of plumbing materials
- Temperature and its measurement
- Properties of water
- Corrosion in plumbing systems
- Pressure in liquids
- Capillarity in plumbing systems
- Flow of water in pipes and channels
- Methods of heat transfer
- Specific heat capacity of a substance
- Principles of electricity supply.

More in-depth detail of each subject area is provided in Chapter 4 of *Plumbing NVQ & Technical Certificate Level 2*, published by Heinemann Educational Publishers.

Properties of materials

Mass and weight of a substance

Mass is the measure of the amount of material or matter contained in an object. The unit of measurement is the kilogram (kg), all measurements of mass are referenced to an 'international prototype kilogram' kept in Sèvres, France.

Weight is the gravitational force acting on an object. The unit of measurement of weight is the Newton (N). Weight is calculated using the following formula:

weight (N) = mass (kg) × acceleration due to gravity (m/s^2)

As the acceleration due to gravity on Earth remains relatively constant at a figure of 9.8 m/s^2, for general business purposes mass and weight are taken to be the same.

Density of a substance

The density of an object is a measurement of the relationship between the mass of the object and its volume. It is calculated by using the following formula:

$$\text{Density (kg/m}^3) = \frac{\text{mass (kg)}}{\text{volume (m}^3)}$$

Density of solids – solid materials, e.g. a bar of copper and a bar of lead of exactly the same size and shape, will have a different mass. This difference in mass is brought about by the molecular structure of the substance or its **density**.

Density of liquids and gases – liquids and gases also have differing densities based on the number of molecules that are contained within a certain volume. Whereas the density of a solid when heated remains relatively constant, the density of a liquid or a gas also changes with an increase or decrease in temperature.

As an example:

- 1 m^3 of water at 4°C has a mass of 1000 kg
- 1 m^3 of water at 60°C has a mass of 983.2 kg

Density of an object being its relationship to mass and volume is used to good effect in the operation of plumbing systems. Figure 3.1, overleaf, shows a hot water storage cylinder being heated by a boiler using the principles of gravity (natural circulation). Circulation by a process known as convection is brought about due to the changes in density of water in the flow and return pipework, i.e. the hotter flow pipe contains a similar volume of water to the cooler return pipe, but will have a slightly different mass due to molecular changes brought about by the heating effect. Essentially the water in the flow pipe is slightly lighter than that in the return pipe, so circulation takes place.

Relative density

Relative density of a substance (previously known as specific gravity) is a comparison of the mass of any volume of a substance in relation to the mass of an equal volume of water.

$$\text{Relative density} = \frac{\text{mass of any volume of a substance}}{\text{mass of an equal volume of water}}$$

1 m^3 of water at 4°C has a mass of 1000 kg – its relative density is 1.0; the relative density of other substances is worked out in relation to this figure for water.

Did you know?

Density is measured in kilograms per metre^3 (kg/m^3).

Did you know?

When a liquid or gas is heated, the molecules inside it move further apart, resulting in a change in its density.

Example:

1 m³ of copper weighs approximately 8900 kg.

Its relative density $= \dfrac{8900 \text{ kg}}{1000 \text{ kg}} = 8.9$ (no measurement units for relative density)

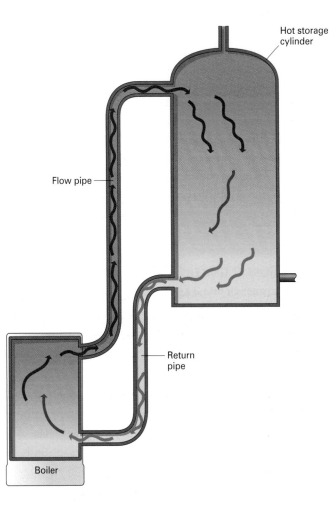

Figure 3.1 Gravity circulation due to density changes in the circulated hot water

Relative density of a gas is a comparison of the mass of any volume of a substance in relation to the mass of an equal volume of dry air. Dry air has a relative density of 1.0.

A number of tables are available, detailing the relative densities of substances in relation to that of water. Relative density can be used in determining densities of comparable substances, their mass and volume.

Thermal expansion and contraction

When a substance is heated the molecules move further apart, which results in a lengthening of the material, or **expansion**. On cooling down, the molecules move closer together, which results in a shortening of the material or **contraction.**

Definition

Coefficient of linear expansion
– a unit for measuring the rate of expansion of different substances.

The rate of expansion or contraction of a solid material will be dependent on three factors:

- the length of the material
- the difference in temperature at the start of the heating process and at the end
- the coefficient of linear expansion.

As a formula this is shown as:

The rate of expansion = length (m) × temperature rise (°C) × coefficient

Coefficients of linear expansion have been determined by scientific experimentation for a range of different materials, with plastics usually having the highest rate of expansion.

Example:

Calculate the expansion that will take place when a 10m length of gutter is heated from 10°C to 30°C if the coefficient for linear expansion of plastics is 0.00018.

Change in length = 10 × (30 − 10) × 0.00018 = 0.036m or 36mm

In the case of the example shown above we need to make an allowance of 36mm in any joints included in the 10m length of gutter, to allow the gutter to expand and avoid undue stresses and in more serious cases possible breakdown of the material.

Temperature and its measurement

In simple language, **temperature** is the degree of hotness or coldness of an object, or of the environment, such as the air temperature.

The scientific unit of measurement of temperature is the Kelvin (K), often known as the absolute temperature. For everyday plumbing purposes we use the metric unit of temperature, the degree Celsius or Centigrade (°C).

We commonly need to measure temperatures when carrying out jobs such as commissioning systems during which the temperature of water will need to be established.

Simple temperature-measuring devices

Simple thermometer

In its simplest form a thermometer is a glass tube containing a substance such as alcohol or mercury that expands or contracts at a constant rate in response to temperature changes. A metal bulb is sited at one end of the thermometer for taking the temperature or immersing in water. This type of thermometer can be used for checking the water temperature at taps or outlets.

Figure 3.2 Simple thermometer

Clip-on thermometer

The clip-on, clamp-on or often called pipe thermometer is used for taking surface temperatures of pipes. The thermometer uses the bi-metallic strip principle. This type of thermometer can be used when commissioning central heating systems, where two clip-on thermometers are used to measure the temperature of both the flow and return pipework in order to establish the correct water flow through each.

Differential digital thermometer

This device comes with a range of attachments that can be used to measure simple water temperatures by immersing a probe in the water stream, or by connecting a device known as a thermistor to pipe surfaces. When commissioning central heating systems two thermistors are attached by means of a strap to the flow and return pipework and the digital thermometer can measure the temperature of each pipe and the difference in temperature between each pipe.

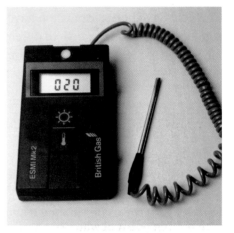

Figure 3.3 Differential digital thermometer

Properties of water

Behaviour of water at different temperatures

Matter such as water can exist in what is known as three different states:

Solid (ice) ⟶ Liquid ⟶ Gas (steam)

In moving from one state to another a **change of state** must take place, during which the water is either cooled or heated.

In its natural state between 0°C to 100°C water is in the form of a **liquid**, see Figure 3.5. When heated during its liquid state the water will increase in volume by up to 4 per cent (it will expand). Using the information previously covered on density, for the same mass of water when heated an increase in volume will take place, the result will be a decrease in density, i.e. it will become lighter. Water is at its maximum density at a temperature of 4°C.

The **freezing point** of water is 0°C; at temperatures of 0°C and below water changes state to **ice**.

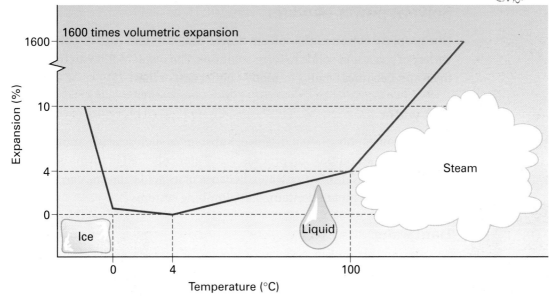

Figure 3.4 Change of state diagram – atmospheric pressure

On cooling below 0°C water turns to ice and expands, this expansion or increase in volume in an enclosed space can result in components rupturing, e.g. a burst pipe.

The **boiling point** of water is 100°C, at temperatures of 100°C and above water under atmospheric conditions changes state to **steam**.

When changing to steam a rapid increase in volume takes place (up to 1600 times its original volume when in liquid form). This can have explosive effects if the water is stored in an enclosed space.

Water stored at above atmospheric pressure

It is worth noting that the pressure at which the water is stored is also linked to water temperature and water volume. So if water is stored in an enclosed space such as a storage cylinder (a constant volume) at above atmospheric pressure, when the water is heated, the temperature at which it boils will rise above 100°C.

As an example the boiling point of water at 1 bar pressure is approximately 120°C.

So why is water stored at above atmospheric pressure and above temperatures of 100°C so dangerous if it's not boiling?

Quite simply, if someone were to open a tap, or a storage cylinder ruptured, then the water pressure would rapidly reduce to atmospheric pressure, almost instantly causing the water to boil, resulting in a change of state from water to steam and causing a rapid increase in volume of the gas (up to 1600 times its original volume). The vessel or system more than likely could not withstand and this would rupture – like a bomb!

> **Did you know?**
>
> Hot water must be very effectively controlled to below 100°C in order to avoid potentially serious explosions.

Solvent power of water

One property of water is its solvent power, that is its ability to dissolve a variety of gases and solids to form solutions. The result of this can be that the water becomes what is termed as either soft or hard.

Soft water

Water becomes soft when it dissolves substances such as acids, soots, by-products of the combustion process, etc. Water collected in towns is more likely to be soft water. Softer water, because of its acidic nature, can lead to the corrosion of metals contained in plumbing systems.

Hard water

Hard water is typically produced when water falls on or flows through ground containing calcium carbonates or sulphates and these solids are taken up into solution. Water hardness can be described as either:

- **Permanent hardness** – the result of nitrates and sulphates being taken into solution. The water does not lather easily and the salts cannot be easily removed by boiling.
- **Temporary hardness** – the result of carbonates being taken into solution. Again the water does not lather easily, but on heating the carbonates can be precipitated out as **limescale**. This limescale can gather on the inside of hot water fittings, causing a restriction to the flow of water, inefficiency of plumbing appliances and possible system failure.

pH value

pH value relates to the level of **acidity** or **alkalinity** of a substance. It is measured on a scale as shown below.

The pH scale of acidity

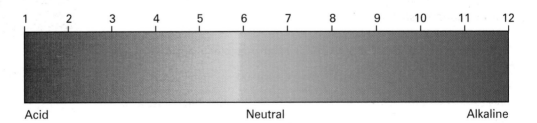

Acid   Neutral   Alkaline

Figure 3.5 pH scale

Neutral water will have a pH of 7. Acidic waters will have a pH value of less than 7, whereas alkali waters will have a pH value greater than 7. Natural rainwater tends to be slightly acidic due to small amounts of gases taken up in the atmosphere during the rainfall process.

High levels of acids and alkalis can lead to corrosion damage in plumbing systems and components.

Corrosion in plumbing systems and components

There are a number of ways in which corrosion of plumbing systems and components can take place.

Atmospheric corrosion

Atmospheric corrosion is caused by the contact of metals and moist air (air containing water vapour). Atmospheric corrosion tends to be more serious with ferrous metals (containing iron), causing a gradual breakdown or rusting of the material that can result in its complete destruction.

Atmospheric corrosion rates increase in areas where there are discharge gases from industrial processes (acidic gases) and also in coastal locations where salt (an alkali) becomes dissolved in the atmosphere.

The corrosive effects of water

The internal corrosion of hot and cold water plumbing system components is usually the result of the water having a relatively high acid or alkali content. In the case of acidic water types, small quantities of materials such as lead or copper can be taken into solution. With lead in particular this can be quite serious, as it is a known poison and can lead to serious medical conditions. A further indication of corrosion in systems is the colour of water inside a central heating system, which discolours over time due to contact between ferrous metals and the water itself showing that corrosion has taken place.

Contact with materials

Metals used in plumbing systems can be corroded by contact with a variety of different materials such as:

- cement – because of its alkali nature cement can be corrosive to plumbing materials such as copper, so we have to protect the copper by wrapping it with a protective material such as tape
- heavy clay – can contain sulphates which can attack copper, lead and steel.

Electrolytic corrosion

Electrolytic corrosion takes place when two dissimilar metals (an anode and a cathode) are placed in a solution known as an electrolyte (water), the

Did you know?

The protective coating formed on the surface of a non-ferrous metal is known as a patina.

Other metals such as copper and lead (non-ferrous metals) tend to have in-built protection against atmospheric corrosion as a protective barrier (usually a sulphate) forms on the metals and protects against further corrosion.

Definition

Anode – positively charged metal.

Cathode – negatively charged metal.

result being the breakdown of the anode. The rate of corrosion will depend on:

- the properties of the electrolyte (if it is hotter or more acidic, the rate of corrosion will increase)
- the metal's position in the electromotive series as shown below (the further apart the metals in the series, the greater the destruction of the anode).

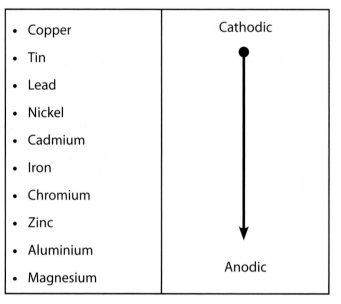

- Copper
- Tin
- Lead
- Nickel
- Cadmium
- Iron
- Chromium
- Zinc
- Aluminium
- Magnesium

Cathodic

Anodic

Figure 3.6 The electromotive series

Pressure in liquids

The pressure in a liquid increases with depth, so in a plumbing system water pressure is higher at the lowest points of the system and lower at the highest points of the system.

Water is measured using a number of different units:

- metres head (m)
- the pascal (Pa) also the Newton per metre squared (N/m^2)
- bar pressure (bar).

1 metre head = approx. 10,000 Pa (10 kPa) = approx. 0.1 bar

An understanding of the **pressure head** created in systems is important in determining component sizes, e.g. pipe sizes, and confirming that components will be able to withstand the pressure of water created within them.

Example:

If a tap is sited 5 metres below a plumbing cistern feeding it, the pressure created at the tap will be:

5.0 metres head × 0.1 bar pressure = 0.5 bar

Did you know?

Atmospheric pressure at sea level is equal to 101.3 kPa (or approximately 1 bar pressure).

Atmospheric pressure

Atmospheric pressure is the natural pressure exerted by the weight of the Earth's atmosphere pressing down on the ground. The atmospheric pressure reduces, the higher the location above sea level.

The siphon

The siphon uses atmospheric pressure to operate. A quantity of water is forced through a short leg of pipe (column A) and over the crown of the siphon. The weight of water in column B longer leg (under positive pressure) is greater than in column A. The water continues to flow, owing to the difference in the weight of water with positive atmospheric pressure (in column B) and negative suction pressure (in column A).

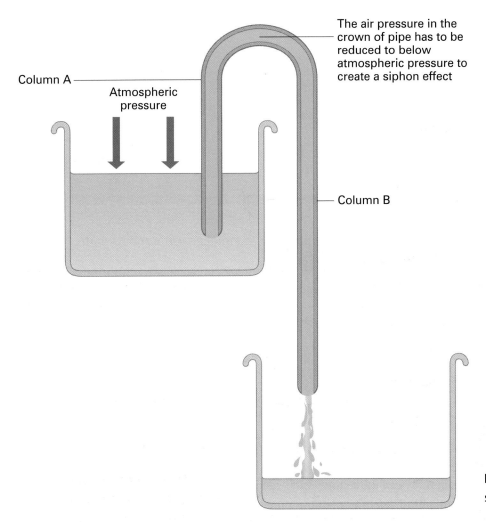

Figure 3.7 The principle of the siphon

Intensity of pressure and total pressure

Intensity of pressure is the force created (Pa) by the weight of a given mass of water acting on a unit area (m^2).

Total pressure is the intensity of pressure multiplied by the area acted on.

Example:

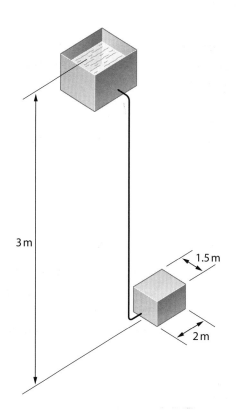

Figure 3.8 Pressure calculation

Calculate the intensity of pressure and total pressure acting on the base of the lower cistern.

Intensity of pressure = head × 9.81 kPa = 3 x 9.81 = 29.43 kPa/m^2

Total pressure – intensity of pressure × area of base = 29.43 × (2 × 1.5)
= 88.29 kPa

Capillarity in plumbing systems

Capillary attraction is the process of drawing water between the gap in two surfaces. The forces of capillary attraction are **surface tension** (cohesive effect of water) which causes the water molecules themselves to 'cling together' and **adhesion** which causes the water molecules to cling to the side of the vessel or container the water is stored in.

Flow of water in pipes and channels

Flow of water in pipes

Plumbers need to be able to calculate the flow of water in pipes in order that the correct quantity of water can be provided to make components work correctly, e.g. a tap or radiator. The flow of water (quantity of water flowing in a pipe) is affected by the following factors:

- the pressure head of water in the pipe
- the diameter of the pipe (smaller diameter pipes will not be able to carry the same amount of water as a larger diameter pipe, unless the pressure and speed of flow are increased, in which case noise in the pipe can occur)
- the roughness (or smoothness) of the pipe walls, the pipe walls creating frictional resistance as the water passes by, resulting in a reduction in available pressure as the water travels further down the pipe.

Self-cleansing velocity

This is a term usually applied to pipes and channels that operate by gravity (not pumped) as applied to sanitation and drainage pipework.

An example is a drainage pipe that is laid at a specific gradient (fall) in order that a minimum speed (velocity) is maintained whilst the drainage products travel along the pipe. This ensures that any solid matter is not permitted to gather at points along the pipe wall, which could result in material build-up and blockage.

Methods of heat transfer

Heat is transferred by one of three methods **conduction**, **convection** and **radiation**.

Conduction

Conduction is the transfer of heat energy, usually through a solid material. Metals tend to be good conductors of heat, whereas wood is a poor conductor of heat (it may be described as the reverse – an insulator).

Convection

Convection is the transfer of heat energy by movement of a locally heated fluid such as air or water. On heating, the fluid increases in volume (molecules move further apart), which reduces its density – it becomes lighter and rises, then is replaced by the denser fluid from below, i.e. a circulation effect is set up.

Radiation

Radiation is the transfer of heat energy by waves from a hot body to a colder one through no substance other than air. Radiated heat is best absorbed by matt (dull, black) surfaces rather than bright, shiny ones.

Did you know?

You can see heating by conduction if you warm a piece of copper pipe at one end: the heat will begin to travel to the other end.

Did you know?

Heating by convection occurs in a hot water system using the principle of gravity circulation to supply the heated water from boiler to cylinder.

Did you know?

Heating by radiation is taking place when you feel the warm glow from sitting in front of a gas fire.

Specific heat capacity

To size various plumbing components such as boilers and radiators, plumbers need to be able to understand the concept of heat. Heat is different from temperature. Heat is a measure of the amount of energy in a substance. The standard unit of measurement of heat is the **joule**.

In order to work out the amount of heat required to heat a substance we need to be able to measure the amount of heat required over time or the **power** required. This is a measure of the energy divided by the time.

Energy is measured in joules (J) or kilowatt-hours (kWh). Power is measured in watts (W) or kilowatts (kW).

In order to be able to undertake plumbing calculations involving heat we usually need to be able to work out the amount of heat required to raise a quantity of a substance such as water from one temperature to another. To do this we need to know the substance's **specific heat capacity**.

The specific heat capacity of a substance is the amount of heat required to raise 1kg of that substance by 1°C. The specific heat capacity of water is 4.186 kJ/kg/°C.

Example:

Calculate the heat energy and power required to raise 200 litres of water from 10°C to 60°C (assume 1 litre of water weighs roughly 1kg).

Heat energy = 200 litres × 4.186 kJ/kg/°C × (60°C – 10°C) = 41,860kJ

Power required to heat the water in 1 hour (assuming no energy is lost)

$$= \frac{41,860}{3600} = 11.63\text{kW}$$

Principles of electricity supply

Electricity can be supplied as either **direct current** or **alternating current**.

In direct current (dc) the electron flow is in the same direction all the time, as may be experienced in a simple circuit between the anode and cathode of a battery.

Most systems that plumbers work on are alternating current (ac), where the electron flow forms what is called a 'sine wave'. Alternating current is produced as a result of **electromagnetism**, where a copper wire wrapped round a soft iron core is rotated in a magnetic field, the result being electricity production.

Electrical units

Voltage can be identified simply as the pressure (driving force) required to push the electricity around the system, measured in volts (V).

Current is a measure of the flow of electricity (amount of electricity) flowing in a circuit over a specific time period, identified in amperes (A) and often given the symbol I.

Resistance is quite simply the resistance to the flow of electrons created by cables (conductors) and electrical components in circuits. Resistance in electrical circuits is created in much the same way as pressure is lost in plumbing systems as it travels along pipework etc. due to the frictional resistance of the pipe and fittings. The electrical unit of resistance is the ohm, often given the symbol Ω.

There is a relationship between voltage current and resistance known as Ohm's Law, which identifies that:

Voltage = Current $\times$ Resistance   or   V = I $\times$ R

Example:

What is the current flowing through a 240-volt circuit which has a resistance of 480 ohms?

$$240\,V = amps \times 480\ ohms$$

$$Amps = \frac{240\,V}{480\ ohms} = 0.5\,A$$

There is also a relationship between the electrical power (measured in kW) required to operate a component and the voltage of the circuit and its rate of current flow.

Power (watts) = voltage (volts) $\times$ current (amps)

Example:

Calculate the current flowing through a cable to a 3kW immersion heater fed by a 240-volt supply.

$$3000\,W = 240\,V \times A$$

$$A = \frac{3000}{240} = 12.5\ amps$$

Size of circuit protection devices in domestic properties

Fuse ratings for 13 amp (maximum) plug tops are determined by the power rating of the appliance that the fuse is protecting. Typically this will be provided by the manufacturer, e.g. low power loaded equipment such as a central heating system will use a 3 amp fuse.

The size of a circuit protection device in the consumer unit in a domestic property will usually be as follows:

Type of device	Fuse	Circuit breaker
Shower	30–45A	32–45A
Cooker	30A	32A
Ring main	30A	32A
Immersion heater	15A	16A
Lighting circuit	5A	6A
Heating circuit	5A	6A

The size of the device being determined by the relationship between power usage, voltage and current as shown above.

Short answer questions

1. If 1m³ water weighs 1000kg, what does 1m³ of mild steel weigh if it has a relative density of 7.7?
2. Which metric unit is density expressed in?
3. Calculate the expansion that will take place in a 6m length of plastic gutter heated from 5 to 30°C, if the coefficient of linear expansion for plastics is 0.00018.
4. Differential temperatures on central heating flow and return pipework can be measured using what type of device?
5. Water boils at what temperature?
6. The scale formation on the inside of hot water system pipework is an example of what type of water hardness?
7. What is the protective coating called that forms on the surface of a non-ferrous metal that is sited outdoors?
8. 10 metres head of water creates approximately how many bars of water pressure?
9. What type of heat travels from one body to another through no substance other than air?
10. What is the resistance in a 240-volt circuit with a current rating of 2 amps?

Multiple-choice test

1. Water is at its maximum density at what temperature?
   a) 100°C
   b) 25°C
   c) 4°C
   d) 0°C

2. The pascal can be expressed in units of:
   a) kg/m^3
   b) N/m^2
   c) Kg/L
   d) N/kg

3. Which of the following has the highest coefficient of linear expansion?
   a) Low carbon steel
   b) Copper
   c) PVCu
   d) Sheet lead

4. How much heat is required to raise 15kg of water from 20°C to 60°C if the specific heat capacity of water is 4.2kJ/kg/°C?
   a) 1225kJ
   b) 2520kJ
   c) 3657kJ
   d) 5252kJ

5. Which of the following metals is the best conductor of heat?
   a) Copper
   b) Low carbon steel
   c) Cast iron
   d) Lead sheet

6. A combination boiler requires a minimum incoming water pressure of 0.8 bar to work correctly. What is this expressed in metres head of water?
   a) 1 metre
   b) 5 metres
   c) 8 metres
   d) 15 metres

7. The rate of electrolytic corrosion between two dissimilar metals in the presence of water will be dependent on:
   a) The density of the two metals
   b) Their relative positions in the electromotive series
   c) The space between the atoms in each metal
   d) The level of hardness of the water

8. The relative density of a substance is:
   a) The pressure exerted by 1m head of water
   b) The weight of a substance per metre squared
   c) Its comparison to the density of water
   d) Its comparison to the volume of water

9. The intensity of pressure at a 15mm bib tap supplied from a storage cistern creating 5m head of water is:
   a) $21.98kPa/m^2$
   b) $49.05kPa/m^2$
   c) $74.32kPa/m^2$
   d) $100.27kPa/m^2$

10. In order for siphonage to occur, the container receiving the water must be sited:
    a) At the same height as the container from which the water is drawn
    b) Above the container from which the water is drawn
    c) Below the container from which the water is drawn
    d) Inside the container from which the water is drawn

11. Siphonage is used in which of the following plumbing components?
    a) *Drop valve*   c) *Double check valve*
    b) *Double trap WC*   d) *Boiler heat exchanger*

12. Gravity circulation in a hot water system takes place by which form of heat transfer?
    a) *Capillary attraction*
    b) *Conduction*
    c) *Convection*
    d) *Radiation*

13. Permanent hardness can occur as a result of which type of salts being taken into solution?
    a) *Chlorides*   c) *Iodides*
    b) *Carbonates*   d) *Nitrates*

14. When water flashes across to steam it can expand by up to how many times its original volume?
    a) *4 times*   c) *100 times*
    b) *50 times*   d) *1600 times*

15. When a substance changes from a liquid to a gas, its molecules:
    a) *Move closer together*
    b) *Move further apart*
    c) *Explode and disintegrate*
    d) *Stay the same*

16. Which of the following will create the greatest frictional resistance to the flow of water in a hot water system?
    a) *Pipe bends*
    b) *Pipe elbows*
    c) *Degree of hardness of the water*
    d) *Thickness of the pipe wall*

17. Which of the following is not a ferrous metal?
    a) *Low carbon steel*   c) *Stainless steel*
    b) *Cast iron*   d) *Lead*

18. What is the SI unit of electrical current?
    a) *Volts*   c) *Watts*
    b) *Amperes*   d) *Ohms*

19. What is the approximate fuse rating required for a pump rated at 700 watts, fed from a 240-volt supply?
    a) *3 amp*   c) *13 amp*
    b) *5 amp*   d) *15 amp*

20. What is the miniature circuit breaker rating for the overcurrent device protecting an immersion heater circuit in a domestic property?
    a) *6A*   c) *16A*
    b) *13A*   d) *32A*

CHAPTER 04

Common plumbing processes

By the end of this chapter you should be able to demonstrate understanding of the following common plumbing processes topics which will assist you in completing knowledge assessment in the Common Plumbing Processes Unit of the Level 2 Certificate in Basic Plumbing Studies:

- Sources of information:
  - Technical standards
  - Site information sources
- Handling material deliveries
- Preparing to carry out the work:
  - Protecting customer property
  - Preparatory work
- Pipework materials and jointing methods:
  - Copper pipework
  - Low carbon steel pipework
  - Plastic pipework
- Bending pipework:
  - Copper pipework
  - LCS pipework
  - Plastic pipework
- Fixing devices and brackets:
  - Screws
  - Plastic plugs
  - Plasterboard fixings
  - Clips and brackets
- Essentials of good plumbing work
- Completing the work.

Sources of information

There are a number of information sources that plumbers may have to use to obtain the necessary detail to undertake their work.

Technical Standards

- Water Regulations – these lay down the statutory requirements that must be carried out when installing, commissioning and maintaining

Did you know?

The Water Supply (Water Fittings) Regulations 1999 detail the water supply requirements that plumbers must work to.

water systems. Responsibility for monitoring compliance with the Water Regulations is given to the local water undertakers. Water Regulations documentation can be freely downloaded from www.defra.gov.uk, who also produce a guidance document to the Water Regulations.

- Building Regulations – these are the main regulations that must be complied with when carrying out the installation of a range of plumbing and heating systems in dwellings. Responsibility for monitoring compliance with the Building Regulations is given to Building Control Officers in local building control bodies, and as with the Water Regulations, certain types of work must be notified to the local building control body before it takes place. Approved documents are provided to detail Building Regulation requirements and these can be freely downloaded from the DCLG website at www.communities.gov.uk.
- Water Fittings and Materials Directory – this is produced by the Water Regulations Advisory Scheme (WRAS), listing approved components and fittings for use in hot and cold water systems in the UK. The guide is freely accessible at www.wras.co.uk.
- British Standards – these support statutory documentation such as the Building Regulations, providing greater detail on installation requirements. Although British Standards are not statutory (legal) documents, they can be used in potential legal action relating to defective systems installation. A range of British Standards are available, dealing with the installation of plumbing and heating systems.
- Manufacturer instructions – these are provided by appliance or component manufacturers to outline the installation, commissioning and maintenance requirements of their products. Manufacturer instructions usually take precedence over British Standards, but should not conflict with Building or Water Regulations, which are statutory (legal) requirements. Manufacturers also produce glossy brochures for use by customers; these tend to contain little information that is useful to the plumber regarding the installation or maintenance requirements of the component.

Site information sources

The following outlines the range of commonly used site information sources:

- site plans – site or location plans show the location of the building or site to adjacent roads, properties or services
- building plans – these are the detailed plans for the property showing key building details – location of doors/windows, room sizes, boiler position, etc.
- services layout plans – detailed drawings of the building services such as pipe runs, position and layout
- job specification – often provided as support to building plans. This details items such as the type, size and position of key components such as boilers and who is responsible for carrying out various items of work including preparatory work

- a quotation is a fixed price, provided either by a plumbers' merchant for supplying materials or by a plumbing company to a customer for carrying out work
- an estimate, as its name suggests, is an estimation of the cost of supplying materials or carrying out work
- an invoice is provided to claim payment either by a merchant when materials have been successfully delivered to a job, or when a plumbing company has completed work for a customer
- a work programme details the point at which various aspects of plumbing work fit into the overall construction programme, e.g. first fix hot and cold water system. Any delays that occur during the construction programme will be built into the overall work programme, which may be adjusted as the work progresses
- a maintenance schedule details the range of activities that should be undertaken by a plumber as part of the planned maintenance programme on a system. In undertaking this type of work the plumber may be required to complete maintenance records to show the work that has been carried out and confirm the proper operation of each system component
- stock control records may be maintained on larger sites; essentially these are a listing of all the materials in stock on the work site. The plumber will usually be required to sign for the items before removing them from stock. This type of system is now usually computerised
- bill of quantities – a bill of quantities details the quantities of components and materials used on a job.

Handling material deliveries

The plumber needs to be aware of the following key points when handling material deliveries:

- initial arrangements will usually have been made by the plumbing company to ensure that a nominated person is present to receive the delivery of plumbing materials, and that where security is an issue (such as on new-build sites), only materials that are going to be installed in the short term (that working day) are left on site
- all materials received on site from the supplier should be checked for correct type and quantity against the specification that you are working to, a check to establish that the components have not been damaged should also be carried out. Any materials that do not meet the specification should be clearly marked on the delivery note and should not be accepted on site, being taken back by the supplier. The supplier will usually require your signature on the delivery note to confirm acceptance of the delivery, so you need to ensure that you only sign for the materials that you have received
- on leaving the site, ensure that all materials are left in a secure location, doors locked, windows closed, etc.

- if a material delivery is expected but does not arrive before you leave the site, your company should be contacted and advised of the position so that they can take the necessary action.

Preparing to carry out the work

It goes without saying that work should be carried out in a tidy manner, taking due care of customer property and leaving the work area in a clean state on completing the work for the day and on completion of the job as a whole. Working like this also assists in keeping the work site safe, as it removes things like tripping hazards.

Protecting customer property

While undertaking work it is important that customer property is fully protected against damage. Examples of customer property relating to work in new-build and owner-occupied properties could be:

- carpets, curtains, furniture, ornaments and wall-coverings
- kitchen units, bathroom suites, etc.
- vehicles (may need to be moved while work is taking place near them)
- lawns, flower beds etc. outside the property.

The greatest risk of damage to property occurs in owner-occupied properties, so a great deal of care is required when working in this type of property, with a good stock of clean dust sheets being essential items of a plumber's tool kit.

Before carrying out the work it's worth checking the work location for existing damage to customer property: now and again plumbers do encounter the odd rogue customer who may claim that the plumber has damaged something that was already damaged before the work took place!

The following are a few key pointers to protection measures in domestic properties:

- keep dirty hands off decorated wall surfaces at all times
- major work in domestic properties such as fireplace, boiler or bathroom replacement will usually require the removal of carpets/curtains and major items of furniture from the room. This is usually the customer's responsibility and needs to be arranged with them before the work takes place. Remaining items in the room will need to be protected by dust sheeting
- when installation work is taking place in domestic properties the walkway (over carpets) needs to be properly sheeted. This is particularly important in poor weather conditions
- discussion should take place with the customer regarding the removal of ornaments and emptying of cupboards, e.g. airing cupboards. This should be planned to take place before the work begins

Safety tip

Care needs to be taken when sheeting stairways, to ensure that the sheets remain constantly flat and do not present a tripping hazard, for major items of work it can be beneficial to recommend the removal of the stair carpet, although this is not always possible.

- building components such as kitchen units and bathroom suites should be properly sheeted over so that they are not marked or damaged
- particular attention needs to be paid to sheeting carpets when removing old components such as cisterns, cylinders and boilers, as they often contain dirty water.

Preparatory work

Cutting holes in masonry surfaces

In order to minimise damage it is preferable to make openings to accommodate pipework or components such as room sealed flues with a large hammer drill. This will minimise damage to the building fabric. Key points in accommodating systems pipework are:

- the hole should be properly measured and marked out
- a pilot drill should be used to first drill through the outer wall surface, in order to avoid a large area of masonry wall being removed during the drilling process
- pipes should be properly sleeved and protected against corrosion when directed through load-bearing masonry walls. Proper sleeving will also accommodate any thermal movement that is required.

Running pipework in joists

Regulations lay down how pipes can be accommodated in timber joists; Figure 4.1 shows the requirements for notching.

Holes that are drilled in joists must be no greater in diameter than 0.25 of the joist depth, they should be drilled at centres of at least 3 diameters apart and should be located between 0.25 and 0.4 of the span from the support.

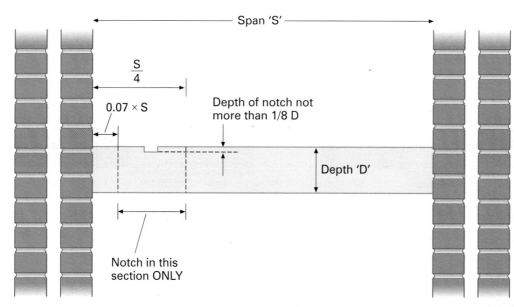

Figure 4.1 Accommodating pipework in timber floor joists

Did you know?

The outlets of old cylinders, cisterns and boilers should be properly plugged when they are being removed from the property, to avoid spillage of dirty water.

The dimensions quoted must be followed at all times in order that the joist is not weakened.

Pipework materials and jointing methods

The following outlines the common materials and jointing methods used for hot, cold and central heating services.

Copper pipework

Types of copper tube

There are a number of specifications for copper tube that can be used for a variety of different applications:

- Half Hard R250 (old grade X) – this is the standard copper tube used for most internal applications in hot, cold and central heating systems. Chromium-plated tube is also available for decorative purposes
- Hard R290 (old grade Z) – this is not commonly used in domestic properties as it is unbendable owing to the thickness of its outer wall and the level of annealing that has taken place
- Soft coil R220 (old grade Y) – used for external underground water supply pipework, the pipework is fully annealed and it is easy to form large radius bends by hand
- Minibore coil R220 (old grade W) – primarily used in central heating applications and for connection to lower-loaded gas appliances such as gas fires.

Methods of jointing copper tube

Copper tube can be jointed by the following methods:

Non-manipulative compression (type A)

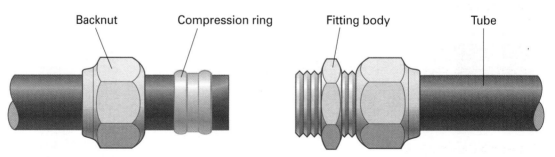

Backnut   Compression ring   Fitting body   Tube

Figure 4.2 Non-manipulative joint

A compression ring or olive is used to make a watertight seal on the pipework. The joint is tightened by means of a fixed-head spanner or grips. No jointing compound should be necessary to form the joint. This type of joint can be used above ground on hot, cold and central heating systems.

Manipulative compression (type B)

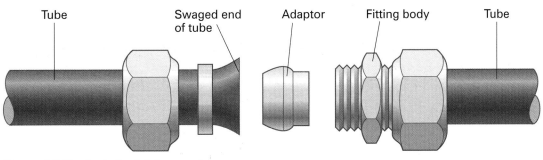

Figure 4.3 Manipulative joint

This type of joint is prepared using a special swaging tool. It is not commonly used other than on below-ground water supply pipework, where it is the only permissible type of compression joint that can be used on copper pipework.

Solder-ring capillary fitting

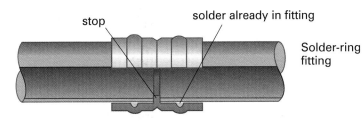

Figure 4.4 Solder-ring capillary fitting

A watertight seal is made with this type of joint, using an integral solder ring built into the fitting, the joint is made by cleaning the pipe ends and the fitting, then applying a flux to permit the solder to flow across the pipe and fitting surfaces when it is heated.

End-feed capillary fitting

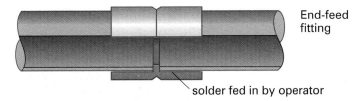

Figure 4.5 End-feed fitting

The joint is made using a similar process to the solder-ring fitting, with the exception that solder is end-fed into the fitting from a spool of wire solder.

Safety tip

A heat-resistant mat is an essential part of the toolkit when heating pipework near to combustible materials such as wood.

Push-fit fittings

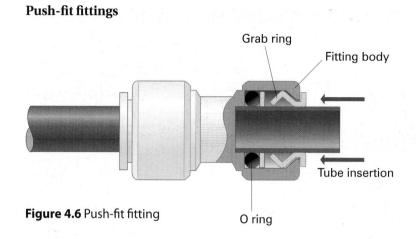

Figure 4.6 Push-fit fitting

There are a number of different types of push-fit fitting available. In most cases the fitting contains a grab ring and O-ring washer to make a seal. A key issue when making this type of joint is to ensure that the pipework is properly inserted into the fitting.

Low carbon steel pipework

Types of LCS tube

LCS is supplied in three colour-coded grades:

- light – colour-coded brown
- medium – colour-coded blue
- heavy – colour-coded red.

LCS is available painted black for use in central heating, gas- and oil-fitting applications, or galvanised for use in hot and cold water applications, although galvanised pipe is not now commonly used for hot and cold water as it can be susceptible to corrosion.

Methods of jointing LCS tube

LCS tube in domestic applications is usually jointed by:

Threaded joints

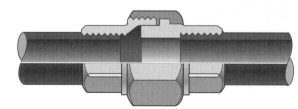

Figure 4.7 Threaded LCS pipe joints

Figure 4.8 Electric pipe-threading machine

A variety of threaded fittings is available for LCS pipework. Pipework is cut to length and a thread cut into the pipe ends using a threading machine or a chaser die stock. A sealant material such as PTFE tape is then applied to the pipe end and the fitting tightened on to the pipe end by using a stillson wrench.

Compression joints

There is a variety of different types of LCS compression joint available. The fitting is designed to be formed without threading, owing to their cost they tend only to be used for repair-type work.

Stainless steel   Rubber
backing washer   compression ring

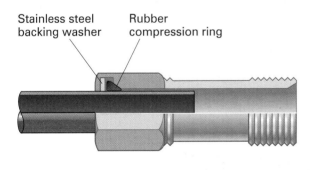

Figure 4.9 LCS compression joint

Plastic pipework

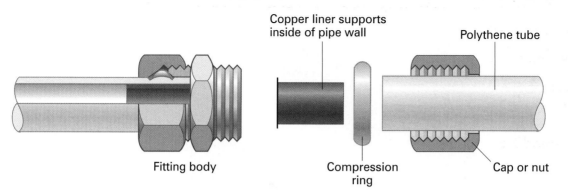

Figure 4.10 Typical polythene pipe fitting

Polythene pipe (colour-coded blue) is used for below ground cold water supply pipework. Joints on this type of pipework are made using gunmetal or plastic fittings. This type of pipework should not be exposed to strong sunlight as it can eventually degrade.

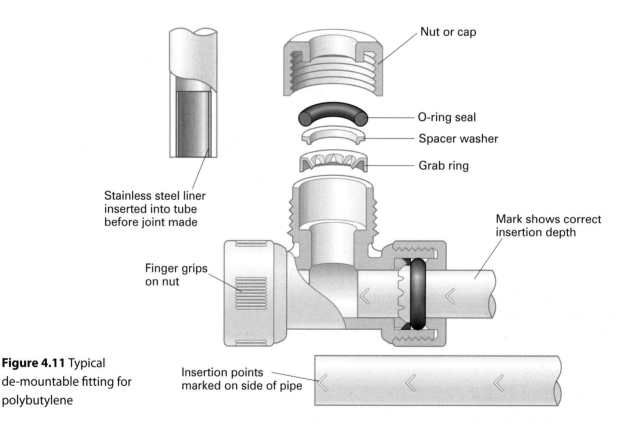

Figure 4.11 Typical de-mountable fitting for polybutylene

Polybutylene pipe can be used for above ground hot, cold and central heating applications. This type of pipework system is usually jointed using manufacturer proprietary push-fit fittings. The pipe used for central heating applications is usually a special 'barrier pipe' which prevents permeation of air through the pipework material in order to avoid corrosion.

Bending pipework

Copper pipework

This can be bent using:

- a bending machine
- a spring.

Machine bending

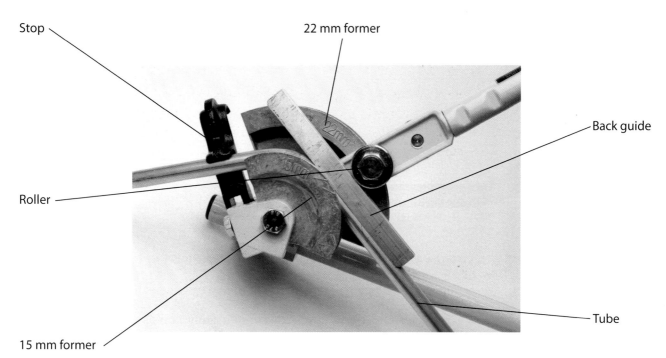

Stop

22 mm former

Back guide

Roller

Tube

15 mm former

Figure 4.12 Hand bender

Machine bending working on the principle of leverage tends to be the most popular method of bending copper tube, because:

- it eliminates possible damage to the knees
- the bend is usually tighter and neater in appearance
- it minimises the risk of 'rippling' of the pipe taking place during bending.

Spring bending

Internal or external bending springs may be used and the pipework may require annealing to bend it successfully. Here are a few key points:

- don't try to bend a piece of pipe that is too short
- when making 90° bends, always overpull the bend as this will make it easier to remove an internal spring
- it is possible to calculate the correct length of pipework to make a bend, this is particularly important with spring bending.

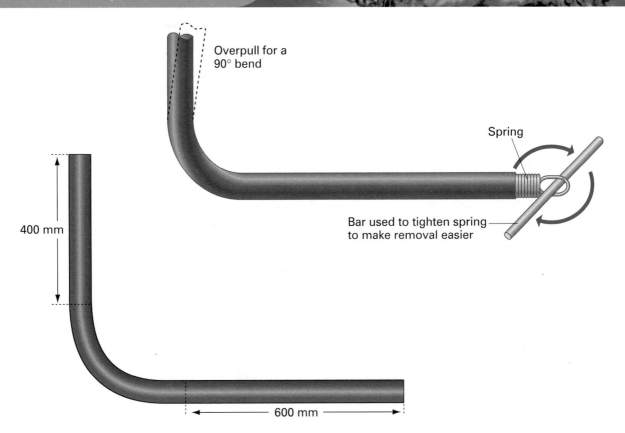

Overpull for a
90° bend

Spring

Bar used to tighten spring
to make removal easier

400 mm

600 mm

Figure 4.13 Apparent gain in length when tubing is bent

Calculate the length of pipe required to make the bend in the diagram.

First, determine the radius of the bend (usually 4 times the diameter of the pipe).

For a 15mm pipe:

$$\text{Bend length} = \frac{(4 \times \text{diameter}) \times 2 \times 3.14}{4 \text{ (quarter of a circle)}}$$

$$= \frac{15 \times 4 \times 2 \times 3.14}{4}$$

$$= 94\text{mm}$$

The length of pipe required to make the bend is therefore (600 + 400) + 94 = 1094mm.

LCS pipework

LCS pipe is bent using a hydraulic bending machine; the hydraulic machine is needed to bend the pipe, owing to its additional thickness. The hydraulic machine uses incompressible oil to exert force on the pipework. The oil level will need topping up in the machine from time to time. It should be noted that galvanised pipe is not suitable for bending as the coating may be lost during the bending process.

Figure 4.14 Hydraulic bending machine

Plastic pipework

Plastic pipework is hand-bent to shape using techniques similar to installing electric cables.

Fixing devices and brackets

Screws

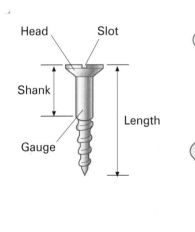

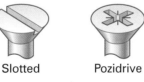
Slotted   Pozidrive

Phillips   Countersunk

Roundhead

Raised head

Pan head   Mirror screw head

Figure 4.15 Commonly used screws

Screws are specified by their length and gauge. Typical screw applications are:

- steel countersunk – for general purpose applications such as fixing pipe clips
- brass or alloy – for fixing components where moisture is present, such as sanitaryware and rainwater fittings
- self-tapping – fixing into metalwork
- chipboard – for fastening chipboard
- mirror – used where appearance is important, such as on bath panels.

Plastic plugs

The wall is drilled with the correct size masonry drill

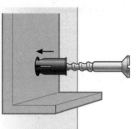
The correct size plug is inserted into the hole

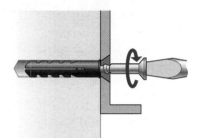
The right size screw is driven into the plug

Figure 4.16 Plug and screw fixings

Plug and screws are used to make fixings into masonry wall surfaces. The size of plug is chosen based on the size of the screw being used.

Figure 4.19 Clip spacing table

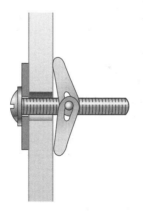

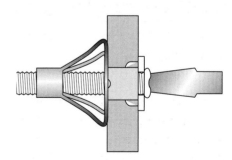

Figure 4.17 Spring toggle fixing

Figure 4.18 Collapsible anchor fixing

Plasterboard fixings

A variety of plasterboard fixings are available, the main types used are the spring toggle and the collapsible anchor, the latter needing a special tool to collapse the anchor.

Clips and brackets

Domestic copper pipework is usually fixed using plastic pipe clips, work on other building types where there is a greater risk of mechanical damage will include using more secure brass brackets.

Steel brackets are used on steel pipework.

Plastic clips of the nail-in or stand-off type are used for plastic pipework.

The following table shows the maximum clip spacing requirements for the various pipework materials:

Pipe size		Copper		LCS		Plastic pipe	
mm	in	horizontal (m)	vertical (m)	horizontal (m)	vertical (m)	horizontal (m)	vertical (m)
15	¾	1.2	1.8	1.8	2.4	0.6	1.2
22	1	1.8	2.4	2.4	3.0	0.7	1.4
28	1¼	1.8	2.4	2.4	3.0	0.8	1.5
35	1½	2.4	3.0	2.7	3.0	0.8	1.7
42	2	2.4	3.0	3.0	3.6	0.9	1.8
54	2½	2.7	3.0	3.0	3.6	1.0	2.1

Essentials of good plumbing work

There are a number of essential points that must be followed when carrying out plumbing work in order that the work runs smoothly:

- establish effective communication with the customer as the work progresses, including confirming items such as ornaments that require moving at the commencement of the job; confirm the location of components that are being fitted, such as radiators; as the work progresses, advise when services are being isolated and provide a general update on the progress of the job
- when working on sites with other trades, effective communication is a must to make sure that you are not interfering with each others' work and that you make provision when isolating services – a plasterer will not be pleased if you have not advised him/her that the water supply is to be turned off all day – at least giving them the opportunity to store some water is helpful!
- the work should be carried out in a logical sequence, with every effort being made to minimise the amount of time the system cannot be used,

so with an extension to an existing system the connection to the supply should be the last item of work carried out rather than the first

- when replacing bathroom suites with only one WC in the property, every attempt should be made to make the WC changeover within the same working day
- keep alert to dangers that you see while carrying out work informing your supervisor/the customer as necessary. Typical dangers could include:
  - building structural problems: woodworm in joists, structural collapse
  - electrical system problems: exposed wires, wires touching hot pipework, lack of earth continuity bonding
  - gas dangers: incorrect flames on gas appliances (burning yellow on radiant gas fires) and soot gathering on the surfaces of gas appliances. These indicate that immediate attention is required to the appliance, this work should only be carried out by a registered installer. Smells of gas at appliances should be checked by a registered installer. Gas smells from meter components and inlet pipework should be referred to the emergency service provider, whose contact details should be on the front of the meter.

Completing the work

- On completing the work the site must be left in a tidy condition, with all rubbish and debris removed from site (unless otherwise agreed with the customer).
- The system must be properly commissioned to ensure that it is working correctly.
- Commissioning records for the system must be completed.
- The user must be instructed on the operation of the system and any user instructions must be provided, together with a copy of the commissioning records.

Short answer questions

1. Which type of document details the type of fixings to be used for a soil and vent pipe?

2. How can stair carpets be protected from damage while carrying out the replacement of a bathroom suite?

3. What type of document details the exact price that a plumbers' merchant will supply materials for?

4. The distance between two tees in a pipeline measures 850mm. The x dimension of each tee (centre line of tee to position of end of pipe) is 12mm, what is the required length of pipe?

5. What is the maximum diameter that a hole can be drilled in a timber floor joist?

6. In what direction should the teeth of a junior hacksaw blade be pointing when fitted to the frame?

7. Tracking on copper tube can occur when using what type of hand tool?

8. When replacing a bathroom suite in a domestic property with no other facilities, which item of sanitary equipment should be replaced the same day?

9. What is the preferred type of exposed screw fixing for a bath panel?

10. A plumber smells gas at the emergency control valve near the meter, what action should be taken?

Multiple-choice test

1. The different phases of work that need to take place to complete the construction of a new dwelling are detailed in a:
   a) *Job specification*
   b) *Work programme*
   c) *Maintenance schedule*
   d) *Site drawing*

2. A plumbers' merchant should provide which one of the following documents when supplying materials to a private dwelling?
   a) *Invoice*   c) *Delivery note*
   b) *Order*   d) *Quotation*

3. Which one of the following shows that plumbing equipment has been manufactured to a recognised UK standard?
   a) *Good manufacturer name*
   b) *BSI Kitemark*
   c) *Trading Standards logo*
   d) *Water company logo*

4. What is the most important action to undertake when removing an old hot water storage cylinder across carpets in a private dwelling?
   a) *Plugging the cylinder tappings*
   b) *Cutting the cylinder up*
   c) *Using dust sheets*
   d) *Refusing to carry out the work*

5. Dust sheets are not onsite when replacing a fire back boiler, what action should be taken?
   a) *Carry on with the work*
   b) *Go and get some to do the work*
   c) *Move all the furniture, carpets etc. out of the room*
   d) *Use some bed linen from the landing cupboard*

6. A non-gas-qualified plumber notices soot marks above the radiants on a gas fire, what action should be taken?
   a) *Ignore it*
   b) *Investigate the cause of the sooting*
   c) *Report a defect in the installation to the customer*
   d) *Report the matter to the Health & Safety Executive*

7. Calculate the exact length of 15mm pipe required to form a spring bend to fit the following dimensions if the radius of the bend is 5 × the pipe diameter.

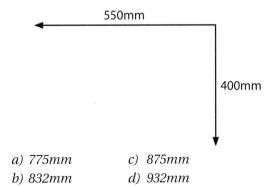

a) *775mm*   c) *875mm*
b) *832mm*   d) *932mm*

8. A first-floor joist has a span of 5m, the maximum distance from a wall that a notch may be cut into it is:
   a) 500mm
   c) 100mm
   b) 750mm
   d) 1250mm

9. What type of joint is shown below?

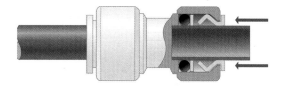

   a) Compression type A
   b) Compression type B
   c) Capillary solder ring
   d) Push fit

10. Which type of copper fitting requires a spool of solder wire to make the joint?
    a) Compression type A
    b) Compression type B
    c) Capillary end feed
    d) Capillary solder ring

11. What type of fitting requires a swaging tool to make the joint?
    a) Compression type A
    b) Compression type B
    c) Capillary end feed
    d) Capillary solder ring

12. What grade of copper tube is used for below-ground water supplies?
    a) Grade W
    c) Grade Y
    b) Grade X
    d) Grade Z

13. What type of bending machine is required to form bends in low carbon steel pipework?
    a) Hand bender
    c) Hydraulic bender
    b) Stand bender
    d) Chaser die set

14. Medium-grade LCS is identified by what colour coded banding?
    a) Red
    c) Blue
    b) Brown
    d) Yellow

15. Damage to ceramic tiles can be avoided when using a masonry drill bit by first:
    a) Applying adhesive tape across the hole to be drilled
    b) Using a small pilot drill to start the hole
    c) Removing the tile and cutting it
    d) Applying cutting oil to the masonry drill bit

16. What is the following type of plasterboard fixing?

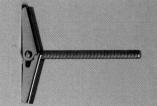

    a) Rubber nut fixing
    b) Spring toggle
    c) Collapsible anchor
    d) Butterfly fixing

17. What is the maximum recommended clip spacing interval for a 22mm vertical copper pipe?
    a) 1.2m
    c) 2.4m
    b) 1.8m
    d) 3.0m

18. A subcontractor working on a construction site is directly responsible to:
    a) The architect
    b) The clerk of works
    c) The site agent
    d) The main contractor

19. Which member of the construction team approves work as conforming with the requirements of the Building Regulations?
    a) Building control officer
    b) Quantity surveyor
    c) Site supervisor
    d) Structural engineer

20. On completing a job the customer:
    a) Should dispose of any rubbish
    b) Should be provided with any user instructions
    c) Must commission the work
    d) Must replace any goods damaged by the plumber

05 Cold water systems

By the end of this chapter you should be able to demonstrate understanding of the following cold water systems topics which will assist you in completing knowledge assessment in the Cold Water Systems Unit of the Level 2 Certificate in Basic Plumbing Studies:

- Sources of information:
  - Technical standards
  - Site information sources
- Types of system:
  - Direct system
  - Indirect system
  - Key features of cold water supply systems
- Cold water storage cisterns:
  - Linking cold water storage cisterns
- Soundness testing cold water storage cisterns:
  - Visual inspection
  - Testing for leaks
  - Pressure testing
  - Final checks
- Decommissioning of cold water systems:
  - Permanent decommissioning
  - Temporary decommissioning
- Maintaining cold water systems:
  - Typical cold water component maintenance activities
  - Typical cold water system faults.

Sources of information

There are a number of information sources that plumbers may have to use to obtain the necessary detail to undertake their work.

Technical standards

- Water Regulations – these lay down the statutory requirements that must be carried out when installing, commissioning and maintaining water systems. Responsibility for monitoring compliance with the Water

Did you know?

The Water Supply (Water Fittings) Regulations 1999 detail the water supply requirements that plumbers must work to.

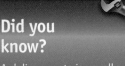

Regulations is given to the local water undertakers. Water Regulations documentation can be freely downloaded from www. defra.gov.uk, who also produce a guidance document to the Water Regulations.

- Water Fittings and Materials Directory – this is produced by the Water Regulations Advisory Scheme (WRAS), listing approved components and fittings for use in hot and cold water systems in the UK. The guide is freely accessible at www.wras.co.uk.
- British Standards – these support statutory documentation such as the Building Regulations, providing greater detail on installation requirements. Although British Standards are not statutory (legal) documents, they can be used in potential legal action relating to defective systems installation. The main British Standard relating to cold water supply is BS 6700 – Specification for design, installation, testing and maintenance of services supplying water for domestic use within buildings and their curtilages.
- Manufacturer instructions – these are provided by appliance or component manufacturers to outline the installation, commissioning and maintenance requirements of their products. Manufacturer instructions usually take precedence over British Standards, but should not conflict with Building or Water Regulations which are statutory (legal) requirements.

Site information sources

The following outlines the range of commonly used site information sources:

- site plans – site or location plans show the location of the building or site to adjacent roads, properties or services
- building plans – detailed plans for the property, showing key building details such as location of doors/windows, room sizes, boiler position, etc.
- services layout plans – detailed drawings of the building services such as pipe runs, position and layout
- job specification – provided as support to building plans, this details items such as the type, size and position of key components such as boilers
- work programme – details the point at which various points of plumbing work fit into the overall construction programme, e.g. first fix hot and cold water system
- bill of quantities – details the quantities of components and materials used on a job.

Types of system

There are two main types of cold water system used in domestic and smaller properties: the direct system and the indirect system.

To understand direct and indirect systems, let's look at some pipework terminology:

- supply pipe – a pipe under direct pressure from the mains
- distributing pipe – a pipe supplying water from a cistern that is under pressure from that cistern.

Direct system

Direct cold water systems should be used in medium to high water-pressure areas in circumstances where a reserve of stored water is not required should the main supply fail. The system is particularly suited to domestic properties.

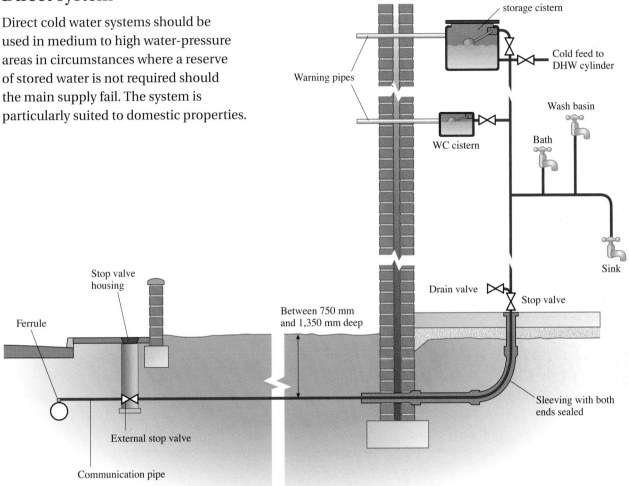

Figure 5.1 Direct cold water system

The advantages of a direct system are:

- it is cheaper to install because:
  - less pipework is required
  - the storage cistern is smaller (100 litre minimum)
- drinking water is available from all draw-off points
- there is less risk of frost damage, due to a smaller amount of pipework.

However, there are disadvantages:

- higher pressure may make the system noisy
- there is no reserve of cold water if the mains or service supply is shut off

Definition

Direct system – all the cold water outlets, e.g. bath, basin, etc. are drawn off the cold water supply pipe.

- there is more wear and tear on taps and valves, due to high pressure
- there is higher demand on the main at peak periods.

Indirect system

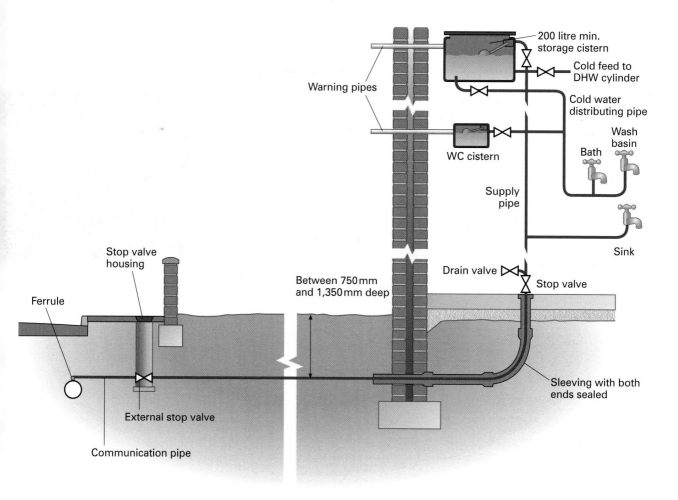

Warning pipes

200 litre min. storage cistern

Cold feed to DHW cylinder

Cold water distributing pipe

Wash basin

Bath

WC cistern

Supply pipe

Sink

Stop valve housing

Drain valve

Stop valve

Between 750 mm and 1,350 mm deep

Ferrule

External stop valve

Sleeving with both ends sealed

Communication pipe

Figure 5.2 Indirect cold water system

This system is normally used in circumstances in which the water supply pressure/flow rate to the property is low or a reserve of stored water is required to guard against mains failure.

The advantages of indirect systems are that there is:

- a reserve of water should the mains supply be turned off
- reduced risk of system noise due to lower pressures
- reduced risk of wear and tear on taps and valves, again due to lower pressure
- lower demand on the main at peak periods.

Definition

Indirect system – usually one outlet (the kitchen sink) is fed from the supply pipe, with the remaining cold water outlets such as WC, bath, etc. being fed from the cold water storage cistern.

The disadvantages are:

- an increased risk of frost damage
- the space occupied by the larger storage cistern (200 litre minimum)
- the additional cost of the storage cistern and pipework.

Key features of cold water supply systems

Determining the incoming water flow rate and pressure

One of the most important checks to be undertaken before carrying out work on a cold water system is to establish whether there is sufficient water pressure and flow rate to feed the appliance/system. There are two specialist tools used to measure this: a pressure gauge and a flow meter (weir cup).

Did you know?

If a flow rate reading is provided in litres/minute, then dividing the figure by 60 will provide the reading in litres/second.

Figure 5.3 Taking water pressure and flow rate readings

Flow rate readings are usually taken in litres/second and water pressure in bars.

Supply pipework to the building

Referring to the previous diagrams of the direct and indirect system (see Figures 5.1 and 5.2), the key features of the below-ground supply pipework are:

- small domestic properties will usually be provided with a minimum 15mm diameter water supply, the size of supply pipework required will increase with a larger property type or with greater demands placed on the system

- the underground service pipework must be laid at a minimum depth of 750mm to guard against frost and mechanical damage, and must be no deeper than 1350mm so that it is accessible for repair
- polythene plastic service pipework tends to be used for the majority of underground service pipework applications, this type of pipework is colour-coded blue and jointed using plastic or gunmetal compression-type fittings
- new underground service pipework in contaminated land may need to be in copper; some substances can permeate through plastic materials, so installing copper overcomes this problem. If copper is used:
  - it may need to be protected against corrosion through plastic coating or wrapping
  - the copper used should be R220 annealed (soft copper) in coils (old Grade Y)
  - there must be a minimum number of joints in underground pipework; acceptable pipe joints for underground supply pipework are soldered capillary firings (provided lead-free solder is used) and manipulative (type B) compression joints (standard non-manipulative type A compression joints are not suitable for underground use).
- service pipework must be ducted into the property so that it can be easily removed/repaired, and protected against ground settlement. The service pipework must rise into the property at least 750mm from the outer wall surface, to guard against frost, if this is not possible then the pipework must be insulated.

Isolation valves on small cold water systems

An accessible supply stop valve must be sited as near to the entry to the property as possible. A drain valve is usually sited near to the outlet of the stop valve to drain the system. On small domestic systems the stop valve will usually be a BS 1010 screwdown stop valve.

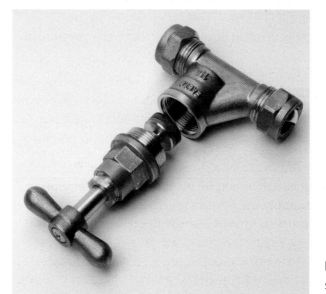

Figure 5.4 Screwdown stop valve

A supply stop valve may also be used on larger systems as an isolation valve for sections or parts of a system, e.g. the cold water supply to a complete bathroom.

Under the Water Regulations the water supply to each appliance fitted with a float-operated valve must be controlled by a service valve. Spherical plug valves will usually be used for this purpose. Care needs to be taken as some spherical plug valves are only suitable for medium- to high-pressure applications.

> **Did you know?**
>
> The common name for a spherical plug valve is a ball-o-fix valve.

Figure 5.5 Gate valve

Figure 5.6 Spherical plug valve

Each outlet from a cold water storage cistern must be fitted with a service valve for maintenance purposes. A gate valve is usually installed for this purpose and for other applications, because of its suitability for low-pressure applications.

Cold water pipework above ground level

The pipework installed inside the building will usually be manufactured from:

- polybutylene (plastic) – usually jointed by manufacturer proprietary push-fit fittings specifically designed for the pipework system; the manufacturer of the pipework system will usually provide guidance on pipe fixing/spacing requirements
- copper – produced in R250 half-hard lengths (old grade X) – pipework is usually jointed by lead-free soldered capillary fittings or by type A non-manipulative compression fittings; Figure 5.7 shows recommended pipe clip spacing requirements for standard tube sizes used for domestic applications.

> **Remember**
>
> Components such as pipework in unheated parts of the building or outside the building will need to be adequately insulated; the thickness of insulation is based on the degree of exposure.

Pipe size		Copper		LCS		Plastic pipe	
mm	in	horizontal (m)	vertical (m)	horizontal (m)	vertical (m)	horizontal (m)	vertical (m)
15	¾	1.2	1.8	1.8	2.4	0.6	1.2
22	1	1.8	2.4	2.4	3.0	0.7	1.4
28	1¼	1.8	2.4	2.4	3.0	0.8	1.5
35	1½	2.4	3.0	2.7	3.0	0.8	1.7
42	2	2.4	3.0	3.0	3.6	0.9	1.8
54	2½	2.7	3.0	3.0	3.6	1.0	2.1

Figure 5.7 Copper pipe clip spacing requirements

The Water Regulations indicate that galvanised steel pipe can be used on cold water installations, however this material is not commonly used in modern systems as the pipework can be susceptible to corrosion.

Cold water storage cisterns

Under the Water Regulations a storage cistern supplying any cold water outlets or feeding a hot water system must only supply wholesome water. Protection measures need to be included in the cistern design as shown in Figure 5.8.

Key requirements of cisterns are that they must be:

- fitted with an effective inlet control device to maintain the correct water level (usually a float-operated valve manufactured to BS 1212 part 2 or 3 with top outlet connection)
- fitted with service valves on inlet and outlet pipes
- fitted with screened warning/overflow pipes to warn of overflow – cisterns up to 1000 litre capacity have a combined warning/overflow pipe, above this capacity the warning and overflow pipes must be separate
- the float-operated valve must be set so that a minimum gap of 25mm is maintained between the water level and the invert of the warning pipe
- cold water distribution pipework should preferably be connected in the bottom of the cistern, this reduces the opportunity for sludge build-up and contamination risk
- as a safety feature, outlet connections to hot water systems must be sited above cold water connections, ensuring that if the water supply fails the hot supply runs out before the cold
- covered to exclude light or insects

Did you know?

WC cisterns usually have a BS 1010 part 4 float-operated valve which may include a collapsible bag as a silencing device, a silencer tube is not permitted on other types of float valve.

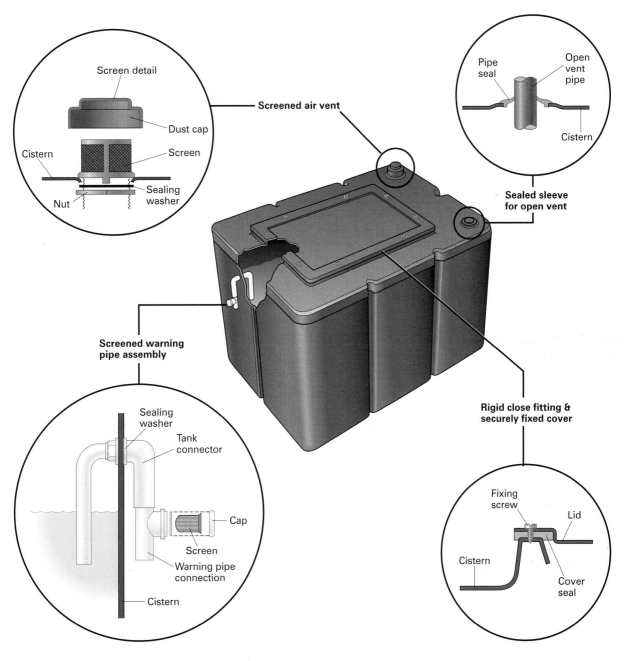

Figure 5.8 Cold water storage cistern supplying wholesome water

- insulated to prevent heat loss and undue warming
- installed so that the risk of contamination is minimised
- arranged so that water can circulate, preventing stagnation
- supported to avoid distortion or damage leading to leaks
- readily accessible for maintenance and cleaning, a minimum height of 350mm between the cistern access point and any adjacent surfaces, e.g. roof surfaces must be provided.

Plastic (polyethylene) cisterns are usually used for domestic properties. Care must be taken when cutting holes in the cisterns (usually carried out using a hole-saw). Pipework joints to the cistern must be made with plastic or rubber washers. On no account should putty or jointing compounds be used as these will degrade the plastic, resulting in cistern failure. Plastic cisterns may also require the installation of a metal stiffener plate (provided by the cistern manufacturer); this supports the cistern wall at the point at which the float valve enters the cistern, and is used to prevent possible pipe-vibration noises that may occur.

Linking cold water storage cisterns

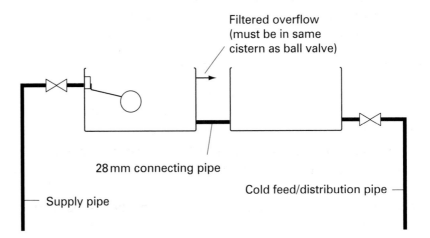

Figure 5.9 Outdated method of linking cisterns

In domestic properties it may be necessary to link two cisterns together. The above arrangement was commonly used in the past, it is possible however that stagnation may occur, so this method of linking is no longer widely used.

A well-designed cistern linking arrangement will include:

- the provision of inlets to *both* cisterns fed via float-operated valves
- the method of connecting the distribution pipes via a manifold arrangement taking equal draw-off from both cisterns simultaneously
- siting outlet connections at the opposite end to inlet connections, to allow effective water distribution across the cistern.

Soundness testing of cold water systems

The soundness testing of cold water systems involves a four stage process:

- visual inspection
- testing for leaks
- pressure testing
- final system checks.

Visual inspection

This is the process of preparing the system to be filled and tested. It will include such things as checking all joints are tight, all pipes are properly clipped, all valves are open, all cisterns are empty and clean, etc.

Testing for leaks

Slowly turn on the supply, fill each section of the pipework system in stages, checking each section for leakage. Open service valves to appliances and check for leaks and make sure the system is vented of air. Finally, ensure that the supply is fully turned on.

Pressure testing

Cold water systems are usually required to be pressure tested under the Water Regulations using a hydraulic (water) test. The following shows the procedures dependent on the pipework materials used in the system.

The procedure for testing rigid pipes (e.g. copper):

- make sure any open-ended pipes are sealed, e.g. vent pipes
- once the system has been filled, it should be allowed to stand for 30 minutes, to allow the water temperature to stabilise
- the system should be pressurised using the hydraulic testing equipment to a pressure of 1.5 times the system working pressure
- leave to stand for 1 hour
- check for visible leakage and loss of pressure; if sound, the test has been satisfactorily completed
- if not sound, repeat the test after locating and repairing any leaks.

The procedure for testing plastic pipes:

BS 6700 has two test procedures for plastic pipes: procedures A and B. See the Water Regulations for more details.

Test A procedure:

- apply test pressure (1.5 times maximum working pressure), which is maintained by pumping for a period of 30 minutes, and visually inspect for leakage
- reduce pressure by bleeding water from the system to 0.33 times maximum working pressure; close the bleed valve
- visually check and monitor for 90 minutes; if the pressure remains at or above 0.33 times working pressure, the system can be regarded as satisfactory.

Test B procedure:

- apply test pressure (1.5 times maximum working pressure) and maintain by pumping for a period of 30 minutes
- note the pressure and inspect visually for leakage
- note the pressure after a further 30 minutes; if the pressure drop is less than 60 kPa (0.6 bar), the system can be considered to have no obvious leakage. Next, visually check and monitor for 120 minutes; if the pressure drop is less than 20 kPa (0.2 bar), the system can be regarded as satisfactory.

Figure 5.10 Hydraulic pressure test

Did you know?

Air can sometimes be used to test pipework; it should only be used in exceptional circumstances on pipework in high-risk areas such as computer suites, as it can give unpredictable results.

Although the Water Regulations only identify the need for the soundness testing of systems and components on completion of the installation work, it may be necessary to undertake interim pressure testing of pipework sections as the installation progresses, this is particularly useful for pipework that is going to be concealed or that will not be accessible at the point of pressure testing.

Final checks

The system should then be thoroughly flushed out, and if it is in a non-domestic property it should be disinfected. It should then be fully performance tested (all controls set and flow rates and pressures measured) to check that it is working properly. It is then handed over to the customer, with any demonstration required on how the system/component works.

Decommissioning cold water systems

Permanent decommissioning

When a cold water system or component is permanently decommissioned, under the Water Regulations no 'dead-legs' (points of stagnation) should be left in the system. So, rather than just capping a tee branch, the whole tee should be removed, or in the case of a redundant water service pipe, it should be terminated as close to the mains as possible (usually by the water company).

When working on cold water systems that include electrical components it will usually be necessary to isolate the electrical supply to the component, this must be carried out using the safe isolation procedure. Whilst carrying out safe isolation in a domestic property it is usually regarded as safer to isolate at the consumer unit if possible, rather than at the appliance supply point (fused spur). The safe isolation procedure is shown in Figure 5.11.

Temporary decommissioning

Temporary decommissioning of a system may need to be carried out while the building is occupied and the following arrangements may need to be considered:

- the length of time that the system is going to be out of service – if it's relatively short then it may be appropriate for the customer to draw off a small supply before the work is carried out; if it's a longer period, or in a commercial building such as an office, it may be necessary to provide a temporary supply
- the customer must always be advised before any cold water supply is turned off, an estimate of the time the water is going to be off should be provided and he/she should be advised when it is turned back on
- in larger buildings, it may be necessary to put a warning notice at the stop valve (isolation point), confirming that the valve should not be

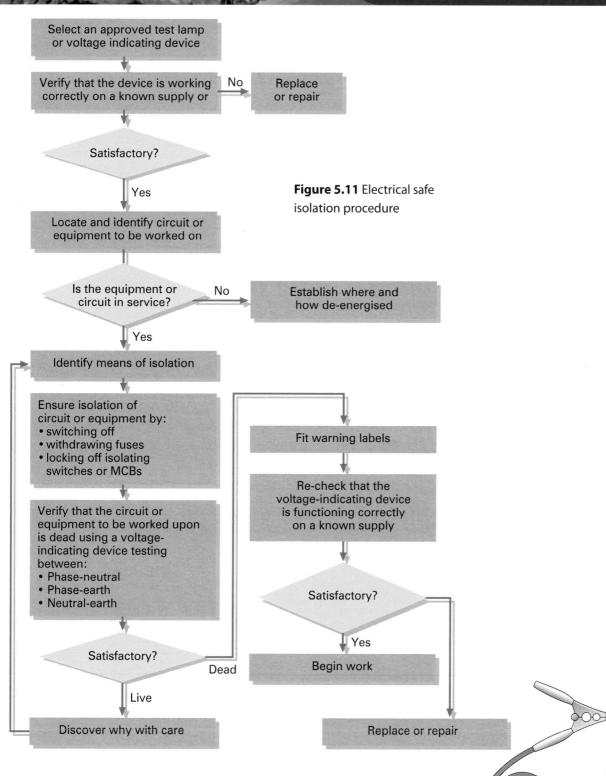

Figure 5.11 Electrical safe isolation procedure

Select an approved test lamp or voltage indicating device

Verify that the device is working correctly on a known supply or → No → Replace or repair

Satisfactory? → Yes

Locate and identify circuit or equipment to be worked on

Is the equipment or circuit in service? → No → Establish where and how de-energised

Yes

Identify means of isolation

Ensure isolation of circuit or equipment by:
• switching off
• withdrawing fuses
• locking off isolating switches or MCBs

Verify that the circuit or equipment to be worked upon is dead using a voltage-indicating device testing between:
• Phase-neutral
• Phase-earth
• Neutral-earth

Satisfactory? → Dead / Live → Discover why with care

Fit warning labels

Re-check that the voltage-indicating device is functioning correctly on a known supply

Satisfactory? → Yes → Begin work

Replace or repair

turned on. This is particularly important if the work that is being carried out is sited in a room away from the stop valve

• all open ends should be capped on systems connected to the mains while plumbers are not onsite, e.g. in the evenings; this guards against damage through the supply being turned on

• a temporary continuity bond must be applied to system components such as pipework, if the pipework is cut into or parts are removed; this

Figure 5.12 Temporary continuity bond

is to ensure that the earth protection and continuity of the system are maintained.

Maintaining cold water systems

Maintenance work is likely to involve communication with the customer, particularly relating to diagnosing the fault and agreeing to the work carried out. Companies have different policies relating to the job responsibilities of plumbers, particularly in relation to providing costs for undertaking work. In general terms, typical job responsibilities are as follows:

- plumbing apprentice – limited job responsibility – normally working with someone else who will assist in diagnosing faults, not normally involved in negotiating cost with customers
- Level 2 qualified plumber – will usually have significant responsibility in diagnosing faults but may need to refer back to his/her supervisor to deal with costing information/ordering parts and confirming costs with customers
- Level 3 qualified plumber – will usually have complete responsibility for diagnosing faults, including ordering parts and confirming costs/orders with customers.

Remember – the golden rule is always to fully communicate to customers the action that is needed to repair or replace parts, this includes the cost of the work. If this doesn't take place, complaints are likely to occur.

Typical cold water component maintenance activities

The following outlines the maintenance work/faults that may occur on a simple range of cold water system components.

Stop valve

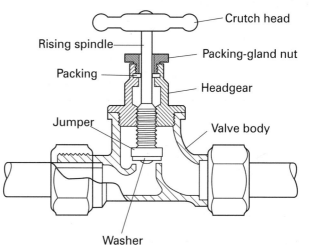

Figure 5.13 Stop valve

Common faults:

- the stop valve headgear is jammed and the valve will not turn off. It may be possible to remove the headgear, loosen the packing gland nut and lubricate the spindle and re-pack the gland; alternatively the valve may be replaced, or if a similar pattern of valve is available it may be possible to replace the headgear only

- the stop valve is leaking at the packing gland – re-pack the gland or in more serious cases replace the stop valve or its complete headgear
- the stop valve is passing water – the valve may be washered or if the valve seat is damaged the complete valve may require replacement.

Pillar tap

Common faults

Standard pillar tap:

- the tap is passing water when turned off – re-washer it; if the seat is damaged it may be necessary to use a re-seating tool to ensure that the washer properly seats
- the headgear is jammed or tight – the rising spindle will need lubricating and the gland re-packing; in more serious cases it may be necessary to replace the tap heads using a tap conversion kit, or replace the complete taps
- water appears under the head of the tap only when it is turned on – the gland requires re-packing, in more serious cases it may be necessary to replace the tap heads using a tap conversion kit, or replace the complete taps.

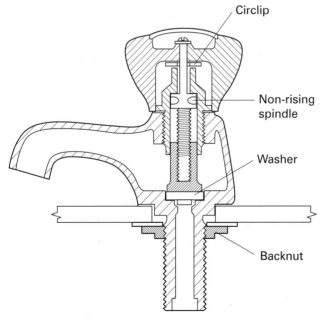

Figure 5.14 Pillar tap with non-rising spindle

Pillar tap with non-rising spindle:

- the tap is passing water when turned off – re-washer it; if the seat is damaged it may be necessary to use a re-seating tool to ensure that the washer properly seats
- faults associated with operation of the tap headgear usually require replacement of the tap heads using a conversion kit, or replacement of the complete taps.

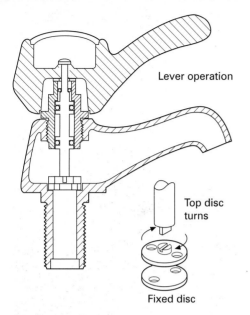

Figure 5.15 Ceramic disc tap

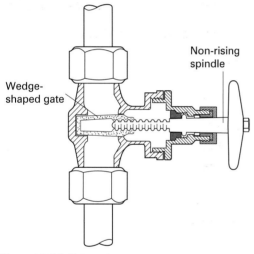

Figure 5.16 Gate valve

Quarter-turn (ceramic disc) taps

Common faults:

- the tap is passing water when turned off or the headgear is jammed – complete replacement of the ceramic disc cartridge.

Gate valve

Common faults:

- water leaking from the packing gland – re-pack the gland; in more serious cases replace the valve
- the headgear is stuck – re-pack the gland; in more serious cases replace the valve
- the valve passes water – replace the valve.

Float-operated valve

Common faults:

- the overflow is running over – here there are a number of possible solutions: re-washer the valve; if there's a piston sticking in the valve body it can be cleaned off; in more serious cases the whole valve may require replacement
- no water discharging from the valve, or poor flow and noise – a build-up of grit in the valve seat which requires removal; the lever arm is stuck in the valve body.

Figure 5.17 Float-operated valve

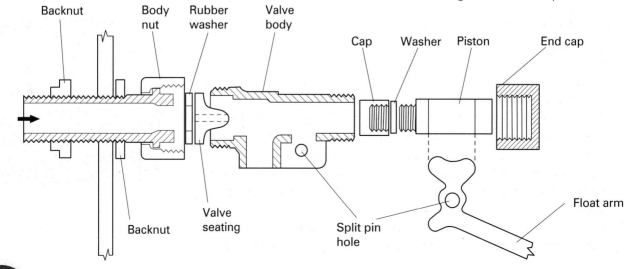

Shower mixer valve

The first check on a shower mixer valve is to ensure that the hot and cold supplies to the shower are functioning correctly, i.e. adequate flow rate and pressure.

Common faults:

Thermostatic mixers

- poor spray from the shower head – before moving on to check the mixer valve, it's worth looking to see if the spray plates in the shower head are blocked with scale
- poor flow rate – check to ensure that any strainers in the valve assembly are clear of grit; alternatively the cartridge may require replacement
- imbalance in the hot/cold water supply or the hot supply will not work – check the valve for correct adjustment, the cartridge may require replacement, the valve may also contain check valves that may be blocked or defective
- valve passes water when turned off – the cartridge needs replacement.

Figure 5.18 Shower mixer valve

Manual mixers

- poor flow rate – check to ensure that any strainers in the valve assembly are clear of grit
- imbalance in the hot/cold water supply or the hot supply will not work – check the valve for correct adjustment, check the pipework connections to see if the cold and hot water supplies are operating at equal pressure (both usually from storage), the valve headgear may require replacement
- valve passes water when turned off – the manufacturer may provide a re-washering kit or alternatively the complete valve headgear may require replacement.

Typical cold water system faults

Noise in systems

Common faults:

- flow noise – this is usually created by water travelling along the pipe at too high a speed. It may be possible to reduce the flow rate and hence the speed at which the water is flowing by installing a device known as a pressure-reducing valve. Blockages or grit build-up in components such as float-operated valves can create flow noise as well
- water hammer – usually created by valves shutting off suddenly, making a loud hammering noise, badly clipped pipework makes the problem worse
- vibration-type noises – they can be caused by loose or split tap washers, poorly clipped pipework and on cold water storage cisterns by stiffener

Remember

It's good practice when installing cold water pipework to use bends as opposed to elbows; they reduce frictional resistance in the pipework and assist in reducing noise levels.

plates not being fitted, usually in association with badly clipped pipework.

Copper pipework corrosion

Common faults:

- old brass fittings corroded via a process known as dezincification, a classic sign of this is a white powder on fitting surfaces
- pipework in contact with corrosive substances – pipework in contact with substances such as mortar and through constant contact with some cleaning materials can corrode and require replacement – the solution here is to ensure that the replacement pipework includes a protective coating
- acidic water supplies can cause rapid corrosion in copper pipework systems, typically a pin-holing effect will be seen.

Low cold water pressure

Common faults:

- valves that are not fully open may cause this problem and should usually be checked first
- some cold water components contain strainers or filters designed to prevent grit entering them, these require cleaning from time to time; if they haven't been cleaned for some time complete blockage can occur
- it's possible that there is an underground burst on the service pipework – this can be checked by listening for any water-flow noise in the supply pipework when no water is being drawn off in the property.

Leaks

It goes without saying that these need repairing wherever they occur. Remember that condensation can form on pipework and components and appear like a leak when there isn't actually one there.

Did you know?

Air locks causing no, or limited, water flow from outlets can occur in low-pressure cold water distribution pipework not laid to the proper self-venting falls.

Short answer questions

1. What is the minimum diameter of a cold water supply (service) pipe to a domestic property?
2. The incoming flow rate to a property is measured as 10 litres/minute, what is this expressed in litres/second?
3. What is the following BS symbol?

4. Under the Water Regulations a common warning and overflow pipe may be used with cold water storage cisterns up to what capacity?
5. What are the key points in safely isolating an electrical pump on a cold water supply before working on it?
6. When temporarily decommissioning a cold water system in order to carry out work in a room a distance from where the isolation valve is sited, what action is considered to be good practice?
7. When carrying out cold water systems maintenance work, when may it be a requirement to complete a maintenance record?
8. Replacement ceramic discs may be required to undertake maintenance on which type of plumbing component?
9. Under the Water Regulations, which type of float-operated valve must not be used on a new WC cistern?
10. What is the most likely cause of a high-pitched vibrating-type noise when the screwdown pillar tap on a basin is opened?

Multiple-choice test

1. The legal requirements for installing cold water systems are laid down in which document for England and Wales?
   a) Water Byelaws
   b) Water Regulations
   c) BS 6700
   d) Building Regulations

2. The detailed installation requirements for a domestic water softener will be found in:
   a) BS 5449
   b) Water Regulations
   c) Manufacturer instructions
   d) Building Regulations

3. The maximum depth at which an incoming water supply pipe should be laid is:
   a) 500mm
   b) 740mm
   c) 1350mm
   d) 2000mm

4. What action should be taken when a supply pipe enters a building through a solid floor at a distance of less than 750mm from the outside wall surface?
   a) The vertical pipe length to below ground must be insulated
   b) Trace heating must be applied to the pipework
   c) The installation is not permitted
   d) The pipe must be moved so that it is more than 750mm from the outer wall

5. Polythene cold water service pipe for underground use is colour coded:
   a) Blue
   b) Red
   c) Brown
   d) Yellow

6. What component must be sited immediately after the supply stop valve on entry to a property?
   a) Drain valve
   b) Service valve
   c) Single-check valve
   d) Double-check valve

7. Which type of cold water system should be used where there is a poor incoming water supply pressure?
   a) Direct
   b) Indirect
   c) Pump on the supply
   d) Combination

8. What is the recommended minimum capacity of a cold water storage cistern in a domestic property?
   a) 50 litre
   b) 100 litre
   c) 200 litre
   d) 350 litre

9. What type of valve should be fitted to isolate a cold water storage cistern?
   a) Globe valve
   b) Service valve
   c) Supply stop valve
   d) Float-operated valve

10. Under the Water Regulations, what is the preferred method of connecting cold water distribution pipework into storage cisterns?
    a) In the base of the cistern
    b) In the side wall at high level
    c) In the side wall at low level
    d) In the cistern lid

11. Which of the following includes a filter when connected to a cold water storage cistern?
    a) Supply pipe
    b) Distribution pipe
    c) Vent pipe
    d) Warning pipe

12. A method of checking to confirm whether a cold water system is direct or indirect is to:
    a) Take a measurement of the incoming water-flow rate into the property
    b) Establish the number and type of connections from the cold water storage cistern
    c) Pressure test the installation and take readings
    d) Check the records kept by the local water company

13. The greatest risk of water contamination will be created by:
    a) A cold water storage cistern fitted without a lid
    b) A supply pipe over 12 metres in length
    c) A bath left filled with dirty water
    d) A WC cistern fitted without a lid

14. The minimum distance between the water level in a cold water storage cistern and the invert level of the overflow should be:
    a) 15mm
    b) 25mm
    c) 50mm
    d) 75mm

15. Which type of pipework must not be installed in cold water systems?
    a) Low-carbon steel
    b) Galvanised low-carbon steel
    c) Polybutylene
    d) Copper

16. What is the recommended maximum clip distance for a horizontal 15mm copper pipe?
    a) 1.2m
    b) 1.8m
    c) 2.4m
    d) 3.0m

17. The cold water test pressure for metallic pipework should be:
    a) At least 3 bar pressure
    b) At least 5 bar pressure
    c) Twice the maximum working pressure
    d) 1.5 times the maximum working pressure

18. The soundness test on a cold water system with metallic pipework should last for:
    a) 15 minutes
    b) 30 minutes
    c) 45 minutes
    d) 60 minutes

19. When removing a cold water storage cistern as part of a conversion to a system fed by a combination boiler, the cold water supply to the cistern:
    a) Must be capped in the loft space
    b) Must be capped in the airing cupboard
    c) Must be completely removed by removing the tee supplying it from the supply pipework
    d) Must be capped at the branch on the tee supplying it

20. Before you leave site for the night, open-ended pipework connected to a live cold water system must be:
    a) Blanked with rag
    b) Sealed with watertight caps
    c) Blanked by crimping the copper pipe ends
    d) Blanked with wooden wedges

21. A stop valve that is passing water can be repaired by:
    a) Re-washering the valve
    b) Re-packing the gland
    c) Replacing the packing gland
    d) Heating it with a blow torch

22. Which kind of tap includes a circlip as part of its headgear assembly?
 a) A standard pillar tap
 b) A quarter-turn ceramic disc
 c) A pillar tap with non-rising spindle
 d) A globe tap

23. Where it is necessary to isolate the cold water supply to the only toilet block in an office for a period of up to 4 hours, what is the best advice to minimise disruption to the company?
 a) Do the work outside normal hours
 b) Get on with the job as quickly as possible
 c) Provide temporary portable toilet facilities
 d) Ask the water company to provide a temporary supply

24. A high-pitched vibrating noise is coming from the float-operated valve to a plastic cold water storage cistern. Which of the following is the likeliest cause of the problem?
 a) The wrong type of float valve has been fitted
 b) The cistern has been fitted without its float valve support plate
 c) The water level in the cistern is too high
 d) The water level in the cistern is too low

25. A supply stop valve has been fitted as the service valve to a cold water storage cistern. What action is necessary?
 a) Fit a spherical plug valve
 b) Fit a gate valve
 c) Fit a globe valve
 d) No action is necessary

26. The cold water distribution pipe from a storage cistern to a bath does not appear to be passing water after the system has been filled. All valves have been checked to establish that they are open, what is the most likely cause of the problem?
 a) An air lock in the pipework
 b) The float valve has been incorrectly set
 c) A build up of sludge in the cistern
 d) The cistern lid has been left off

27. A defect in the valve seat can be repaired in which of the following components?
 a) Gate valve
 b) Spherical plug valve
 c) Pillar tap
 d) Double-check valve

28. Pipework joints to a cold water storage cistern should be made with:
 a) Putty
 b) Jointing compound
 c) Plastic washers
 d) Silicone sealant

29. Pinholing of copper tube is more likely to be caused by:
 a) Acidic water
 b) Alkaline water
 c) Water containing nitrates
 d) Water containing carbonates

30. When cutting into metallic pipework for safety purposes, which of the following types of equipment must be applied to the pipework?
 a) De-sludging device
 b) Pipe freezing kit
 c) Temporary continuity bond
 d) Pipe jig

By the end of this chapter you should be able to demonstrate understanding of the following hot water systems topics which will assist you in completing knowledge assessment in the Domestic Hot Water Systems Unit of the Level 2 Certificate in Basic Plumbing Studies:

- Sources of information:
  - Technical standards
  - Site information sources
- Types of system:
  - Vented direct system
  - Vented indirect system
  - Hot water storage cylinders
  - Feed and expansion cisterns to indirect systems
  - Water heaters
  - Secondary hot water circulation systems
  - Showers
  - Hot water pipework above ground level
- Soundness testing hot water systems:
  - Visual inspection
  - Testing for leaks
  - Pressure testing
  - Final checks
- Decommissioning hot water systems:
  - Permanent decommissioning
  - Temporary decommissioning
- Maintaining hot water systems:
  - Typical hot water component maintenance activities
  - Typical hot water system faults.

Sources of information

There are a number of information sources that plumbers may have to use to obtain the necessary detail to undertake their work.

Technical standards

- Water Regulations – these lay down the statutory requirements that must be carried out when installing, commissioning and maintaining water systems. Responsibility for monitoring compliance with the Water Regulations is given to the local water undertakers. Water Regulations documentation can be freely downloaded from www. defra.gov.uk, who also produce a guidance document to the Water Regulations.
- Water Fittings and Materials Directory – this is produced by the Water Regulations Advisory Scheme (WRAS), listing approved components and fittings for use in hot and cold water systems in the UK, the guide is freely accessible at www.wras.co.uk.
- British Standards – these support statutory documentation such as the Building Regulations, providing greater detail on installation requirements. Although British Standards are not statutory (legal) documents, they can be used in potential legal action relating to defective systems installation. The main British Standard relating to hot water supply is BS 6700 – Specification for design, installation, testing and maintenance of services supplying water for domestic use within buildings and their curtilages.
- Manufacturer instructions – these are provided by appliance or component manufacturers to outline the installation, commissioning and maintenance requirements of their products. Manufacturer instructions usually take precedence over British Standards, but should not conflict with Building or Water Regulations which are statutory (legal) requirements.

Site information sources

The following outlines the range of site information sources that are commonly used:

- site plans – site or location plans show the location of the building or site to adjacent roads, properties or services
- building plans – detailed plans for the property, showing key building details such as location of doors/windows, room sizes, boiler position, etc.
- services layout plans – detailed drawings of the building services such as pipe runs, position and layout
- job specification – often provided as support to building plans, this details items such as the type, size and position of key components such as boilers
- work programme – details the point at which various aspects of plumbing work fit into the overall construction programme, e.g. first fix hot and cold water system
- A delivery note is usually provided by a merchant when delivering materials and an advice note is usually provided when payment of an invoice has been received.

Did you know?

Water undertakers refers to the local water authority/company who supplies water in your area, e.g. Severn Trent, Thames Water.

Key fact

British Standards
BS 8000 Part 15 details the requirements for the correct installation of hot and cold pipework in domestic properties.

Did you know?

A bill of quantities details the quantities of components and materials used on a job.

Types of system

Vented direct system

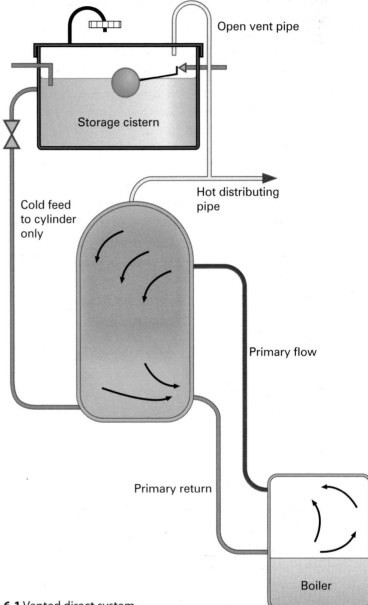

Figure 6.1 Vented direct system

This system is no longer widely used. It works on the principle of water heated in a boiler which rises (when heated) using the process of gravity circulation, causing hot water to circulate to the hot water storage cylinder. The cooler water returning to the boiler from the cylinder by the return pipe is heavier – so a circulation effect is set up.

A more common form of direct system used today is one that uses electric immersion heaters as the heat source (no boiler used); typically there are two immersion heaters sited in the cylinder: one at high level, one at low level. Two immersion heaters are used as an environmental/economy measure, with the upper immersion heater heating only a small portion of the cylinder, usually for daytime use, and the lower heater heating the whole of the cylinder for early-morning and evening use.

Key additional points of systems installed in domestic properties are:

- short runs of primary flow and return pipework will usually be 22mm in diameter (28mm may be required for longer runs)
- the system pipework must be laid to proper falls, otherwise it will air lock and fail to operate correctly
- there must be a clear open path (not valved) from the boiler through the primary flow, cylinder and to the storage cistern via the open vent pipe
- in a small domestic property the open vent and cold feed pipework will usually be 22mm, larger properties will have larger pipe sizes
- there should be a minimum of 450mm between the hot water draw-off from the cylinder and the point at which the open vent pipe is connected into the system; this is to prevent one-pipe circulation and wastage of heat
- the system is not suitable for use in hard-water areas, as a constant supply of fresh water in the system will lead to potential blockage of the pipework, which can be very dangerous
- the boiler and system pipework must be manufactured from a material that will not contaminate the water supply, such as copper
- no other supplies should be connected into the cold feed pipe.

Vented indirect system

Here there are two types of cylinder that can be used:

Double-feed indirect system

Key features of the double-feed indirect system are:

- water in the primary circuit does not mix with that in the secondary circuit, so the system is particularly suited for use in hard-water areas as the primary circuit will not be constantly exposed to circulating fresh water. The boiler and primary circuit pipework can therefore be manufactured from a variety of different materials including steels
- the primary flow and return pipework to this type of system will usually be a minimum of 28mm diameter as the system will usually be fed by a higher-output back boiler
- a separate feed and expansion cistern (f&e) is provided to supply primary water to the system
- the open vent pipe from the primary circuit must discharge over the f&e cistern and not the cold water cistern, and the open vent pipe from the secondary circuit must discharge over the cold water storage cistern and not the f&e cistern – this is for safety purposes in the event of overheating and to prevent water in the cold water storage cistern from becoming contaminated.

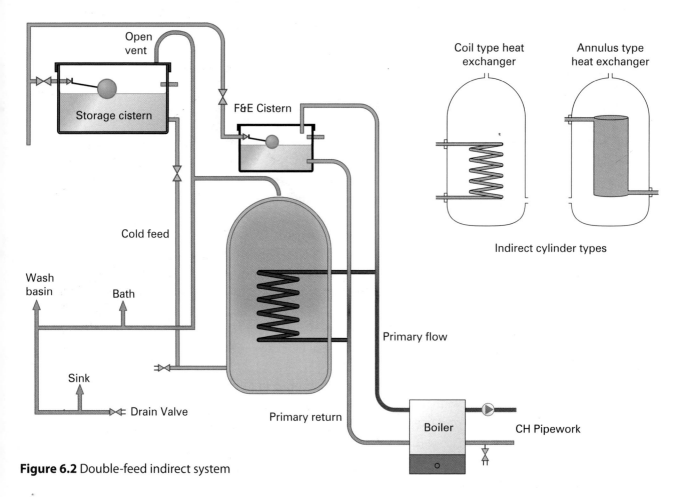

Figure 6.2 Double-feed indirect system

Single-feed indirect system

Key points of the single-feed type of cylinder (see Figure 6.3):

- water enters the primary circuit via a number of holes at the top of the vertical pipe immediately under the upper dome
- the system is self-venting through the air vent pipe while the primary circuit is filling
- once the primary circuit is filled, the filling of the secondary supply (the one that feeds the appliances) continues
- when the secondary supply is full, two air seals are formed and a permanent seal is maintained
- once the water is heated, expansion of the water in the primary circuit is taken up by forcing the air from the upper dome.

Other factors that need to be considered:

- if the primary circulation system is too large, an excessive amount of expanded water could remove the air bubble in the cylinder, causing the mixing of the two waters with possible corrosion effects/contaminated hot water

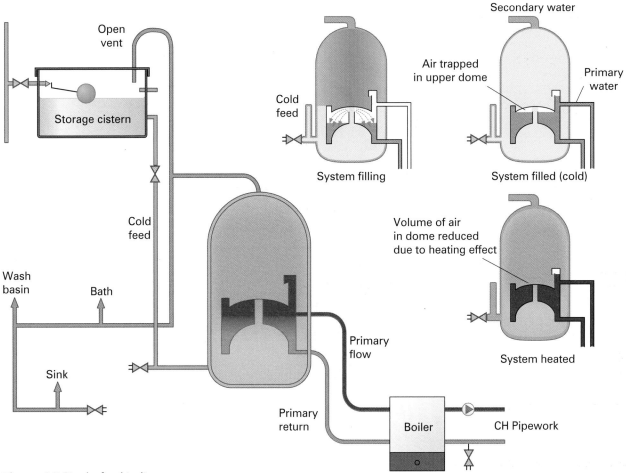

Figure 6.3 Single-feed indirect system

- circulating pumps on the primary pipework can also cause loss of the air bubble
- corrosion inhibitors cannot be added to protect the primary system.

There are quite a few disadvantages to using single-feed indirect cylinders and therefore their installation is not now normally considered.

Hot water storage cylinders

Standard direct and indirect cylinders

Key requirements of hot water storage cylinders are:

- the following cylinders must be manufactured to the following standards:
  - direct cylinder – BS 699
  - indirect single-feed cylinder (self priming) – BS 1566 part 2
  - indirect double-feed cylinder – BS 1566 part 1
- new and replacement cylinders must be adequately insulated; most cylinders are now pre-insulated

Did you know?

Under Part L1 of the Building Regulations the primary flow and return pipework and the secondary outlet from the cylinder must be insulated for a length of at least 1 metre from the cylinder, or up to a point where it becomes concealed.

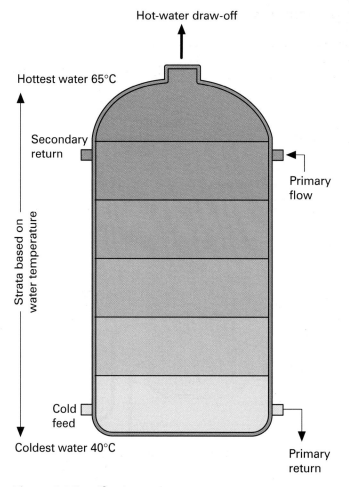

Figure 6.4 Stratification

- storage cylinders in domestic properties need to be properly sized to meet hot water demands, a typical small domestic property will have a minimum 100 litre capacity cylinder
- a drain-off point must be provided, either at the bottom of the cylinder or at the point where the cold-feed pipe enters the cylinder
- a process known as stratification (layers of water of differing temperatures) usually takes place in the cylinder and this needs to be taken into account when siting thermostats and sizing cylinders
- a thermostat on a standard cylinder is usually sited approximately one-third up from the base of the cylinder
- cylinders sometimes contain a sacrificial anode manufactured from magnesium, to guard against pitting corrosion
- new and replacement cylinders must be properly commissioned following their installation, this includes the proper completion of a commissioning certificate, usually in the form of a 'sticky label' fixed to the cylinder.

Combination-type cylinders

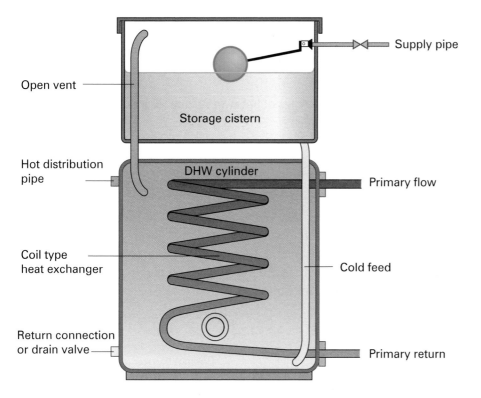

Figure 6.5 Combination storage cylinder

You may come across combination-type cylinders such as that shown in Figure 6.5. The cold water storage cistern and hot water storage cylinder are part of one complete unit. They tended to be used in flats, but their use is now somewhat limited as the head (pressure) of water generated in the hot water system is low and typically will not now meet minimum Water Regulation requirements.

Feed and expansion cisterns to indirect systems

There are a number of requirements that need to be considered regarding feed and expansion cisterns to indirect hot water systems:

- the size of cistern for a normal domestic application will be 10 litre nominal capacity
- there is no requirement to protect the cistern with filtered vents as in the cold water storage cistern, it should however be provided with a suitable lid and be insulated if installed in an unheated or exposed location
- there should be at least a 25mm air gap between the water level in the cistern and the invert level of the overflow, (remember water in a hot water system expands so the air gap referred to must be maintained when the system is in its heated condition)
- there must be no service valve on the cold-feed pipe to the primary circuit, this is a safety feature and ensures that in the event of overheating a constant supply of cooler water can enter the system

Did you know?

Combination-type storage cylinders should be manufactured to BS 3198.

- the vent pipe from the primary circuit must discharge over the feed and expansion cistern and not over the cold water storage cistern. This would present a water contamination risk and could be dangerous in the event of the system overheating.

Water heaters

There are essentially two types of hot water heater working on the following principles:

- storage system
- non-storage system.

Storage systems

Heaters such as the gas-fired one shown in Figure 6.6 are used to supply multiple hot water outlets in the property. The amount of stored water in the heater is dependent on the hot water usage in the property; the heater is therefore available in a range of sizes.

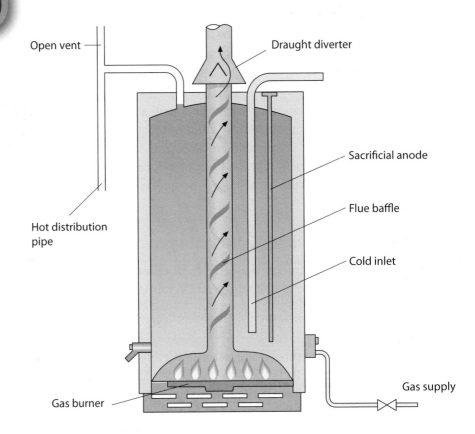

Figure 6.6 Multiple-outlet direct-fired water heater

Open vent

Draught diverter

Hot distribution pipe

Sacrificial anode

Flue baffle

Cold inlet

Gas supply

Gas burner

Single-point storage heaters, such as that shown in Figure 6.7, are also available. They can be inlet- or outlet-controlled and are designed to supply hot water to one appliance only.

Non-storage systems

These are often called instantaneous water heaters. They are usually supplied direct from the mains water supply and work on the principle of heating cold water by passing it through a heat exchanger. The speed at which the water is heated is limited, due to the amount of heat that can be put into the water over a relatively short period of time. This type of heater is not therefore suitable for supplying a large number of outlets at once, as the flow rate from the heater will be unsuitable to meet the demands of all the outlets at once.

There are essentially two types of non-storage heater, the first as shown in Figure 6.8 is the multipoint (this is the type of heater that the combination boiler is based on).

A single-point instantaneous heater is also available, as shown in Figure 6.9. This type of heater is used to feed single appliances, typically sinks; an electric shower is a type of single-point instantaneous water heater.

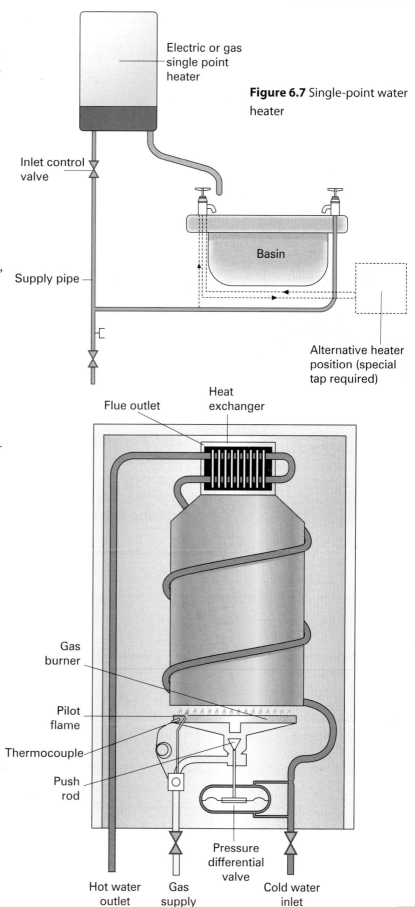

Figure 6.7 Single-point water heater

Figure 6.8 Multipoint water heater

Figure 6.9 Single-point instantaneous heater

Secondary hot water circulation systems

Long dead legs between hot water storage cylinders and hot water outlets should be avoided because:

- they waste water, as a significant volume of cold water needs to be run off before it turns hot; this problem can be the cause of customer complaint
- they waste energy as the hot water contained in the dead leg will rapidly cool, meaning that it will have to be completely drawn off for hot water to be available at the tap again.

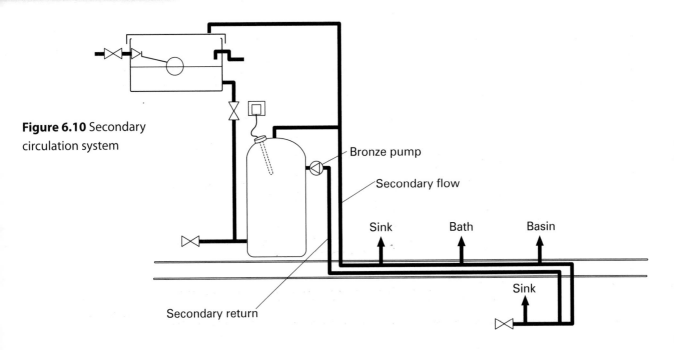

Figure 6.10 Secondary circulation system

Bronze pump

Secondary flow

Sink   Bath   Basin

Sink

Secondary return

A common method of overcoming this problem, particularly in larger systems, is to install a secondary circulation system. A flow and return pipework loop is installed, circulating water around the appliances; the water is usually circulated around the loop by means of a non-corroding bronze pump.

The return pipe is connected in the top one-third of the cylinder to prevent the cooler water at lower levels in the cylinder mixing with the hot water. In buildings where the hot water is not used 24 hours a day, such as an office block, a time clock will be fitted to control the operation of the pump to prevent water circulation taking place when the system is not in use.

Did you know?

Energy saving
The use of a time clock on a secondary circuit saves energy by preventing the pump from operating when the building is not in use.

Showers

Mains fed

Showers can be fed directly from the mains supply. Care should be taken to ensure that the shower mixer valve being used is suitable for the supply pressure; the shower mixer valve must be a thermostatic type to guard against scalding should the cold water supply reduce. Valves of this type will also require protection against backflow under the Water Regulations.

Gravity-fed from storage

There usually needs to be a minimum head of 1 metre between the top of the shower rose and the base of the cold water storage cistern to establish

Did you know?

It is possible that the water supply pressure in the property may be too high for a particular shower valve, in which case it may be necessary to install a pressure-reducing valve.

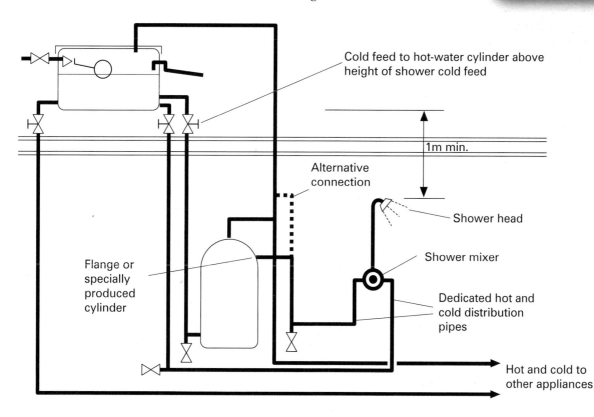

Figure 6.11 Gravity-fed shower from storage

an adequate water pressure. The supplies to the shower (both hot and cold) in a domestic system should come from their own dedicated supplies (not feeding other appliances); this ensures that the supply is not interrupted while the shower is being used. Low-pressure manual shower mixer valves or thermostatic valves may be used; thermostatic mixers are a safer alternative. The storage capacity of the cold water storage cistern will need to be increased if it is used to supply a shower. Typical storage volumes start at 200 litres.

Pumped showers

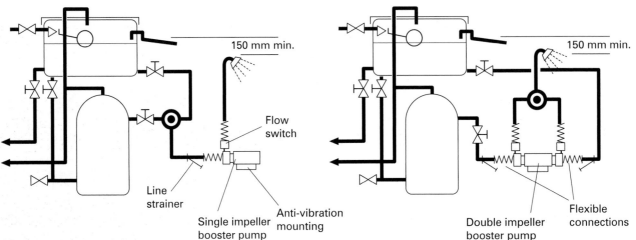

Figure 6.12 Pumped shower

A shower booster pump may be used to provide better performance from showers in storage systems. There are two types of pump that can be used:

- single impellor – sited between the shower mixer and the shower rose (although these are available they are not used very often as they provide a lower performance and can be difficult to site)
- double impellor – sited before the shower mixer valve.

Shower pumps are suitable for low-head applications, only usually requiring a minimum head of 150mm to make the flow switch work correctly. The pump must be carefully sited in order to avoid customer complaints, and it must have:

- anti-vibration mountings at its base to minimise noise production and damage through movement of the pump whilst in operation
- flexible connections at the inlets and outlets to avoid possible leakage through cracking of joints owing to pump movement whilst in operation.

Hot water pipework above ground level

The pipework installed inside the building will usually be manufactured from:

- polybutylene (plastic) – usually jointed by manufacturer proprietary push-fit fittings specifically designed for the pipework system, the manufacturer of the pipework system will usually provide guidance on pipe fixing/spacing requirements
- copper – produced in R250 half-hard lengths (old Grade X) – pipework is usually jointed by lead-free soldered capillary fittings or by type A non-manipulative compression fittings; the following chart shows recommended pipe clip spacing requirements for standard tube sizes used for domestic applications.

Pipe size		Copper		LCS		Plastic pipe	
mm	in	horizontal (m)	vertical (m)	horizontal (m)	vertical (m)	horizontal (m)	vertical (m)
15	¾	1.2	1.8	1.8	2.4	0.6	1.2
22	1	1.8	2.4	2.4	3.0	0.7	1.4
28	1¼	1.8	2.4	2.4	3.0	0.8	1.5
35	1½	2.4	3.0	2.7	3.0	0.8	1.7
42	2	2.4	3.0	3.0	3.6	0.9	1.8
54	2½	2.7	3.0	3.0	3.6	1.0	2.1

Figure 6.13 Copper pipe clip spacing requirements

The Water Regulations indicate that galvanised steel pipe can be used on hot water installations, it is not however commonly used in modern systems as the pipework can be susceptible to corrosion.

Service valves in the form of gate valves which are more suited to low-pressure applications are usually fitted on the outlets from cold water storage cisterns, on cold-feed supplies to hot water storage cylinders and as individual appliance isolation valves, such as on supplies to showers.

Soundness testing hot water systems

The soundness testing of hot water systems involves a four-stage process:

- visual inspection
- testing for leaks
- pressure testing
- final system checks.

Visual inspection

This is the process of preparing the system to be filled and tested, and will include such things as checking all joints are tight, all pipes are properly clipped, all valves are open, all cisterns are empty and clean, etc.

Testing for leaks

Slowly turn on the supply, fill each section of the pipework system in stages, checking each section for leakage. Open service valves to appliances and check for leaks, and make sure the system is vented of air, finally ensure that the supply is fully turned on.

Pressure testing

Hot water systems are usually required to be pressure tested under the Water Regulations using a hydraulic (water) test. The following shows the procedures dependent on the pipework materials used in the system:

The procedure for testing rigid pipes, e.g. copper:

- make sure any open-ended pipes are sealed, e.g. vent pipes
- once the system has been filled, it should be allowed to stand for 30 minutes, to allow the water temperature to stabilise
- the system should be pressurised using the hydraulic testing equipment to a pressure of 1.5 times the system working pressure
- leave to stand for 1 hour
- check for visible leakage and loss of pressure; if sound, the test has been satisfactorily completed
- if not sound, repeat the test after locating and repairing any leaks.

The procedure for testing plastic pipes:

BS 6700 has two test procedures for plastic pipes: procedures A and B. See Water Regulations for more details.

Test A procedure:

- apply test pressure (1.5 times maximum working pressure), which is maintained by pumping for a period of 30 minutes, and visually inspect for leakage
- reduce pressure by bleeding water from the system to 0.33 times maximum working pressure; close the bleed valve
- visually check and monitor for 90 minutes; if the pressure remains at or above 0.33 times working pressure, the system can be regarded as satisfactory.

Test B procedure:

- apply test pressure (1.5 times maximum working pressure) and maintain by pumping for a period of 30 minutes
- note the pressure and inspect visually for leakage

- note the pressure after a further 30 minutes. If the pressure drop is less than 60 kPa (0.6 bar), the system can be considered to have no obvious leakage; next, visually check and monitor for 120 minutes. If the pressure drop is less than 20 kPa (0.2 bar), the system can be regarded as satisfactory.

Although the Water Regulations only identify the need for the soundness testing of systems and components on completion of the installation work, it may be necessary to undertake interim pressure testing of pipework sections as the installation progresses, this is particularly useful for pipework that is going to be concealed or will not be accessible at the point of pressure testing.

Final system checks

The system should then be thoroughly flushed out and if it's in a non-domestic property it should be disinfected. It should then be fully performance tested (all controls set and flow rates and temperatures measured to check that it is working properly). It is then handed over to the customer, including any demonstration required on how the system/component works.

Decommissioning hot water systems

Permanent decommissioning

When a hot water system or component is permanently decommissioned, under the Water Regulations no 'dead legs' (points of stagnation) should be left in the system. So rather than just capping a tee branch, the whole tee should be removed.

When working on hot water systems that include electrical components it will usually be necessary to isolate the electrical supply to the component; this must be carried out using the safe isolation procedure. Whilst carrying out safe isolation in a domestic property it is usually regarded as safer to isolate at the consumer unit if possible, rather than isolating at the appliance supply point (fused spur).

Temporary decommissioning

Temporary decommissioning of a system may need to be carried out while the building is occupied. The following arrangements may need to be considered:

- the length of time that the system is going to be out of service – if it's relatively short then it may not be necessary to advise the customer of turning off the hot water supply
- in larger buildings, it may be necessary to put a warning notice at the service valve (isolation point), confirming that the valve should not be turned on; this is particularly important if the work that is being carried out is sited in a room away from the valve

Definition

Temporary decommissioning – the process of taking a system or component out of action for a short time to work on it.

Permanent decommissioning – the process of taking a system or component permanently out of action and completely removing it from the building.

Did you know?

On larger systems it may be necessary to complete a decommissioning record for both temporary and permanent decommissioning.

- all open ends should be capped on systems connected to live supplies while plumbers are not on site, e.g. in the evenings, this guards against damage through the supply being turned on
- a temporary continuity bond must be applied to system components such as pipework, if the pipework is cut into or parts are removed; this is to ensure that the earth protection and continuity of the system is maintained.

Maintaining hot water systems

Maintenance work is likely to involve communication with the customer, particularly relating to diagnosing the fault and agreeing to the work carried out. Companies have different policies relating to the job responsibilities of plumbers, particularly in relation to providing costs for undertaking work. In general terms typical job responsibilities are as follows:

Did you know?

Maintenance specification – a document that lays down what activities a plumber needs to carry out when maintaining a system.

Maintenance record – a document completed by the plumber to indicate the maintenance work actually carried out.

- plumbing apprentice – limited job responsibility – normally working with someone else who will assist in diagnosing faults; not normally involved in negotiating cost with customers
- Level 2 qualified plumber – will usually have significant responsibility in diagnosing faults but may need to refer back to his/her supervisor to deal with costing information/ordering parts and confirming costs with customers
- Level 3 qualified plumber – will usually have complete responsibility for diagnosing faults, ordering parts and confirming costs/orders with customers.

Remember – the golden rule is to always fully communicate to customers the action needed to repair or replace parts, this includes the cost of the work. If this doesn't take place, complaints are likely to occur.

Typical hot water component maintenance activities

The following outlines the maintenance work/faults that may occur on a simple range of hot water system components:

Pillar tap

Common faults

Standard pillar tap:

- the tap is passing water when turned off – re-washer it; if the seat is damaged it may be necessary to use a re-seating tool to ensure that the washer properly seats
- the headgear is jammed or tight – the rising spindle will need lubricating and the gland re-packing, in more serious cases it may be necessary to replace the tap heads using a tap conversion kit or replace the complete taps

- water appears under the head of the tap only when it is turned on – the gland requires re-packing, in more serious cases it may be necessary to replace the tap heads using a tap conversion kit or replace the complete taps.

Pillar tap with non-rising spindle:

- the tap is passing water when turned off – re-washer it, if the seat is damaged it may be necessary to use a re-seating tool to ensure that the washer properly seats
- faults associated with operation of the tap headgear usually require replacement of the tap heads using a conversion kit, or replacement of the complete taps.

Quarter turn (ceramic disc) taps

Common faults:

- the tap is passing water when turned off or the headgear is jammed – complete replacement of the ceramic disc cartridge.

Gate valve

Common faults:

- water leaking from the packing gland – re-pack the gland or in more serious cases replace the valve
- the headgear is stuck – re-pack the gland or in more serious cases replace the valve
- the valve passes water – replace the valve.

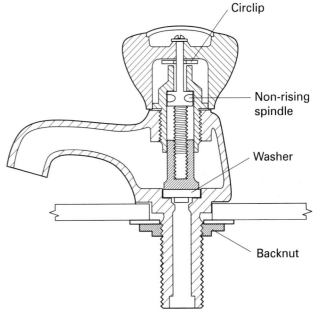

Figure 6.14 Pillar tap with non-rising spindle

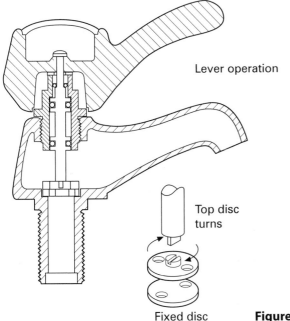

Lever operation

Top disc turns

Fixed disc

Figure 6.15 Ceramic disc tap

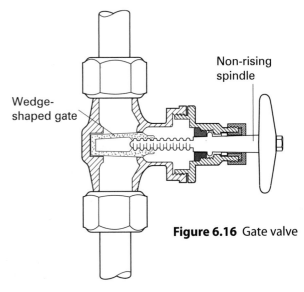

Figure 6.16 Gate valve

Figure 6.17 Shower mixer valve

Shower mixer valve

The first check on a shower mixer valve is to ensure that the hot and cold supplies to the shower are functioning correctly, i.e. adequate flow rate and pressure.

Common faults:

Thermostatic mixers

- poor spray from the shower head – before moving on to check the mixer valve it's worth looking to see if the spray plates in the shower head are blocked with scale
- poor flow rate – check to ensure that any strainers in the valve assembly are clear of grit, alternatively the cartridge may require replacement
- imbalance in the hot/cold water supply – check the valve for correct adjustment, the cartridge may require replacement; the valve may also contain check valves which may be blocked or defective
- valve passes water when turned off – the cartridge needs replacement.

Manual mixers

- poor flow rate – check to ensure that any strainers in the valve assembly are clear of grit
- imbalance in the hot/cold water supply or the hot supply will not work – check the valve for correct adjustment, check the pipework connections to see if the cold and hot water supplies are operating at equal pressure (both usually from storage); the valve headgear may require replacement
- valve passes water when turned off – the manufacturer may provide a re-washering kit, or alternatively the complete valve headgear may require replacement.

With boosted showers that use a pump, problems can occur with failure of the shower pump or its controlling switch, in which case a very poor flow rate or no flow will occur from the shower rose.

Thermostat failure

Appliances may suffer from control thermostat failure, resulting in an overheating or boiling effect in the system; this can usually be identified by noise (boiling) occurring in the system. The solution to the problem is usually replacement of the thermostat.

Some hot water systems include a second thermostat called an overheat thermostat (energy cut-out device); this is installed to prevent the system from overheating and causes the system to shut down if a higher than normal temperature is reached.

Single-feed cylinders

This type of cylinder is susceptible to the loss of its integral air bubble. This can create real problems in the system with corrosion. The main sign of the loss of air bubble is discoloured water from the hot taps. The solution to the problem is to drain down the system and re-form the air bubble; if the problem continues to happen then the reasons for the air-bubble loss need to be fully investigated or alternatively it may be better to replace the cylinder with a double-feed-type and f&e cistern.

Typical hot water system faults

Copper pipework corrosion

Common faults:

- old brass fittings corroded via a process known as dezincification, a classic sign of this is a white powder on fitting surfaces
- pipework in contact with corrosive substances – pipework in contact with substances such as mortar and through constant contact with some cleaning materials can corrode and require replacement – the solution here is to ensure that the replacement pipework includes a protective coating
- acidic water supplies can cause rapid corrosion in copper pipework systems, typically a pin-holing effect will be seen.

No supply at outlets

Common faults:

- valves that are not fully open may cause this problem and should usually be checked first
- some hot water components contain strainers or filters designed to prevent grit entering them, these require cleaning from time to time, if they haven't been cleaned for some time complete blockage can occur.

Heated cold water

This problem usually occurs when hot water pipes are run close to cold water pipes (usually touching). When the cold water is not being drawn off it is heated through contact with the hot pipe, customers will often complain about this problem. The solution is to ensure that there is a gap between the hot and cold pipes when they are installed.

Expansion noises

The process of drawing hot water through pipework results in the pipework materials being heated and expansion occurring. This expansion of pipework needs to be catered for in hot water systems as it may result in a creaking-type noise occurring. The solution is to make sure that pipework

Did you know?

Air locks causing no, or limited water flow from outlets can occur in low-pressure hot water distribution pipework not laid to the proper self-venting falls.

has the ability to move in pipe clips and pipes are not securely anchored at the end of pipe runs, i.e. the pipe can extend in length. It may be necessary to apply a sound-absorbent material under copper pipework when notched in floor joists, to allow movement without creaking.

Limescale build-up

Areas supplied with temporary hard water can be susceptible to limescale build-up in hot water systems. The result of this will be a gradual reduction in water-flow rates at appliances; in more serious cases the result can be a complete blockage of the pipework or plumbing component. The solution to more serious cases of limescale build-up and expensive early replacement of plumbing components is to install a water-conditioning device to treat the water supply in the property.

Leaks

It goes without saying that these need repairing wherever they occur.

Short answer questions

1. Which two items of legislation deal with the installation of hot water systems?
2. Which component is detailed by the following symbol?

3. The cold feed to a hot water cylinder will usually be isolated by which type of valve?
4. Why should the cold feed to the hot water storage cylinder from a cold water storage cistern be sited above cold water distributing pipe connections?
5. Which type of shower pump would be sited between the shower mixer valve and the shower rose to a shower?
6. Plastic pipe materials for use in hot and cold water systems are usually manufactured from which type of plastic material?
7. Which type of hot water fitting contains a circlip to retain the valve spindle?
8. Why should there be a minimum gap of 450mm between the hot water outlet of a cylinder and the vent pipe connection?
9. What is the likely cause of a creaking noise under the floorboards in a domestic property when water is drawn through the hot taps?
10. Which electrical safety precaution should be applied when branching into an existing length of hot water pipeline?

Multiple-choice test

1. The location of a hot water cylinder in a new-build domestic property will usually be detailed in which of the following documents?
   a) *Job specification*   c) *Site plan*
   b) *Work programme*   d) *Building plan*

2. A schedule of materials brought to site by a plumbers' merchant will usually be listed in which type of document?
   a) *Delivery note*   c) *Quotation*
   b) *Variation order*   d) *Work programme*

3. Which type of hot water cylinder separates the primary and secondary hot water system by means of an air bubble?
   a) *Single-feed indirect*
   b) *Double-feed indirect*
   c) *Direct*
   d) *Alternating*

4. The recommended minimum size of circulators from a solid-fuel high-output back boiler to a hot water storage cylinder is:
   a) *15mm*   c) *28mm*
   b) *22mm*   d) *35mm*

5. The minimum size of open vent pipe from a hot water storage cylinder is:
   a) *15mm*   c) *28mm*
   b) *22mm*   d) *35mm*

6. Shower manufacturers will usually recommend a minimum distance between the base of a cold water storage cistern and the shower rose of a gravity-fed shower of:
   a) *500mm*   c) *1000mm*
   b) *750mm*   d) *1500mm*

7. The primary open vent pipe to a hot water system should discharge over which of the following?
   a) *Feed and expansion cistern*
   b) *Hot water storage cylinder*
   c) *Cold water storage cistern*
   d) *Boiler*

8. The cold feed to the primary circuit of an indirect hot water system must contain which of the following types of isolation valve?
   a) *Gate valve*
   b) *Stop valve*
   c) *Spherical plug valve*
   d) *No valve must be fitted*

9. A water heater capable of providing hot water to a number of outlets is said to be what type of appliance?
   a) *Condensing*   c) *Multipoint*
   b) *Single outlet*   d) *Indirect*

10. The effects of dead legs in hot water system pipework can be minimised by using:
a) Long pipe runs
b) Trace heating
c) Galvanised pipework
d) Larger boilers

11. A feed and expansion cistern to a hot water storage cistern should be sufficiently sized to:
a) Ensure sufficient storage for hot water purposes
b) Contain the expanded water in the system when heated and without overflowing
c) Contain the expanded water in the system when heated with overflow taking place
d) Convert the hot water to steam during the heating process

12. The secondary open vent pipe to a hot water storage cylinder must include:
a) A check valve
b) A gate valve
c) An anti-gravity valve
d) No valve

13. The operation of a pump to a secondary hot water circulation system is controlled by:
a) Time clock
b) Thermostatic valve
c) Frost thermostat
d) Boiler thermostat

14. A sacrificial anode in a hot water storage cylinder is made from:
a) Copper   c) Iron
b) Magnesium   d) Lead

15. The minimum size of hot water storage cylinder for a domestic property is:
a) 60 litres   c) 160 litres
b) 110 litres   d) 220 litres

16. Limescale in a hot water storage cylinder is caused by which of the following?
a) Permanently hard water
b) Temporarily hard water
c) Permanently acidic water
d) Temporarily acidic water

17. The immersion heater to a hot water storage cylinder will usually be set at which of the following temperatures?
a) 20°C   c) 60°C
b) 40°C   d) 80°C

18. The water temperature in a hot water storage cylinder will be:
a) Greater at the top
b) Greater at the bottom
c) Greater in the middle
d) The same throughout the cylinder

19. The following hot water system is described as:

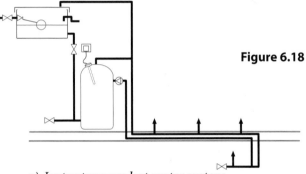

Figure 6.18

a) Instantaneous hot water system
b) Secondary circulation system
c) Unvented system
d) Gravity circulation system

20. Which of the following fittings should not be used for making joints to hot water pipework?
a) Leaded capillary solder ring
b) Compression type A
c) Push-fit fittings
d) Compression type B

21. What action should be taken to open ended pipework from a live supply before leaving site for the evening?
a) Place rags in the open pipe ends
b) Crimp the pipe ends with a pair of grips
c) Seal the pipe end with a watertight cap
d) No action is necessary

22. During a soundness test on metallic pipe on a hot water storage system, the standing time before the test period commences is of what duration?
a) 15 minutes   c) 60 minutes
b) 30 minutes   d) 90 minutes

23. A decommissioning record is more likely to be required to be completed when working on which of the following types of hot water system?
a) A combination unit in a domestic property
b) A direct system in a domestic property
c) An indirect system in an industrial property
d) Any work in any type of property

24. A check valve is most likely to be found in which of the following?
a) Hot water storage cylinder
b) Cold water storage cistern
c) Thermostatic shower mixer valve
d) Gate valve

25. Hot water coming from under the hand-wheel of a pillar tap only when it is opened is likely to be caused by which of the following?
a) Loose tap headgear
b) Leaking packing gland
c) Worn tap washer
d) Loose hand-wheel

26. Excessively high water temperatures at the taps in a hot water system fed by an immersion heater could be caused by:
a) Blockage of the vent pipe
b) Closure of the cold feed pipe
c) An over-sized fuse fitted
d) Thermostat failure

27. The simplest method of isolating a hot water pillar tap in order to washer it is to isolate the:
a) Cold water stop valve under the sink
b) Cold feed gate valve to the cylinder
c) Cold water service valve to the cistern
d) Cold water distribution pipe to the bath

28. Hot water discharging from cold water taps for a short period of time after turning them on could be the cause of:
a) The boiler thermostat being set too high
b) An electrical component in the system failing
c) Cold pipework touching hot pipework
d) Pipework to the taps connected the wrong way round

29. The cold water pressure at a low-pressure manual shower mixer valve is much greater than the hot, with the customer complaining that the valve is difficult to control. Which of the following could be a cause of the problem?
a) The immersion heater is set too low
b) The cold water is connected to the supply pipe
c) The cold water distribution valve is partially closed
d) The cylinder is under-sized

30. An air lock in the supply from a hot water storage cistern is most likely to be caused by:
a) The open vent pipe rising above the storage cistern
b) The cold feed pipe falling back into the storage cistern
c) The cold feed pipe falling into the cylinder
d) The cold water supply pipework falling into the storage cistern

By the end of this chapter you should be able to demonstrate understanding of the following central heating systems topics which will assist you in completing knowledge assessment in the Central Heating Systems Unit of the Level 2 Certificate in Basic Plumbing Studies:

- Sources of information:
  - Technical standards
  - Site information sources
- Types of system:
  - One-pipe central heating circuits
  - Two-pipe central heating circuits
  - Central heating system layouts complying with the Building Regulations
  - Key components of fully pumped open-vented central heating systems
- Types of heat emitter
- Central heating control components:
  - Thermostatic radiator valves
  - Programmer
  - Room thermostat
  - Cylinder thermostat
  - Frost thermostat
  - Automatic bypass valve
  - Motorised valves
  - Automatic air vents
  - Junction box (wiring centre)
- Types of boiler:
  - Solid-fuel boilers
  - Gas- and oil-fired boilers
- Soundness testing central heating systems:
  - Visual inspection
  - Testing for leaks
  - Pressure testing
  - Final system checks
- Decommissioning central heating systems:
  - Permanent decommissioning.
  - Temporary decommissioning.
- Maintaining central heating systems:
  - Typical central heating system faults.

Sources of information

There are a number of information sources that plumbers may have to use to obtain the necessary detail to undertake their work.

Technical standards

- Building Regulations – these are the main regulations that must be complied with when installing central heating systems. Approved documents L1 (energy conservation) and J (heat-producing appliances) detail the main requirements for central heating systems; these can be freely downloaded from the DCLG website at www.communities.gov.uk.
- Water Regulations – these lay down the statutory requirements that must be carried out when installing, commissioning and maintaining water systems. Some aspects of central heating installation fall under the requirements of the Water Regulations. Water Regulations documentation can be freely downloaded from www.defra.gov.uk, who also produce a guidance document to the Water Regulations.
- British Standards – these support statutory documentation such as the Building Regulations, providing greater detail on installation requirements. Although British Standards are not statutory (legal) documents, they can be used in potential legal action relating to defective systems installation. The main British Standard relating to central heating systems is BS 5449 – Specification for forced circulation hot water central heating systems for domestic premises (some aspects have been replaced by other standards).
- Manufacturer instructions – these are provided by appliance or component manufacturers to outline the installation, commissioning and maintenance requirements of their products. Manufacturer instructions usually take precedence over British Standards but should not conflict with Building or Water Regulations, which are statutory (legal) requirements.

Site information sources

The following outlines the range of site information sources that are commonly used:

- site plans – site or location plans show the location of the building or site to adjacent roads, properties or services
- building plans – detailed plans for the property, showing key building details such as location of doors/windows, room sizes, boiler position, etc.
- services layout plans – detailed drawings of the building services such as pipe runs, position and layout
- job specification – often provided as support to building plans, this details items such as the type, size and position of key components such as boilers

- work programme – details the points at which various aspects of plumbing work fit into the overall construction programme, e.g. first fix hot & cold water system
- bill of quantities – details the quantities of components and materials used on a job.

Types of system

Circuits to central heating systems are either:

- one-pipe (not commonly used on domestic systems)
- two-pipe.

One-pipe central heating circuit

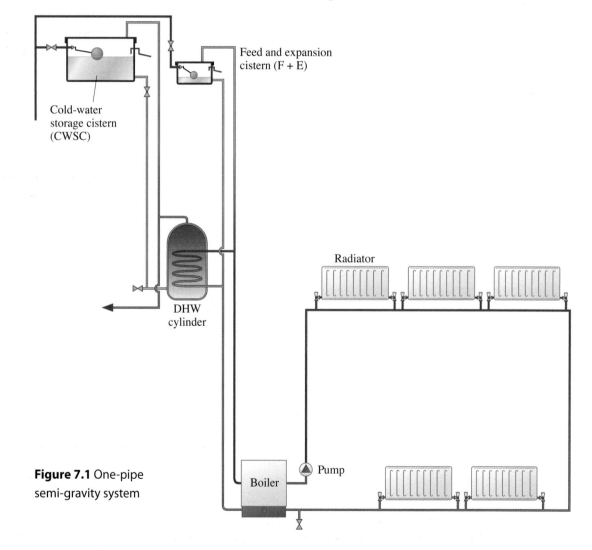

Figure 7.1 One-pipe semi-gravity system

In this system the central heating circuit is in the form of a loop running from and returning to the boiler. The disadvantages of this system tend to outweigh the advantages.

Advantages	Disadvantages
Lower installation cost compared to a two-pipe system	The heat emitters on the system pass cooler water back into the circuit. This means that the heat emitters at the end of the system are cooler
Quicker to install	The pump only forces water around the main circuit and not directly through the radiators. This means it is important to select radiators that allow minimum resistance to the flow of water
Lower maintenance costs	The 'flow' side to the radiator is usually installed at high level to improve circulation, creating additional unsightly pipework

Figure 7.2 Advantages/disadvantages of the one-pipe system

Two-pipe central heating circuit

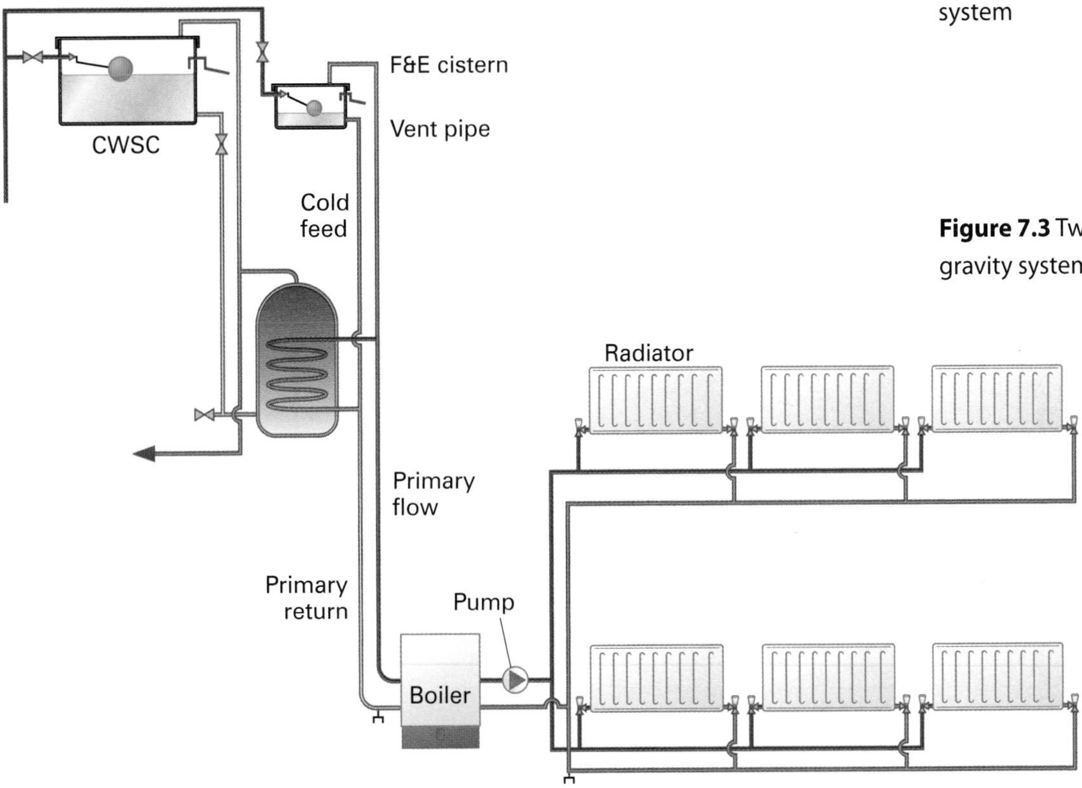

Figure 7.3 Two-pipe semi-gravity system

In this system the flow and return pipework to the radiators is kept completely separate, this permits the radiators to heat up evenly and the heat-up period is quicker. The two-pipe system is commonly used in domestic properties. This type of semi-gravity system has very limited control of hot water temperatures and a lack of boiler interlock means that it is only now suitable for solid-fuel systems.

Did you know?

The pipework to the hot water cylinder in semi-gravity systems (domestic primaries) should be a minimum 28mm diameter.

Central heating system layouts complying with the Building Regulations

Part L1 of the Building Regulations lays down the requirements for energy conservation and the minimum requirements for central heating controls. The following are the recommended control systems for domestic properties fuelled by gas and oil.

Fully pumped system using three-port mid-position valve

This type of system is fully pumped, and both circuits are subject to accelerated circulation of the system contents by means of a circulating pump. This type of system provides considerable flexibility in terms of system design options, for example the boiler may be sited above the hot water cylinder.

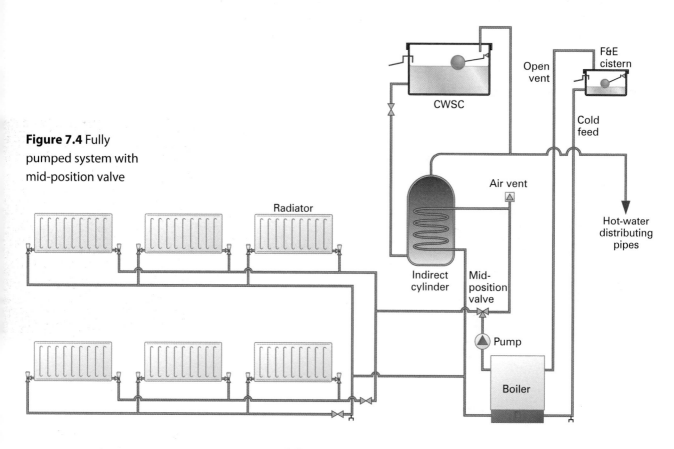

Figure 7.4 Fully pumped system with mid-position valve

Key points of the system are:

- independent time and temperature control of the central heating circuits is provided
- a full boiler interlock is provided (the last circuit to close causes the pump and boiler to shut off)
- the mid-position valve permits the heating and hot water circuits to operate together or independently

- care needs to be taken when piping the mid-position valve to ensure that the correct pipe is connected to the correct valve port:
  - Port AB – common supply from boiler
  - Port A – to heating circuit
  - Port B – to hot water circuit.

In all fully pumped systems, the hot water return must be the last connection to the common return before the boiler. This ensures that unwanted circulation does not take place in the heating circuit during summer months (radiators heat up when the central heating circuit is turned off). If the returns cannot be piped to meet this requirement, then one or more anti-gravity (non-return) valves may have to be fitted to ensure that unwanted circulation does not take place.

Earlier fully pumped systems included a diverter valve, this is a type of valve that looks similar to the mid-position valve but is only able to provide a flow of water to one circuit at a time. These valves are not commonly used, but you may come across one on a job – it operates quite differently, so be careful.

> **Did you know?**
>
> A special type of non-return valve (anti-gravity) should be selected for use in central heating systems, it needs to operate under low circulating head – so don't just use a standard valve for hot or cold applications, as it probably won't work!

Fully pumped system using 2 × two-port valves

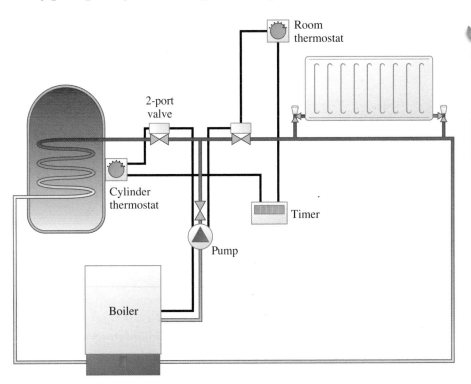

> **Did you know?**
>
> A 2 × two-port valve arrangement will need a system bypass to ensure a supply of cool water to the return pipework should the boiler overheat (the two-port valves when closed prevent this happening).

Figure 7.5 Fully pumped system with 2 × two-port valves

Key features of this system are:

- independent time and temperature control of heating and hot water circuits is provided as well as a full boiler interlock
- the system is particularly suited to larger properties, usually above 150m² floor area where the two-port valve is capable of delivering a greater flow rate compared with its mid-position counterpart

- this type of system is also readily suited to the provision of additional central heating zones (circuits), e.g. separate upstairs and downstairs circuits.

Key components of fully pumped open-vented central heating systems

Feed and expansion cistern

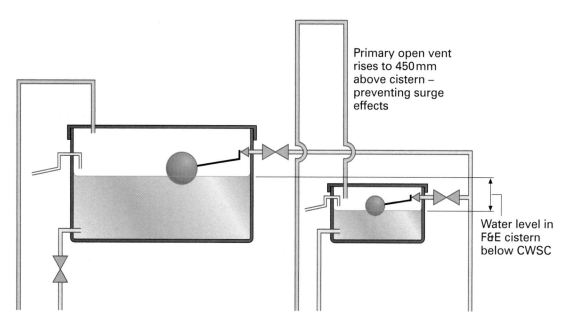

Primary open vent rises to 450mm above cistern – preventing surge effects

Water level in F&E cistern below CWSC

Figure 7.6 Feed and expansion cistern

Key features of the cistern are:

- a cistern of 10-litre nominal capacity is provided
- the vent pipe will usually be 22mm and the cold feed pipe 15mm
- the purpose of the open-vent pipe is to provide a safety outlet in the event of the system overheating and to ensure that the system is maintained at around atmospheric pressure
- a service valve should be provided on the cold water inlet to the f&e cistern for maintenance purposes, on no account should this be sited on the cold feed pipe, as it can be dangerous in an overheat situation
- sufficient space must be provided in the f&e cistern for expansion when the system heats up (an approximate increase of 4% in total system volume); this ensures that an adequate space is maintained between the overflow and the finished water level in the cistern
- the vent pipe in a fully pumped system should rise approximately 450mm above the height of the cistern to overcome any pressure surge effects
- the cistern should have a close-fitting lid and be insulated if installed in an unheated space
- the open-vent pipe to the central heating system must discharge over the f&e cistern and not the cold water storage cistern; this is in order to avoid the risk of contamination and potential danger should the system overheat.

Air separators

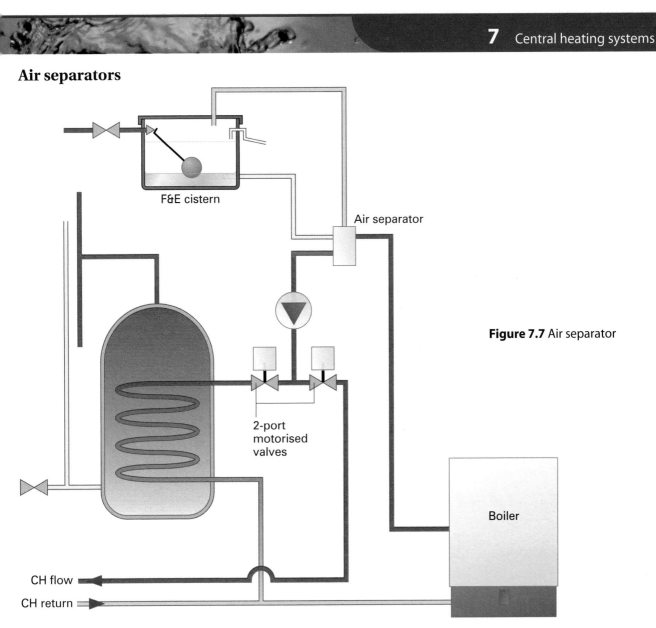

F&E cistern

Air separator

Figure 7.7 Air separator

2-port motorised valves

Boiler

CH flow

CH return

The use of an air separator permits:

- system pipework to be properly and closely grouped (pump position in relation to cold feed and vent pipe)
- turbulence of water flow in the separator causing air to be removed from the system, so reducing the risk of noise and corrosion.

Pump/cold feed/open vent positioning

- in Figure 7.8, Diagram 1 shows a system working largely under negative pressure, resulting in the possibility of air being drawn into the system through micro-leaks, e.g. at radiator valves, resulting in corrosion

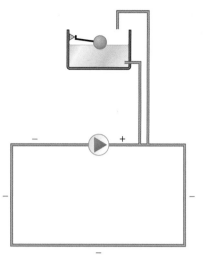

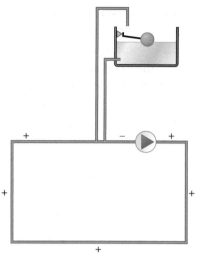

System under negative pressure (undesirable)

System under positive pressure 'pumping over' may occur

System under positive pressure (desirable connection)

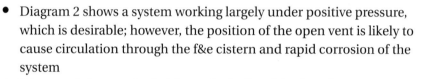

Figure 7.8 Pump position in relation to cold feed and vent pipe

- Diagram 2 shows a system working largely under positive pressure, which is desirable; however, the position of the open vent is likely to cause circulation through the f&e cistern and rapid corrosion of the system
- Diagram 3 shows a desirable method of positioning, the system operates largely under positive pressure and the open-vent pipe is connected at the point of lowest possible circulating pressure.

Types of heat emitter

A range of heat emitters are available, including:

- cast-iron radiators – these are not commonly installed in domestic systems but may be used in the refurbishment of luxury properties
- panel radiators – these are the most common form of heat emitter in domestic properties and are available in a range of styles, sizes and outputs, including double panel options. This type of radiator is

Installation tip

When installing panel radiators, sufficient gap must be left between the top of the radiator and any shelf or window cill and the bottom of the radiator and the skirting board, this is to ensure proper air circulation and heat output.

Figure 7.9 Typical panel radiator

manufactured from low carbon steel and may include fins welded on the back to increase the heat output. About 80% of the heat emitted from a panel radiator is by convection

- skirting heaters – now little used in domestic properties, these are fixed at skirting board level and heat the air by natural convection
- fan-assisted convector heaters – these force air (by means of a fan) over a heat exchanger; they therefore require an electrical connection via the central heating control system
- low surface temperature radiators – similar to panel radiators, these are used in properties where there is a risk of the elderly, the infirm or the young coming into contact with the radiator
- towel rails – used in bathrooms to provide heating and towel warming, a towel rail may also include an integral radiator.

Central heating control components

Thermostatic radiator valves (TRVs)

A thermostatic radiator valve is a device designed to control the heat output from the radiator by adjusting the rate of water flowing through it.

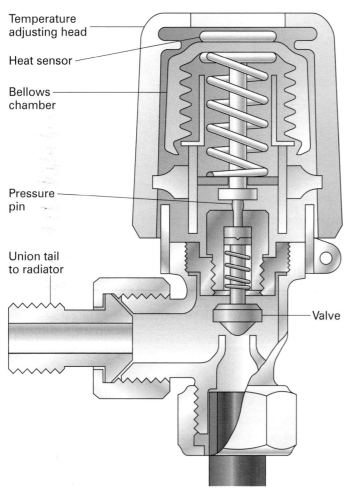

Temperature adjusting head
Heat sensor
Bellows chamber
Pressure pin
Union tail to radiator
Valve

Figure 7.10 Thermostatic radiator valve

Did you know?

The sensor on a TRV should be sited in an area of free air flow in the room so that it can sense the air temperature properly, if this is not possible, e.g. when sited behind long curtains, then a special valve head with a remote sensor is available.

TRVs include a sensor of liquid, gas or wax which expands or contracts a chamber or bellows which in turn moves a pressure pin in the valve body, so adjusting the amount of water flowing through the radiator.

It is now common practice to provide TRVs on radiators in domestic properties to meet the requirements of the Building Regulations. There must, however, be a room thermostat installed in the system, and the radiator in the room in which the thermostat is sited must not be fitted with a thermostatic radiator valve. It may also be necessary to install an automatic bypass valve to the system to ensure that a minimum water-flow rate is maintained through the boiler should the majority of thermostatic radiator valves close down together.

Programmer

A programmer is an electrically operated device allowing for independent timing and operation of the central heating and hot water circuits.

Did you know?

A cylinder thermostat is usually sited about one-third height from the bottom of the cylinder, in order to control the water temperature.

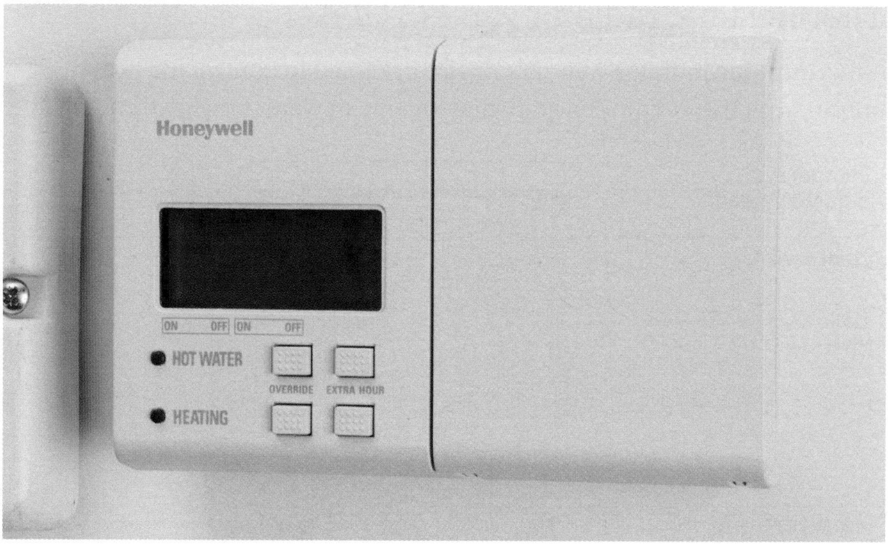

Figure 7.11 Programmer

Room thermostat

This device measures air temperature in the room where it is sited and controls the operation of the heating circuit. The room thermostat should not be sited in direct draughts and must be capable of freely measuring the air temperature in the room. The thermostat should usually be mounted at a height of 1.5m from floor level.

Cylinder thermostat

A cylinder thermostat is fixed to a hot water storage cylinder, usually by a strap, and senses the temperature of the hot water in the cylinder. When the cylinder reaches the setting on the thermostat, usually 60°C, the hot water circuit is isolated.

Figure 7.12 Room thermostat

Frost thermostat

A frost thermostat is fitted to a system that has components such as the boiler and system pipework which may be susceptible to freezing, such as when installed in an unheated boiler house. The frost thermostat will sense the temperature in the boiler house and bring the heating system on if it reaches a level where it may begin to freeze, typically 4°C.

Figure 7.13 Frost thermostat

Figure 7.14 Automatic bypass valve

Did you know?

An electrical pipe thermostat will often be used with a frost thermostat to conserve energy. The pipe thermostat minimises the heat required to prevent the components from freezing by controlling the central heating water level at a lower temperature than the boiler thermostat.

Automatic bypass valve

An automatic bypass valve ensures a minimum flow rate is maintained around a central heating circuit, particularly when TRVs are installed. Once set, the valve opens automatically as the TRVs or circuits close. A bypass valve will minimise the potential for system noise and damage to the boiler heat exchanger and pump.

Motorised valves

There are two main types of motorised valves in use:

- two-port valves – controlling the operation of single circuits such as the hot water circuit
- mid-position valve (three-port valve) controls the operation of both central heating and hot water circuits on an independent basis.

Key fact

Regulation requirement

If it's necessary to fit a bypass to a system, under the Building Regulations, the bypass must be of the automatic type and not just a simple gate valve.

Automatic air vents

These are used in the high points of central heating systems to automatically vent the system of air and ensure correct water flow through the system. They should only be installed on the positive pressure parts of the circuit, so ensuring that if they leak, water discharges from the vent, (if installed on negative parts then air may be drawn into the system).

Figure 7.15 Automatic air vent

Junction box (wiring centre)

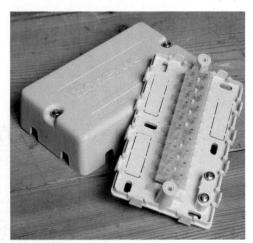

Figure 7.16 Wiring centre

A wiring centre is used to make all the electrical connections for the electrical components in the system, its use makes for easier maintenance and repair of components.

Types of boiler

There are quite a number of different types of boilers available for use in central heating systems; the type of boiler used is normally dependent on fuel supply and flueing options.

Solid-fuel boilers

For domestic use, solid-fuel boilers are only available with open flues. Typical boiler options are:

- wrap-around back boiler – the simplest of solid-fuel boilers. The rate of burning in the appliance is not effectively controlled and hence the water temperature from the boiler can vary considerably, being dependent on the amount of fuel on the appliance

Definition

An open-flued appliance is one where the flue products are discharged by means of a chimney or flue pipe to outside air, usually at high level. The combustion air supply to the heating appliance comes from the room in which the appliance is situated.

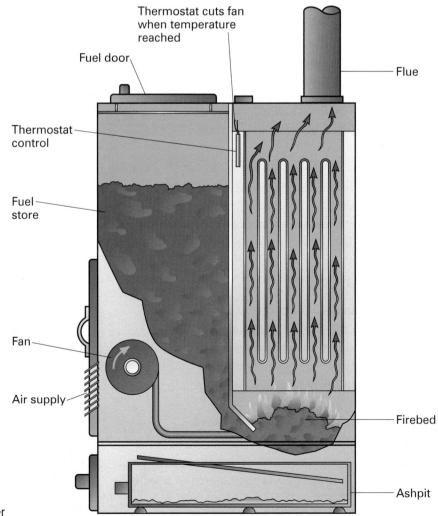

Figure 7.17 Independent gravity-fed solid-fuel boiler

- room heater with back boiler – this is a more sophisticated type of boiler where fuel is burnt in an enclosed firebox that heats the room in which the appliance is sited, as well as a heat exchanger containing water to heat the radiators. Better control of the water temperature is achieved by the use of a water thermostat that regulates the amount of air allowed to enter the appliance fire-bed to burn the fuel. If the air supply is reduced, the rate of fuel burning decreases
- independent free-standing boiler – this is the most sophisticated type of solid-fuel boiler. Control of the boiler temperature is still by regulation of the air supply, which in this case is provided by an electrical fan, so achieving close control of the water temperature. The hopper in the boiler can usually store sufficient fuel for at least a full day's operation, making the boiler relatively automatic in operation.

Gas- and oil-fired boilers

There are a number of options for gas- and oil-fired boilers with either open-flued or room-sealed flueing options. Boilers fuelled by gas and oil can be:

- floor mounted
- wall mounted
- installed in a fireplace opening.

Further options available are:

- traditional boilers – the installation of these is largely not permitted under the Building Regulations as they don't tend to meet the stringent energy efficiency requirements that have been set
- condensing boilers – these are the most energy-efficient boilers and are now the norm under the Building Regulations. This type of boiler is able to extract more useful heat from the combustion process, making it more efficient. Owing to the lower flue gas temperatures from this type of appliance, water vapour collects in the appliance and must be disposed of safely via a condensate pipe from the boiler
- combination boilers – this type of boiler is designed to provide central heating and instantaneous hot water (rather like a multipoint water heater); the boiler removes the need for a separate hot water storage cylinder and associated controls. Care should be taken when specifying this type of boiler as hot water flow rates may be an issue with the customer (some manufacturers do produce higher-rated appliances)
- system boilers – this is a boiler that contains key operating components within its casing such as pump, bypass valve and sealed system components. System boilers may be of the condensing type.

Definition

A room-sealed boiler is one that discharges its combustion products to a terminal, usually sited on the outside wall of a building. The combustion air supply is drawn directly from the outside air at the terminal – hence the term 'room-sealed'.

Did you know?

Condensing combination boilers are available.

Figure 7.18 Gas-fired combination boiler

Soundness testing central heating systems

The soundness testing of central heating systems involves a four-stage process:

- visual inspection
- testing for leaks
- pressure testing
- final system checks.

Visual inspection

This is the process of preparing the system to be filled and tested, including thoroughly inspecting all pipework and fittings to ensure:

- they are fully supported, including f&e cisterns and hot water storage cylinders
- they are free from jointing compound and flux
- that all connections are tight
- that in-line valves and radiator valves have been properly tightened and are closed to allow stage filling
- that the inside of the f&e cistern is clean
- that all the air vents are closed.

Before filling, it is a good idea to remove the pump and replace it with a section of pipe. This will prevent any system debris entering the pump's workings.

Testing for leaks

- Turn on the stop tap if the installation was for a complete cold-water, domestic hot-water and central heating system, or the service valve to the f&e cistern if only the central heating circuit has been installed.
- Allow the system to fill.
- Turn on the radiator valves fully and bleed each radiator.
- Visually check all the joints for signs of leaks.
- Reinstall the pump.
- Refill and test for leaks again.
- Make sure the water level in the f&e cistern is at a level that allows for expansion of water in the system when hot.
- Heat the system and flush while hot.

Pressure testing

The system is usually pressure tested at a test pressure of 1.5 times the normal system working pressure, up to a maximum of 3 bar pressure. The system is left to stand for 1 hour, during which time there should be no visible loss in pressure.

Did you know?

Corrosion inhibitor manufacturers may require the system to be treated with a special neutralising compound prior to adding the corrosion inhibitor.

Following the pressure test and if required, the system should be treated with corrosion inhibitor following the manufacturer instructions.

Final system checks

Once the system has been pressure tested and proved sound and any corrosion protection applied, it is ready for performance testing; this will include:

- setting and adjusting controls, including commissioning the boiler
- balancing the heating circuits to ensure that they heat up evenly and to specification
- completing any commissioning records
- handing over and demonstrating the operation of the system to the user.

Decommissioning central heating systems

Permanent decommissioning

It's fairly rare, but on certain occasions you may be asked to permanently remove a central heating system from a building, this will include disconnecting the system from its essential services.

When working on central heating systems that include electrical components it will usually be necessary to isolate the electrical supply to the component. This must be carried out using the safe isolation procedure. Whilst carrying out safe isolation in a domestic property it is usually regarded safer to isolate at the consumer unit if possible, rather than isolating at the appliance supply point (fused spur). The safe isolation procedure is shown in Figure 7.19.

Temporary decommissioning

Temporary decommissioning of a system may need to be carried out while a building is occupied. The following arrangements may need to be considered:

- the length of time that the system is going to be out of service – care must be taken with the young, the elderly or the infirm to ensure that if the system is going to be out of action for a period of time in cold weather (usually in excess of 4 hours), an alternative source of heating is available to them
- the customer must always be advised before any central heating system is turned off, an estimate of the time it is going to be off should be provided and he/she should be advised when it is turned back on
- in larger buildings, it may be necessary to put a warning notice at the isolation point, confirming that the valve should not be turned on. This is particularly important if the work that is being carried out is sited in a room away from the isolation valve

> **Definition**
>
> A plumber that is completely removing a system is said to be permanently decommissioning it.
>
> A plumber that is taking a system out of action to service or modify it is said to be temporarily decommissioning it.

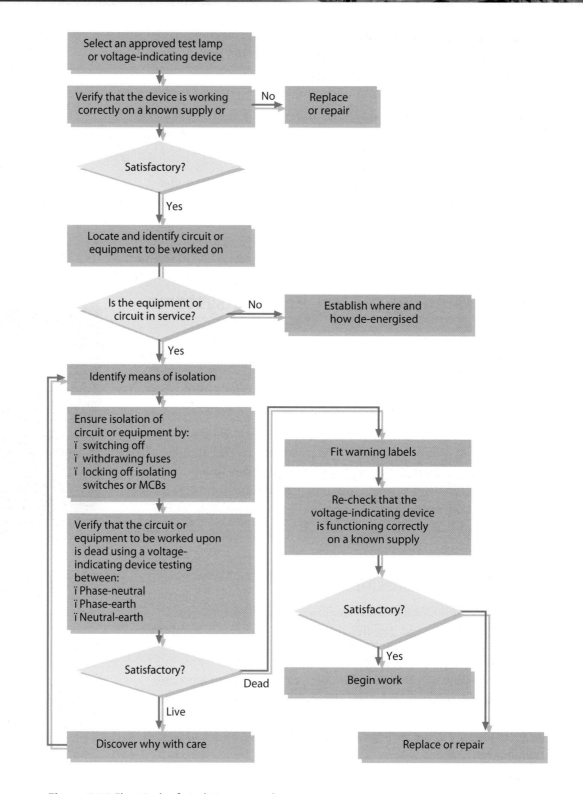

Figure 7.19 Electrical safe isolation procedure

- all open ends should be capped on systems connected to the supply while plumbers are not on site, e.g. in the evenings; this guards against damage through the supply being turned on
- a temporary continuity bond must be applied to system components such as pipework, if the pipework is cut into or parts are removed. This is to ensure that the earth protection and continuity of the system is maintained
- when making modifications or additions to wet central heating systems, such as adding or removing radiators, there are a number of ways of decommissioning the system/component:
  - removing a radiator for decorating purposes – modern systems will include a radiator valve at either end of the radiator, both these valves can be isolated and the radiator individually drained and removed without the need to drain the rest of the system.
  - replacing a radiator valve – here there are a number of options; the simplest is creating a partial vacuum in the system, provided that the pipe is vertical and the system is leak free, pipe freezing is an option, or taking longer the system could be drained to below the height of the valve
  - adding a new component to the circuit such as a radiator – here options include pipe freezing and draining the system to below the level of the connections to be made.

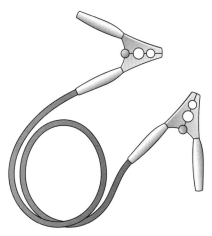

Figure 7.20 Temporary continuity bond

Maintaining central heating systems

Maintenance work is likely to involve communication with the customer, particularly relating to diagnosing the fault and agreeing to the work carried out. Companies have different policies relating to the job responsibilities of plumbers, particularly in relation to providing costs for undertaking work. In general terms the following outlines typical job responsibilities:

- plumbing apprentice – limited job responsibility – normally working with someone else who will assist in diagnosing faults, not normally involved in negotiating cost with customers
- Level 2 qualified plumber – will usually have significant responsibility in diagnosing faults but may need to refer back to his/her supervisor to deal with costing information/ordering parts and confirming costs with customers
- Level 3 qualified plumber – will usually have complete responsibility for diagnosing faults, ordering parts and confirming costs/orders with customers.

Remember – the golden rule is to always fully communicate to customers the action needed to repair or replace parts, this includes the cost of the work. If this doesn't take place, complaints are likely to occur.

Did you know?

A special isolating cap may be required when removing a radiator with TRVs. Some TRVs do not provide a full shut-off when the sensing head is closed, therefore the sensing head needs to be replaced with an isolation cap before the radiator is drained.

Did you know?

If a system is drained down you need to open the air taps (air-release points) in the system, to allow the water in the system to be replaced by air in order for it to empty.

Typical central heating system faults

The range of faults that can occur with central heating systems is quite extensive, the following identifies some typical faults that may occur:

Leakage from radiator valves

- Wheelhead radiator valves in particular are eventually susceptible to leakage as they may be subject to constant turning on and off. Typically, leakage may occur from the packing gland, which may be re-packed or in more severe cases the valve may require replacement.

Radiators failing to warm up

There are a number of different faults associated with this:

- a first check should be to ensure that the system electrical components are working correctly – electrical supply is available, programmer, thermostats, zone valves and pump are working correctly and the boiler is firing
- on older systems a sign of pump failure will be that the radiators upstairs and the hot water circuit are lukewarm while the downstairs radiators are cold. On more modern systems pump failure is likely to cause the boiler to overheat and cut out on its overheat cut-out device
- a sign of thermostat or zone valve failure will be failure for the heating circuit to receive a supply of warm water to any radiators
- TRVs can be subject to the pressure pin sticking in the valve, so it's worth checking this as an early action in systems in which a number of radiators are not heating up – the solution is to grease the pressure pin or replace it.

Hot water circuit failing to warm up

- with the exception of TRVs, similar points as shown for radiators failing to heat up.

The boiler never shuts off (no overheating occurs)

- here it's likely that an electrical component fault has occurred; typically this could be a programmer fault (not switching correctly) or the zone valve is defective, causing a permanent electrical supply to the pump and boiler.

Heating and hot water cannot be run independently

- this is likely to be the result of an electrical component fault, such as a defect in the programmer or in the motorised valves, the problem is more likely to occur with three-port valves.

Unwanted circulation in the heating circuit when it is turned off

- this is usually associated with the domestic hot water return from the cylinder not being the last connection to the common return before the boiler. The solution to the problem is to alter the connection position of the domestic return or install one or more anti-gravity valves.

System noise

There are a number of causes of system noise, including:

- poor initial design practices – pipe size too small and flow rates through them too high, the only solution here is to re-pipe affected circuits
- boiler noise – noise from boilers can often be associated with a lack of water flow through them, which results in noise being created. Solutions may include increasing the water flow through the heat exchanger by increasing the pump size and the inclusion of a system bypass
- noise created as thermostatic radiator valves begin to close. The solution is the correct installation and adjustment of a system bypass.

Short answer questions

1. Legislation relating to the energy efficiency of domestic central heating systems is laid down in which document?

2. What is the name of the following type of domestic central heating system?

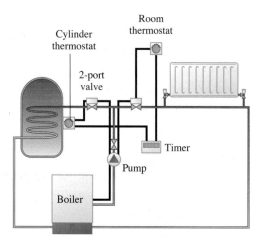

3. Why should the domestic return from the hot water storage cylinder be the last pipe to connect to the common return pipe before the boiler in a fully pumped system?

4. What is the size of f&e cistern used in an indirect heating and hot water system to a small domestic property?

5. What is the purpose of an injector tee fitted to a solid-fuel central heating system?

6. What are the key features of siting a room thermostat?

7. A boiler heat exchanger that requires a greater flow rate than required in the heating and hot water circuits should be fitted with what type of device?

8. The primary open-vent pipe in a central heating system must discharge over which cistern?

9. Two radiators controlled by thermostatic radiator valves in a property are failing to heat up, whilst all other radiators are working correctly. What is the first check to make in overcoming the problem?

10. When isolating the electricity supply to a central heating system at a fused spur switch to replace a central heating pump, what are the key requirements?

Multiple-choice test

1. Details of the fixing requirements for a boiler would be found in:
   a) *Water Fittings & Materials Directory*
   b) *BS 6700*
   c) *Manufacturer instructions*
   d) *Building Regulations L1*

2. One of the features of a one-pipe ring-main circuit is:
   a) *The first radiator on the circuit is cooler than the last*
   b) *The last radiator on the circuit is cooler than the first*
   c) *Equal temperatures at all radiators*
   d) *Larger radiators at the beginning of a circuit*

3. What is the minimum recommended size of gravity primary circuit pipework to a hot water storage cylinder fed by a high-output solid-fuel boiler?
   a) *15mm*
   b) *22mm*
   c) *28mm*
   d) *35mm*

4. What is the minimum recommended size of open-vent pipe to a fully pumped central heating system?
   a) *15mm*
   b) *22mm*
   c) *28mm*
   d) *35mm*

5. What is the minimum recommended size of cold-feed pipe to a fully pumped central heating system?
   a) *15mm*
   b) *22mm*
   c) *28mm*
   d) *35mm*

6. A device that closely groups the connection of cold-feed pipe and open-vent pipe in a fully pumped central heating system is called:
   a) *A check valve*
   b) *An injector tee*
   c) *A diverter valve*
   d) *An air separator*

7. The positioning of the pump and cold-feed and open-vent pipes as shown in the following diagram could be described as:

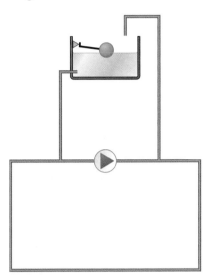

   a) *A system largely operating under negative pressure*
   b) *A system in which 'pumping over' of the vent pipe is likely*
   c) *A system in which 'sucking down' of the vent pipe is likely*
   d) *A system in which the open vent is connected at the point of lowest pressure*

8. It is normal practice to raise the open vent pipe to what height above the f&e cistern in a fully pumped system?
   a) *150mm*   c) *450mm*
   b) *250mm*   d) *600mm*

9. The minimum distance between the water level in an f&e cistern and the invert level of the overflow when the system is fully heated should be:
   a) *10mm*   c) *25mm*
   b) *15mm*   d) *50mm*

10. Which of the following types of central heating control valve could be used to provide heat to the water and central heating circuits at the same time?
    a) *Mid-position valve*
    b) *Anti-gravity valve*
    c) *Diverter valve*
    d) *Thermostatic valve*

11. A remote sensor could be used with which of the following central heating controls?
    a) *Programmer*
    b) *Thermostatic radiator valve*
    c) *Mid-position valve*
    d) *Anti-gravity valve*

12. Which control can be used with a frost thermostat to conserve energy when exposed central heating components are being protected against frost?
    a) *Cylinder thermostat*
    b) *Pipe thermostat*
    c) *Thermostatic radiator valve*
    d) *Programmer*

13. The thermostat to a solid-fuel room heater controls:
    a) *The quantity of water flowing through the boiler heat exchanger*
    b) *The quantity of air entering the boiler fire-box for heating purposes*
    c) *The quantity of fuel entering the boiler fire-box for heating purposes*
    d) *A flap in the flue controlling the rate of burning*

14. A boiler that requires a discharge pipe to waste is called a:
    a) *Traditional boiler*
    b) *Room sealed boiler*
    c) *Condensing boiler*
    d) *System boiler*

15. The common pipe connection to a three-port valve is usually marked:
    a) *Port A*
    b) *Port B*
    c) *Port C*
    d) *Port AB*

16. An automatic air vent should be sited in a system:
 a) *At its lowest point*
 b) *At its highest point*
 c) *At a point of negative pressure*
 d) *On each radiator*

17. A sufficient gap is provided between the top of a panel radiator and a window cill in order that:
 a) *Correct air circulation occurs across all surfaces of the radiator*
 b) *Risk of fire is minimised through contact with the radiator*
 c) *The radiator back can be painted easily*
 d) *The thermostatic valve operates correctly*

18. A soundness test on a central heating system will include testing at which of the following test pressures?
 a) *The maximum working pressure of the system*
 b) *1.5 times the maximum working pressure of the system*
 c) *Twice the maximum working pressure of the system*
 d) *10 bar pressure at radiators and 6 bar pressure at boilers*

19. A new central heating system should be treated with which of the following compounds prior to treatment with a corrosion inhibitor?
 a) *System descaler*
 b) *System neutraliser*
 c) *Anti-limescale solution*
 d) *Strong acid solution*

20. The most important action to take when carrying out a boiler change during the winter in a domestic property owned by an elderly person is to:
 a) *Carry out the work as quickly as possible*
 b) *Refuse to do the work until summer*
 c) *Establish that a temporary method of heating is available*
 d) *Provide a connection to a temporary boiler*

21. Which is the most economical method of replacing a radiator valve to a first-floor radiator in an occupied domestic property?
 a) *Draining the contents of the system*
 b) *Draining the system to below first-floor level*
 c) *Creating a temporary vacuum in the system*
 d) *Replacing the valve under full pressure*

22. The upstairs radiators and hot water in a domestic property are getting lukewarm whilst the downstairs radiators are not working at all, which of the following is the likely fault?
 a) *Room thermostat failure*
 b) *Pump failure*
 c) *Programmer failure*
 d) *Blown fuse in the fused spur switch*

23. A customer complaining that a radiator does not work properly with the TRV sited behind the edge of a bookcase would be best advised to:
 a) *Raise the temperature at the boiler thermostat*
 b) *Raise the temperature at the room thermostat*
 c) *Fit a remote sensor to the TRV*
 d) *Fit an anti-gravity valve to the radiator*

24. The source of a leak from under the head of a wheelhead radiator valve will usually be a defective:
 a) *Valve seat*
 b) *Packing gland*
 c) *Olive*
 d) *Boiler thermostat*

25. The most likely cause of the boiler and pump in a central heating system not turning off when both circuits in the programmer have switched off is:
 a) *Defective two-port valve*
 b) *Defective pump*
 c) *Room thermostat failure*
 d) *Cylinder thermostat failure*

By the end of this chapter you should be able to demonstrate understanding of the following electrical systems topics which will assist you in completing knowledge assessment in the Electrical Supply & Earth Continuity Unit of the Level 2 Certificate in Basic Plumbing Studies:

- Sources of information:
  - Technical standards
- Electrical circuits in a domestic property:
  - Electrical supply to the property
  - Basic domestic circuits
  - Equipotential bonding
- Components used in electrical systems related to plumbing work:
  - Electrical cables and cords
  - Socket outlets
  - Fused spur switch
  - Unswitched connection unit
  - Pull-cord switch
  - Sheathing
  - Trunking
  - Junction box
  - Terminal connections
- Electrical testing
- Decommissioning electrical systems.

Sources of information

There are a number of information sources that plumbers may have to use to obtain the necessary detail to undertake work on electrical systems.

Technical standards

- Electricity at Work Regulations – these lay down the requirements under health and safety law for safety in working with electricity.
- Building Regulations – these are the main regulations which must be complied with when installing electrical systems in properties. Approved document P – electrical safety details the main requirements of electrical systems, this can be freely downloaded from the DCLG website at www.communities.gov.uk.
- British Standards – these support statutory documentation such as the Building Regulations, providing greater detail on installation requirements. Although British Standards are not statutory (legal) documents, they can be used in potential legal action relating to defective systems installation. The main British Standard relating to electrical systems is BS 7671 – Requirements for electrical installations.
- Manufacturer instructions – these are provided by appliance or component manufacturers to outline the installation, commissioning and maintenance requirements of their products. Manufacturer instructions usually take precedence over British Standards but should not conflict with Building or Water Regulations, which are statutory (legal) requirements.

Electrical circuits in a domestic property

Electrical supply to the property

The electrical supply to a domestic property will usually be single-phase 240V alternating current (ac).

The main intake to a domestic property will usually include:

- a sealed over-current device – protecting the supply company's cable
- a metering system.

The supplier's equipment then connects to the customer's equipment in the form of a consumer unit sited near to the meter. The consumer unit contains the equipment necessary to distribute and protect the final circuits to the electrical equipment, including a main switch.

Did you know?

The incoming cable, over-current device and meter are the property of the supply company and should not be tampered with by anyone other than supply company personnel. Any damage to the equipment must be reported direct to the supply company.

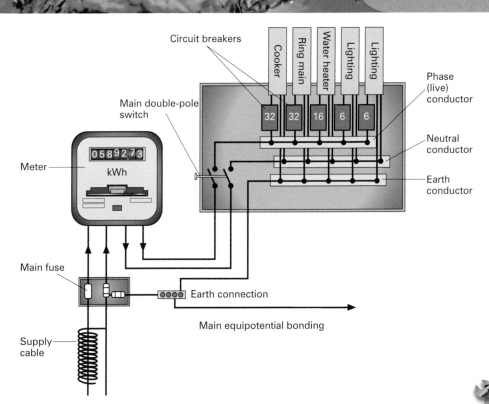

Circuit breakers

Cooker

Ring main

Water heater

Lighting

Lighting

Main double-pole switch

Phase (live) conductor

32 32 16 6 6

Neutral conductor

Meter

kWh

0589273

Earth conductor

Main fuse

Earth connection

Main equipotential bonding

Supply cable

Figure 8.1 Meter installation and consumer unit

Figure 8.2 Fuses

Each circuit is protected by an over-current protection device:

- fuses – these were used in older consumer units that contained either rewirable fuses or cartridge fuses; they contain a fuse wire that melts if an electric current above a specified level passes through it
- miniature circuit breakers (MCBs) are used in modern consumer units, a switch is tripped and the electrical circuit is broken if an excessively high current is detected
- residual current device (RCD) – higher-risk circuits such as the ring main or shower circuits may include additional protection against earth faults, provided by a residual current device. The RCD measures very small differences in current between the electrical conductors in the system, typically for domestic properties this will be 30mA. If a small change occurs the system is automatically disconnected.

Figure 8.3 Miniature circuit breaker

Basic domestic circuits

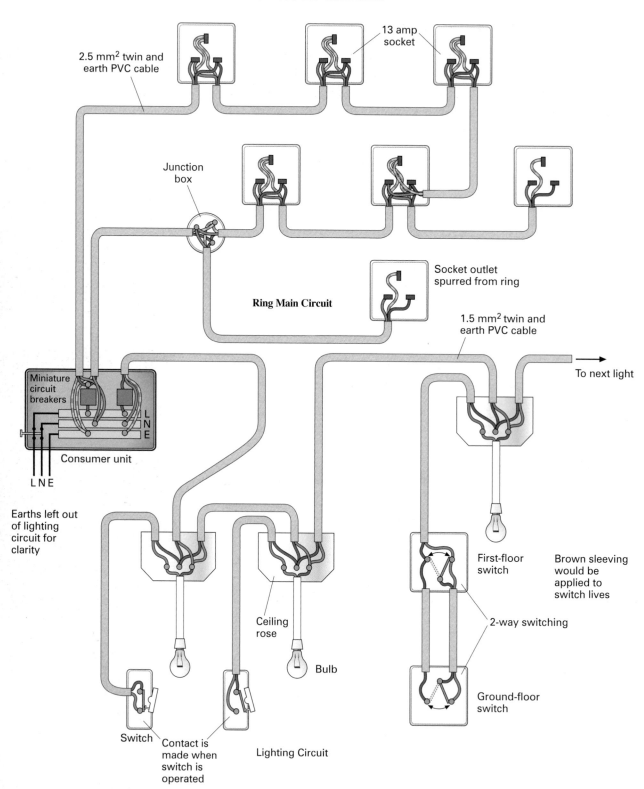

Figure 8.4 Basic electrical layout in a domestic property

Circuits are split into two types:

Ring main – feeding portable appliances

A ring main is a continuous circuit to and from the consumer unit and feeds portable appliances such as kettles, TV sets, etc. The cable feeding the ring main is kept to an optimum size as electricity is permitted to flow in two directions to reach the socket. Most properties will be served by more than one ring main, e.g. upstairs sockets and downstairs sockets.

The ring main is fed using a 2.5mm twin and earthed PVC cable and is protected by a 32A MCB or a 30A fuse.

Fixed circuits – fixed appliances connected to the electrical supply

Lighting circuit

The lighting circuit is known as a radial circuit which feeds each overhead light or wall light in turn. The lighting circuit is usually fed by a 1.5mm twin and earthed PVC cable and is protected by a 6A MCB or a 5A fuse.

Cooker circuit

A cooker circuit is an independent circuit connecting directly to a cooker. The circuit is usually fed by a 6mm twin and earthed PVC cable and is protected by a 30A MCB or a 32A fuse.

Immersion heater circuit

This circuit is independently connected to an immersion heater. The circuit is usually fed by a 2.5mm twin and earthed PVC cable and is protected by a 16A MCB or a 15A fuse.

Shower circuit

This circuit is independently connected to an electric shower. The cable size needs to be carefully selected for this type of higher-loaded appliance, based on the cable load and run. Typically cable size will be 6–10mm twin and earthed PVC cable and protection provided by a 32–45A MCB or 30–45A fuse.

Other circuits

It is preferable on new properties for other fixed appliances such as macerator WCs, central heating controls, shower pumps etc. to be fed directly from the consumer unit via their own circuit. In most cases these are lower loaded appliances and typically will be fed by 1.5mm twin and earthed PVC cable and protected by a 6A MCB or 5A fuse.

Spurs from the ring

As an alternative to independent fixed circuits, certain lower-loaded appliances such as central heating controls and macerator WCs may be spurred from the ring main, as shown in Figure 8.4. The spur is connected to the ring main through a junction box or taken from the back of an existing

Did you know?

Fixed circuits to individual appliances such as water heaters, showers, central heating controls, etc. will usually require further switches in the circuit, either to control the operation of the appliance or to isolate it for servicing purposes. These switches must be of the double-pole type – switching both the live and neutral conductor.

Did you know?

Cables should be properly sized for each circuit, based on its load, length and position in the building. Cable size is affected by the ability of the cable to lose heat when electricity is being drawn through it, so cables should not be laid under insulating materials such as loft insulation.

Did you know?

For safety purposes electrical sockets or wall switches must not be installed in bathrooms. Isolation switches in bathrooms controlling shower circuits must be of the pull-cord type and electrical connections to a macerator WC must be by an unswitched connection unit.

socket on the ring. A spur usually then feeds to a fused spur switch acting as the appliance isolation point, and also including the correctly sized over-current protection device.

Equipotential bonding

Bonding is provided in the event of a fault occuring on the electrical system and contact being made with metalwork in properties such as piped systems, radiators, kitchen sinks, baths, etc. System components need to be bonded to earth to ensure that all metalwork is kept at equal potential in the event of a fault.

Main equipotential bonding

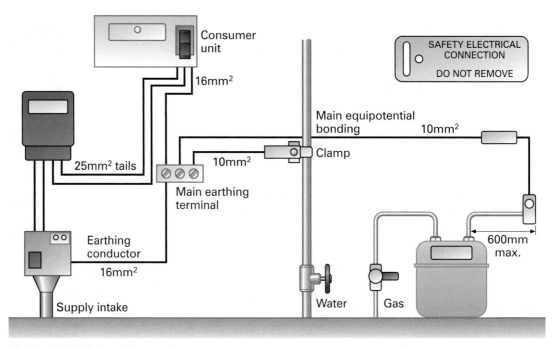

Figure 8.5 Earth-bonding conductors

The main pipework systems in a building are bonded to the main earth terminal in the property, this is in order to provide a route for any stray electric current to go to earth (fault). The bonding conductor from the main terminal to the earthing clamp is 10mm. All services are bonded – gas, water or oil. The earthing clamp should be located on the pipework, as near to the point of entry as possible, and for the gas supply within 600mm of the meter.

Supplementary bonding

There are likely to be other points of exposed metalwork in a building that may not be protected as they have been isolated from the earth by plastic fittings, cisterns, etc. This affects the conductivity of the pipework and disconnects them from the main bonding conductor. To maintain the earth, supplementary cross bonding is used, with typical supplementary bonding as shown in Figure 8.6.

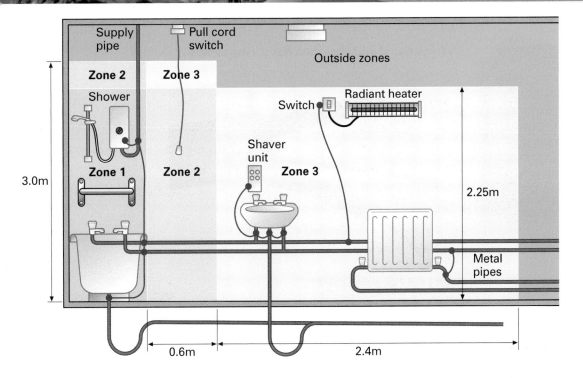

Figure 8.6 Earthing zones in bathrooms

Temporary bonding

A temporary continuity bond is an essential part of the toolkit when cutting into metal pipework. The bond maintains the electrical continuity of the pipework whilst you are working on it, retaining a continuous connection to the main bonding conductor whilst the two sections of the pipework are separated. A typical temporary bond is made from two crocodile clips and a 10mm piece of cable. The bond should be placed in position so that it bridges the gap in the pipework section being removed.

Components used in electrical systems related to plumbing work

Electrical cables and cords

All electrical cables and cords are now colour coded as follows:

- brown – live
- blue – neutral
- green/yellow – earth.

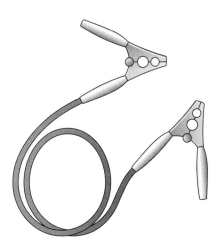

Figure 8.7 Temporary continuity bond

In domestic properties the following types of cable/cords are generally used:

PVC insulated and sheathed flat wiring cables

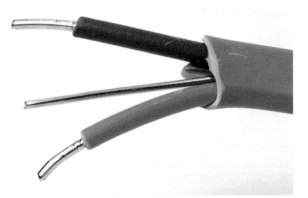

Figure 8.8 Flat wiring cable

This is general-purpose cable available in a range of cable sizes suitable for wiring where there is little risk of mechanical damage. The cable is available containing a range of different cores, and includes an uninsulated plain copper circuit protective conductor (earth) between the coloured cores. When the cable termination is being made at, for example, a socket, the uninsulated earth must be protected with a section of green/yellow marked earth sleeving. If it is intended to run flat wiring cable on exposed wall surfaces, it must be protected by trunking, and cables sunk into masonry walls must be protected by plastic or metal sheathing.

PVC insulated and sheathed flexible cords

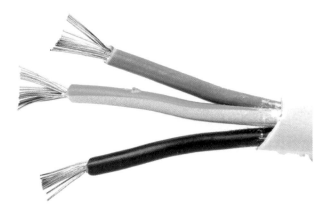

Figure 8.9 Multi-strand cord

Multi-strand cord is used to make the final connection from component to appliance, such as a double-pole switch to an immersion heater. Cords used to connect heating system components such as pumps and immersion heaters should be of the heat-resisting type capable of withstanding temperatures of up to 85°C.

Socket outlets

This is the typical socket outlet used on the ring main to feed portable appliances; multiple sockets (gangs) may form part of a single unit, e.g. a double socket. The socket outlet is capable of feeding portable appliances up to 13A current loading.

Figure 8.10 Socket outlet

Figure 8.11 Countersunk metal box

The socket outlet can either be surface-mounted using a plastic moulded box, or can be concealed using a metal countersunk box.

Did you know?

Cable entry to countersunk metal boxes must be protected by the use of rubber grommets.

Fused spur switch

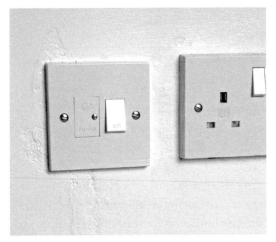

Figure 8.12 Fused spur switch

A fused spur switch is shown to the left of the socket outlet. These are used to provide over-current protection to individual appliances such as shower pumps and central heating controls, and as a means of isolation.

Unswitched connection unit

This is used to make the connection of the cable to the flex on appliances sited in areas where moisture may be a problem. Examples include macerator WCs and sink waste-disposal units. The connection unit may be fused or unfused, depending on the design of the circuit.

Figure 8.13 Unswitched connection unit

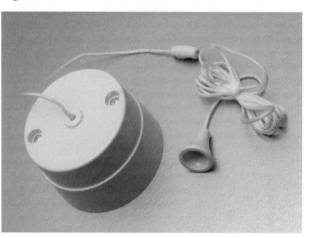

Figure 8.14 Pull-cord switch

Pull-cord switch

This is a user control (switch) to turn off an appliance. In plumbing this type of switch is likely to be found as a user control for an electric shower, with the switch being ceiling mounted in the bathroom controlling the supply to the shower.

Sheathing

A plastic or metal u-shaped sheath is used to protect electrical cables that are countersunk into masonry wall surfaces.

Trunking

Plastic trunking is used to protect surface mounted cables against mechanical damage.

Junction box

Figure 8.15 Junction box

A junction box is used to connect two or more electrical cables together, such as when an appliance is 'spurred' into the ring main. A central heating wiring centre is a more sophisticated form of junction box, providing terminals for many electrical connections to be made.

Terminal connections

Electrical components contain a variety of different methods of making terminal connections to individual wires. The main types used in components in domestic properties are shown below:

- pillar terminal
- screw terminal
- claw washer
- strip connector.

Electrical testing

On completion of the work the electrical system must be properly tested for electrical safety. Electrical tests are carried out whilst the system is in a safe (non-live) condition. The main electrical tests related to plumbing systems are:

- polarity – this makes sure that the phased conductors are not crossed somewhere – neutral from mains connected to live and vice versa. If this is not checked, the system could function correctly, but when isolated by a switch the system would still be in a dangerous mode
- earth continuity – testing to make sure that should there be an electrical fault, all exposed metalwork in a building is connected together (main and supplementary bonding) to the main supply earthing terminal

Pillar terminal

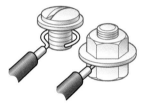
Screw terminal

Claw terminal

Strip terminal

Figure 8.16 Electrical connections

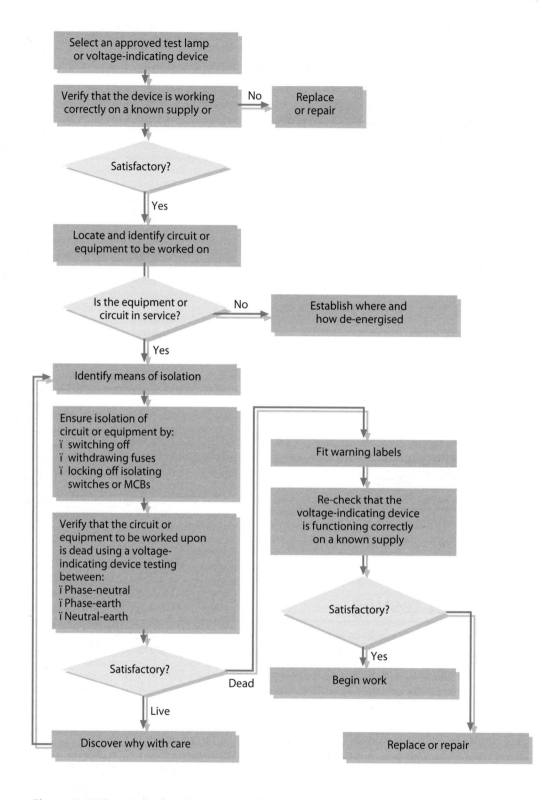

Figure 8.17 Electrical safe isolation procedure

- continuity of ring final circuit conductors – this test is carried out on a ring-main circuit, particularly when additions have been made to the circuit such as a spur. It confirms that supplies to the ring from both directions are taking place
- insulation resistance – an insulation resistance test makes sure that the insulation of conductors, electrical appliances and components is satisfactory.

Decommissioning electrical systems

When working on plumbing systems that include electrical components it will be necessary to isolate the electrical supply to the component, this must be carried out using the safe isolation procedure shown in Figure 8.17. Don't forget that you'll need to advise the customer that the system is being isolated, giving an indication of the likely time it is going to be turned off. Whilst carrying out safe isolation in a domestic property it is usually regarded as safer to isolate at the consumer unit if possible, rather than isolating at the appliance supply point (fused spur).

Did you know?

An approved voltage-indicating device is the key instrument to be used for ensuring effective isolation of an electrical circuit.

Did you know?

When permanently decommissioning an appliance such as an immersion heater it's usually necessary to remove cabling right back to the consumer unit – that will mean isolating the complete electrical supply to the building. The work should only be carried out by a competent person.

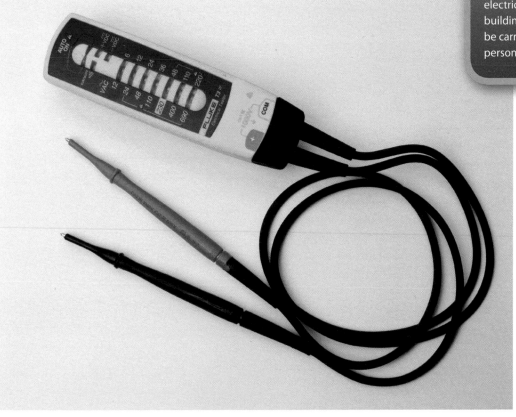

Figure 8.18 Approved voltage-indicating device

Key features of the safe isolation procedure are:

- the fuse or circuit breaker must be isolated, if it's a fuse that means removing it and keeping it in your pocket, if it's an mcb this should be locked closed with a special locking device
- the circuit should be checked to prove that it is dead. This check should be made using an approved voltage-indicating device, which should be visually inspected for damage each time it is used. Prior to the test it should be checked on a known supply such as a proving unit, to make sure that it works correctly
- when the device has been checked and is known to be working it can then be used to check that the supply is dead, checking phase to neutral conductors, phase to earth conductors and neutral to earth conductors
- before work begins, the approved voltage-indicating device should be checked again on a known supply, to make sure that it has worked correctly during the test
- finally, a warning notice should be placed at the system isolation point; only then can work begin.

Short answer questions

1. Identify two items of legislation dealing with the installation of electrical systems.
2. Who can carry out work on the main fuse in a domestic property?
3. Which type of device can be used to protect higher-risk circuits against earth faults?
4. The immersion heater circuit from a consumer unit is defined as what type of circuit?
5. The ring-main circuit from a consumer unit is defined as what type of circuit?
6. Calculate the size of overcurrent protection device required to protect an 8.5kW shower circuit when supplied at 240V ac.
7. A kitchen sink drainer should be connected to earth by means of which type of bonding?
8. The cord connecting to a domestic central heating pump should be of which type?
9. What protection is usually provided in domestic properties to surface-mounted twin and earth cable?
10. An MCB is safely isolated using what type of device?

Multiple-choice test

1. Which British Standard details the requirements for electrical installations in domestic properties?
   a) BS 5449   c) BS 7671
   b) BS 6700   d) BS EN 12056

2. The standard electricity supply to a domestic property is:
   a) 110V ac   c) 240V ac
   b) 110V dc   d) 240V dc

3. The over-current protection devices in a domestic property are contained in which of the following?
   a) Residual current device
   b) Main fuse
   c) Consumer unit
   d) Meter

4. The main isolation switch for all the electrical circuits in a domestic property is usually sited in which of the following components?
   a) Main fuse
   b) Meter
   c) Residual current device
   d) Consumer unit

5. A standard Residual Current device (RCD) protecting a domestic ring-main circuit is usually pre-set to activate when detecting an earth fault above:
   a) 15mA   c) 100mA
   b) 30mA   d) 1 amp

6. The standard MCB rating supplying a central heating circuit only is:
   a) 3A   c) 16A
   b) 6A   d) 32A

7. A rewirable fuse to an immersion heater circuit is usually rated at:
   a) 5A   c) 30A
   b) 15A   d) 45A

8. The twin and earth cable feeding an immersion heater in a domestic property is usually a minimum size of:
   a) 1.5mm   c) 4.0mm
   b) 2.5mm   d) 6.0mm

9. The main continuity bonding conductor to gas pipework in a domestic property is sized at:
   a) 2.5mm   c) 6.0mm
   b) 4.0mm   d) 10.0mm

10. The live conductor in a cord to a sink waste disposal unit is coloured:
    a) Brown   c) Green
    b) Blue   d) Yellow

11. The final connection to a macerator WC is made using which of the following?
    a) Fused spur switch
    b) Double-pole switch
    c) Pull cord
    d) Unswitched connection unit

12. A grommet is used:
   a) *As a cable enters a plastic surface-mounted box*
   b) *As a cable enters a concealed metal box*
   c) *To sleeve the earth conductor*
   d) *As insulation for cables*

13. The user isolation switch to an electric shower when sited in a bathroom should be which of the following types?
   a) *Pull-cord single pole*
   b) *Pull-cord double pole*
   c) *Rocker plate single pole*
   d) *Rocker plate double pole*

14. The wiring connections to the controls of a domestic central heating system will usually be grouped (connected) in which of the components?
   a) *Consumer unit*
   b) *Residual current device*
   c) *Wiring centre*
   d) *Meter*

15. Which of the following components must be provided with its own circuit from the consumer unit?
   a) *Shower pump*   c) *Room thermostat*
   b) *Immersion heater*   d) *Programmer*

16. The main reason for not permitting tight coils in electrical cables when installing them is:
   a) *An excess of cable is used*
   b) *Heating can occur in the cable*
   c) *The circuit will not work*
   d) *The cable will split*

17. What is the following type of electrical connection?

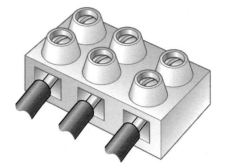

   a) *Pillar terminal*   c) *Claw washer*
   b) *Screw terminal*   d) *Strip connector*

18. What is the following type of electrical connection?

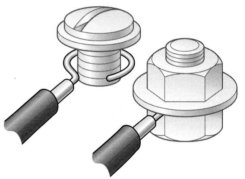

   a) *Pillar terminal*   c) *Claw washer*
   b) *Screw terminal*   d) *Strip connector*

19. Which of the following type of tests would be carried out to ensure that in the event of an electrical fault through contact with a metallic pipe, the current would flow to earth?
   a) *RCD test*
   b) *Polarity test*
   c) *Earth continuity test*
   d) *Insulation resistance test*

20. Which type of test is carried out to ensure that live and neutral conductors are not crossed?
   a) *RCD test*
   b) *Polarity test*
   c) *Earth continuity test*
   d) *Insulation resistance test*

21. Before isolating the main electrical switch at the consumer unit in an occupied domestic property, the plumber should notify the:
   a) *Local building control department*
   b) *Electricity supply company*
   c) *Customer*
   d) *Emergency service provider*

22. What instrument should be used under the safe isolation procedure when checking for safe isolation?
   a) *RCD tester*
   b) *Insulation resistance tester*
   c) *Multi-meter*
   d) *Approved voltage-indicating device*

23. When isolating a circuit at the fused spur switch, which of the following actions is considered the safest?
   a) *Covering the switch with insulating tape*
   b) *Removing and placing the fuse below the switch*
   c) *Removing and retaining the fuse in your pocket*
   d) *Turning the switch off*

24. The isolation of an electric shower should take place at the:
   a) *Pull-cord switch*
   b) *Rocker plate switch*
   c) *Main supplier's fuse*
   d) *Consumer unit*

25. What is the recommended device for checking the correct operation of an approved voltage indicating device?
   a) *Proving unit*
   b) *Multi-meter*
   c) *Earth tester*
   d) *Neon screwdriver*

By the end of this chapter you should be able to demonstrate understanding of the following above-ground discharge systems topics which will assist you in completing knowledge assessment in the Above-Ground Discharge Systems Unit of the Level 2 Certificate in Basic Plumbing Studies:

- Sources of information:
  - Technical standards
  - Site information sources
- Types of sanitary appliance:
  - Baths
  - Water closets
  - Macerator WCs
  - Washbasins
  - Shower trays
  - Bidets
  - Sinks
  - Sink waste-disposal units
  - Urinals
- Traps:
  - Types of trap
- Types of sanitary pipework system:
  - Primary ventilated stack system
  - Larger systems
  - Stub stack
  - Direct WC connection to drain
  - Causes of trap seal loss
- Soundness testing above-ground discharge systems:
  - Visual inspection
  - Pressure testing
  - Final system checks

- Maintaining above-ground discharge systems:
  - Routine maintenance
  - System faults
- Below-ground drainage systems:
  - Combined drainage system
  - Separate drainage system
- Rainwater systems:
  - Typical faults on plastic rainwater systems.

Sources of information

There are a number of information sources that plumbers may have to use to obtain the necessary detail to undertake their work on above-ground discharge systems.

Technical standards

- Building Regulations – these lay down the statutory requirements that must be carried out when dealing with the installation of sanitary appliances and sanitary pipework systems. Copies of the Building Regulations can be freely downloaded from the DCLG website at www.communities.gov.uk.
- Certain types of work on above-ground discharge systems, such as new soil stack installation, must be notified to, and be approved by, the local building control body.
- British Standards – these support statutory documentation such as the Building Regulations, providing greater detail on installation requirements. Although British Standards are not statutory (legal) documents, they can be used in potential legal action relating to defective systems installation. The main British Standards relating to above-ground discharge systems installation are BS EN 12056 Part 2 – sanitary pipework layout and calculation, and BS EN 12056 Part 3 – roof drainage layout and calculation. BS 8000 Part 13 also provides detail on the installation of sanitary pipework systems.
- Manufacturer instructions – these are provided by appliance or component manufacturers to outline the installation, commissioning and maintenance requirements of their products. Manufacturer instructions usually take precedence over British Standards but should not conflict with Building or Water Regulations, which are statutory (legal) requirements.

> **Key fact**
>
> **Key Building Regulations**
>
> Part G of the regulations deals with sanitary appliance requirements.
>
> Part H of the of the regulations deals with sanitary and rainwater pipework systems.

Site information sources

The following outlines the range of site information sources that are commonly used:

- site plans – site or location plans show the location of the building or site to adjacent roads, properties or services
- building plans – detailed plans for the property, showing key building details such as location of doors/windows, room sizes, boiler position, etc.
- services layout plans – detailed drawings of the building services such as pipe runs, position and layout
- job specification – often provided as support to building plans, this details items such as the type, size and position of key components such as boilers
- work programme – details the points at which various aspects of plumbing work fit into the overall construction programme, e.g. first fix hot and cold water system
- bill of quantities – details the quantities of components and materials used on a job.

> **Did you know?**
>
> A maintenance schedule details the equipment and components to be checked as part of a maintenance programme or a planned preventative maintenance programme.

Types of sanitary appliance

Baths

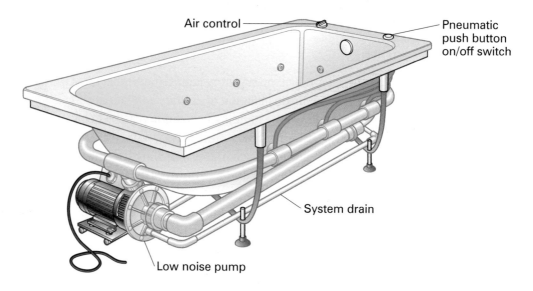

Figure 9.1 Typical jet-system bath

Baths are available in a variety of styles with taps and waste either centre mounted or end mounted. They are usually manufactured from:

- acrylic sheet (plastic)
- heavy gauged enamel steel
- vitreous enamelled cast iron.

More luxurious baths may also include a jet system (whirlpool) as shown in Figure 9.1. Baths are usually supplied with two holes for the taps to suit pillar taps or mixer taps, an overflow hole and a waste hole capable of taking a 1½" threaded waste. A combined overflow and waste connection is usually provided (as shown in Figure 9.2), an alternative to the plug and chain is the pop-up waste.

Water closets (WCs)

Most WCs are manufactured from vitreous china; models used in public conveniences typically will be stainless steel as they are more resistant to vandalism. WCs are available as:

- concealed – the cistern is hidden
- close coupled – the cistern and pan are joined together as one unit
- low level – the cistern is sited usually no more than 1 metre above the height of the pan
- high level – the cistern is sited more than 1 metre above the pan and uses a chain as part of the flushing mechanism.

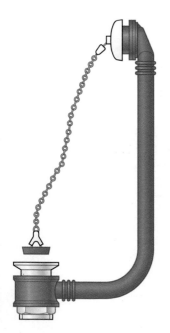

Figure 9.2 Combined waste and overflow fitting

WC pans

WC pans are available in two types:

The wash-down pan tends to be the most popular type of WC pan, it uses the force of water from the cistern to clear the contents of the pan.

Siphonic pans use the principle of the siphon to create negative pressure behind the trap seal. They have been produced as single- and double-trap types. The double-trap type uses a pressure-reducing valve between the cistern and the pan, as water is released into the second trap it draws air from the void between the two traps and siphons the contents from the bowl.

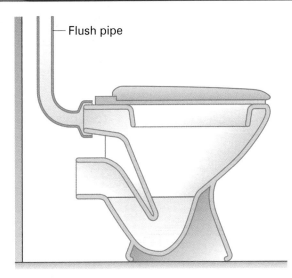

Figure 9.3a Wash-down pan

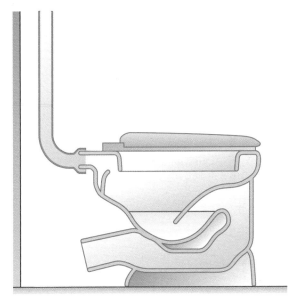

Figure 9.3b Single-trap siphonic pan

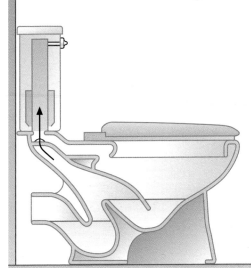

Figure 9.3c Double-trap siphonic pan

WC cisterns

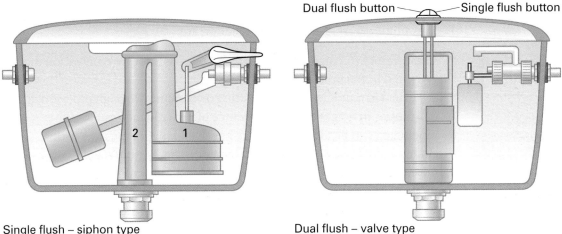

Single flush – siphon type

Dual flush – valve type

Figure 9.4 Different types of cistern-flushing mechanism

WCs in domestic properties are flushed by means of a cistern. The flushing mechanism in the cistern may be either:

- a siphon, or
- a valve such as drop valve or hinged-flap valve.

Cisterns may be either single flush or dual flush. Dual flushing provides for greater water conservation. Maximum WC cistern capacities for new installations are:

- 6 litres single flush
- dual flush – 6 litres large flush and 4 litres small flush.

Older pans, cisterns and flushing mechanisms of 7.5 litre and 9 litre capacity, approved under previous Water Byelaws, are still available for use as replacements, but must not be used on new installations under the Water Regulations.

Macerator WCs

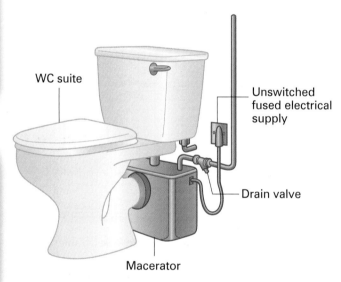

Figure 9.5 WC macerator unit

The key points of WC macerator installation are:

- a macerator WC can only be used when there is another conventional WC fitted in the premises
- the macerator unit is capable of lifting its contents through pipework up to 5 metres in height and for a distance of up to 90 metres
- pipe sizing can be as low as 22mm, however, longer pipe runs with changes in direction will require a larger discharge pipe size
- horizontal pipework must usually be laid to a minimum fall of 10mm per metre run
- the electrical supply to the unit must be via an unswitched connection; the supply must be fused.

Washbasins

There are two types of washbasin:

Fixed-to-the-wall basins come in two types: pedestal wash-hand basins and wall-hung basins. Pedestal wash-hand basins tend to be more popular in domestic properties as they allow the connecting pipework to be easily hidden. There is a wide range of fixing devices available to mount wall-hung basins, manufacturer installation instructions should be referred to for greater detail.

> ### Did you know?
> Some older types of pedestal wash-hand basins were supplied with a fixing device known as a safety bracket to support the edges of the basin and fix the basin to the wall.

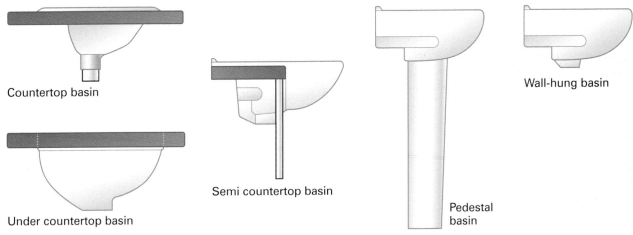

Countertop basin

Under countertop basin

Semi countertop basin

Pedestal basin

Wall-hung basin

Figure 9.7 Counter-top

Figure 9.6 Fixed to the wall

There are three types of counter-top basin:

- counter-top – sits proud of the work surface
- semi counter-top – used to save space
- under counter-top – the basin sits under the counter.

Basins are usually manufactured from vitreous china, counter-tops are however available manufactured from acetyl (plastic), stainless steel wall-hung basins are available for areas such as kitchens, where damage may occur. Basins are available with one, two or three tap-holes, depending on the type of taps being used. A 1¼" waste is usually provided for normal domestic basins. Basins may be supplied with or without an integral overflow, in which case the following applies:

- slotted waste to be used if an integral overflow is provided
- unslotted waste to be used if there is no integral overflow.

> ### Installation tip
> Plastic threaded wastes or threaded wastes to plastic basins should be made water-tight using silicone sealant as the jointing material, on no account must jointing compounds or putty be used, as they cause the plastic to degrade.

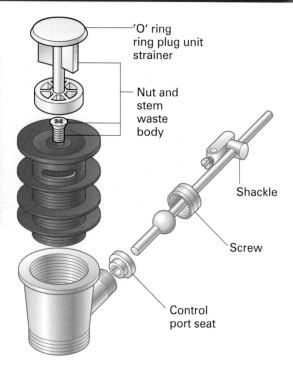

'O' ring
ring plug unit
strainer

Nut and
stem
waste
body

Shackle

Screw

Control
port seat

Figure 9.8 Pop-up waste fitting

Pop-up basin wastes are available, removing the need to use a plug and chain, the basin is filled/emptied using a twist lever or push button. The height that the ring plug unit lifts can be adjusted by turning clockwise to increase the lift or anti-clockwise to reduce the lift.

Shower trays

There are many designs of shower tray available to suit the particular installation circumstance. Trays are manufactured from:

- acrylic sheet (plastic)
- fireclay
- resin bonded.

The waste outlet from the tray will usually take a 1½" threaded waste, most trays do not usually have an integral overflow and therefore the waste will be of the unslotted type. Care must be taken on installing the shower tray to make sure it is level across all its corners, as tiles and enclosures will rest on the tray edges.

Bidets

Bidets are usually manufactured from vitreous china and are available as:

- over-the-rim types which may include a spray head connected via a flexible hose
- ascending spray.

Over-the-rim types with flexible hoses and ascending spray bidets are not suitable for connection directly to the supply pipe and must be fed from storage, with particular care and attention to how they are connected.

A typical bidet will take a 1¼" slotted waste which will accommodate water from an integral overflow.

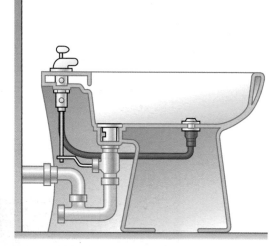

Figure 9.9 Ascending spray bidet

Sinks

Sinks are available in a variety of styles, suited to different applications. Belfast and London sinks are often used for industrial/commercial applications such as cleaners' sinks; they are usually manufactured from heavy-duty fireclay. They come with or without an overflow and usually have a 1½" threaded waste, the waste is slotted or unslotted, depending on whether an overflow is provided.

A wide variety of sinks is available for domestic properties, typical manufacturing materials include:

- stainless steel
- plastic-coated stainless steel
- acetyl (plastic)
- fireclay – London and Belfast type sinks are now popular for domestic kitchens.

Domestic sinks are available with multiple bowls and drainer options. They usually take a 1½" threaded waste which is part of a combined waste/overflow device. The number of tap holes in the sink will depend on the type of tap being used, i.e. one, two or three hole.

Did you know?

Bottle traps should not be used on kitchen sinks and in particular waste-disposal units, as they are susceptible to blockage with food matter.

Sink waste-disposal unit

These are used as a luxury item to dispose of kitchen refuse such as left-over food, vegetable peelings, etc. They are usually sited under the kitchen sink and may require a special sink top with a larger than normal waste outlet. Key features of the unit are:

- a cut-out device must be provided that will turn off the unit if it jams
- a jamming tool is usually provided to assist in freeing any jamming or blockages
- the waste-disposal unit must be connected to the waste pipework by means of a trap
- the electrical connection should be made by an unswitched outlet; the supply must be fused.

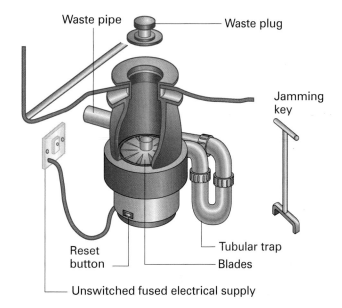

Figure 9.10 Sink waste-disposal unit

Urinals

Urinals are used in non-domestic buildings and can be of the following type:

- slab urinal
- stall urinal
- bowl urinal.

Bowl urinals tend to be the most popular and are usually manufactured from vitreous china, or stainless steel for areas with a higher risk of damage occurring.

Urinals are usually flushed (cleaned) by means of a flushing cistern which contains an automatic flushing siphon. The siphon flushes automatically when a pre-determined water level in the cistern has been reached.

Did you know?

A sparge pipe is a flush pipe fixed to a slab urinal which has a number of holes pre-drilled into it to permit the surface of the slab to be washed during flushing.

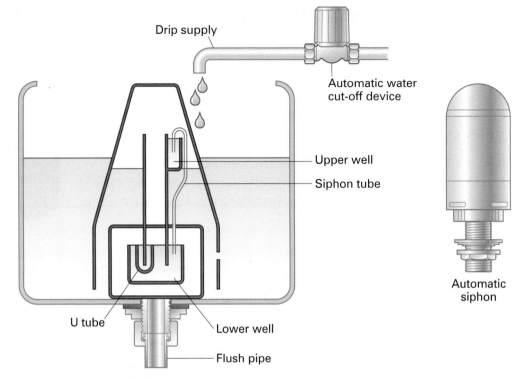

Figure 9.11 Automatic flushing cistern

To ensure adequate water conservation and minimise the amount of flushing taking place, the water flow into the cistern is regulated by a:

- hydraulically operated valve – this permits water to flow into the cistern when other appliances are being used in the public convenience
- solenoid valve and time switch (the time switch prevents the cistern from filling during periods when the building is not in use)
- solenoid valve and infra-red sensor (the infra-red sensor detects movement of persons in the toilets and opens the solenoid valve to allow water to flow into the cistern, if no movement is detected for a period of time, the solenoid closes and the cistern does not flush).

Traps

A trap is designed to retain a plug of water in order to prevent foul air and noxious smells entering a room from the drainage pipework to which sanitary appliances are connected. The depth of trap seal required is dependent on the type of appliance the trap is serving, as detailed in Figure 9.12.

Appliance	Diameter of trap (mm)	Depth of seal (mm of water or equivalent)
Washbasin[1] Bidet	32	75
Bath[2] Shower[2]	40	50
Food waste disposal unit Urinal bowl Sink Washing machine[2] Dishwashing machine[2]	40	75
WC pan - outlet <80mm	75	50
WC pan - outlet >80mm	100	50

[1]The depth of seal may be reduced to 50mm only with flush grated wastes without plugs on spray tap basins
[2]Where these appliances discharge directly to a gully the depth of seal may be reduced to not less than 38mm
[2]Traps used on appliances with flat bottom (trailing waste discharge) and discharging to a gully with a grating may have a reduced water seal of not less than 38mm

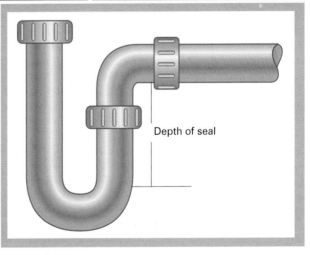

Depth of seal

Figure 9.12 Minimum trap sizes and seal depths

Types of trap

P-traps

Used where the waste pipe discharges directly through a wall into a gulley, or to directly connect into a soil stack.

Figure 9.13 P-trap

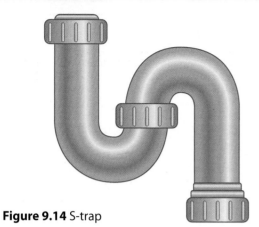

Figure 9.14 S-trap

S-traps

S-traps are used where the waste pipe has to discharge vertically through a floor or into a lower-level horizontal pipe run. Care needs to be taken with their application as it can often lead to trap seal loss.

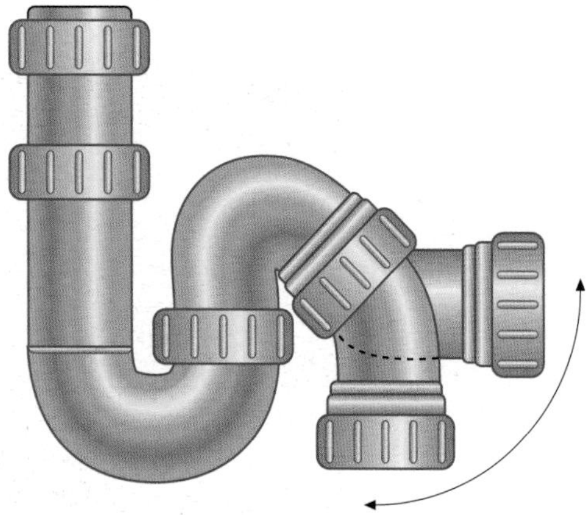

Swivel traps

These traps provide multiple position options and are often used on kitchen sinks with multiple bowls and for sanitary appliance replacement jobs.

Figure 9.15 Swivel trap

Low-level bath traps

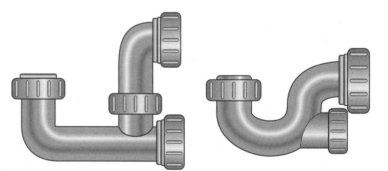

Figure 9.16 Low-level bath trap

This type of trap is designed to fit into a tight space under a bath or shower, it is usually only suited to connection to a gulley, as it only has a 38mm depth of seal.

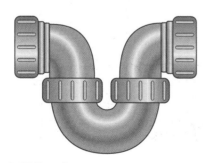

Figure 9.17 Running trap

Running traps

These are used on a range of appliances (normally basins) where one trap provides a seal for more than one appliance.

Washing machine traps

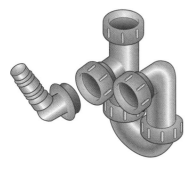
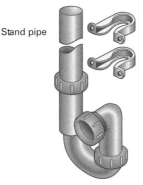
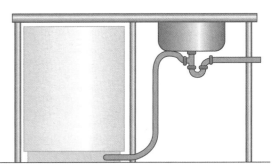

Stand pipe

Figure 9.18 Washing machine traps

These are available as a separate trap serving a washing machine alone and which incorporates a stand-pipe assembly. An alternative to this is to use a combined sink/washing machine or dish washer trap, particularly where space is at a premium.

Bottle traps

These are often used for their neat appearance, particularly on wall-mounted wash-hand basins. They are not suitable for kitchen sink applications, as food deposits can accumulate in them, causing blockages.

Did you know?

When using a combined sink/washing machine trap, the washing machine discharge pipe should be looped above the sink overflow height to ensure that products from the kitchen sink cannot discharge into the washing machine.

Figure 9.19 Bottle trap

Resealing traps

This is a special type of trap fitted in situations where trap seal loss owing to problems with the waste discharge pipework may occur. The trap ensures that the seal in the trap is not lost and noxious smells cannot enter the building.

The trap show contains an anti-vacuum valve letting air into the system if a high-suction pressure occurs.

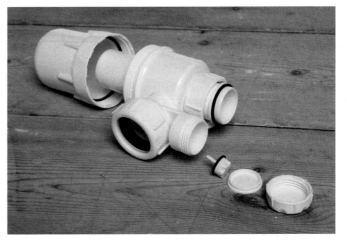

Figure 9.20 Resealing trap

Types of sanitary pipework system

The design of sanitary pipework systems must comply with Part H1 of the Building Regulations, which requires that sanitary pipework systems:

- minimise the risk of blockage or leakage
- prevent foul air from the drainage system from entering a building
- are ventilated to prevent the build-up of dangerous gases
- are accessible for cleaning and clearing of any blockages.

Primary ventilated stack system

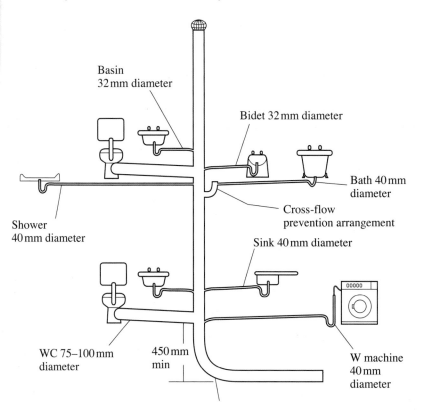

Basin 32 mm diameter

Bidet 32 mm diameter

Bath 40 mm diameter

Cross-flow prevention arrangement

Shower 40 mm diameter

Sink 40 mm diameter

WC 75–100 mm diameter

450 mm min

W machine 40 mm diameter

Figure 9.21 Primary ventilated stack

This tends to be the most popular type of stack system, as it minimises the amount of pipework that needs to be used. It is particularly suited to application in domestic properties where appliances are closely grouped around the main stack. There are however a number of golden rules that need to be considered when designing and installing this type of stack, in order to avoid trap seal loss and noxious smells entering the building:

- no appliances must be connected within 450mm of the invert level of the drain with buildings up to three storeys in height, and a long radius bend must be used to connect the stack to the drainage system
- the following table shows the maximum pipe lengths and pipe gradients that must be applied to the system in order to avoid trap seal loss

	Pipe size	Maximum length	Slope
Basin	32 mm	1.7 m	18–20 mm fall per metre run
Bath	40 mm	3.0 m	19–90 mm/m
Shower	50 mm*	4.0 m	18–90 mm/m
WC	100 mm	6.0 m	18 mm/m min

Figure 9.22 Table of maximum branch discharge pipe lengths and gradients

*Normally 40 mm

- branch connections into the main stack from waste pipes must not occur within a space of 200mm opposite other connections, as shown in Figure 9.23 (this is in order to prevent cross flow)
- an external stack must terminate at least 0.9m above an openable window when it is sited within 3m of that window.

In domestic applications where some of these requirements cannot be met, it may be acceptable to use a resealing trap to prevent trap seal loss.

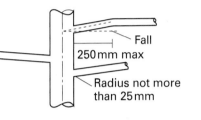

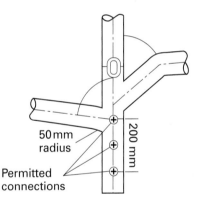

Figure 9.23 Permitted branch pipe connections

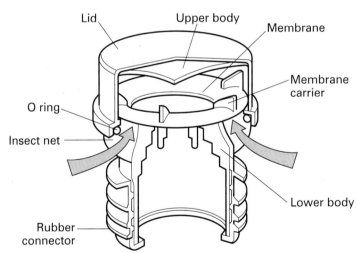

Figure 9.24 Air-admittance valve

It is possible in certain circumstances to install an air-admittance valve as an alternative to the main stack vent pipe in a primary ventilated stack system. The main features of the air-admittance valve are:

- it must only be sited indoors as externally it could freeze and lock up
- the head of the drain to which the stack is connected must be properly ventilated by means of a vent pipe

Did you know?

The minimum size of main soil stack pipework should be the same as the largest WC outlet usually 110mm. Some WCs are sized at 75mm, in which case the stack can be a minimum of 75mm.

- it must be sited for ease of maintenance and air must be supplied to the valve in order for it to work properly.

Larger systems

With larger systems, or indeed where the requirements for the primary ventilated stack cannot be met through the use of resealing traps, an alternative is to use a system employing separate ventilation pipework:

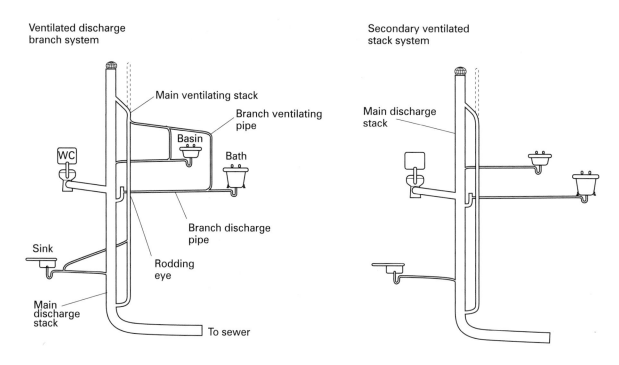

Figure 9.25 Ventilated branch discharge system and secondary stack system

- ventilated branch discharge system – ventilating each separate appliance into a separate stack
- secondary ventilated stack system – directly ventilating the main soil stack.

Stub stack

These can be used on single-storey properties and the lower floors of multiple-storey properties, they eliminate the need for a separate vent pipe. Provided that the installation meets the requirements shown in Figure 9.26, in particular the highest waste connection above the invert of the drain must be no more than 2m and the base of the WC 1.3m.

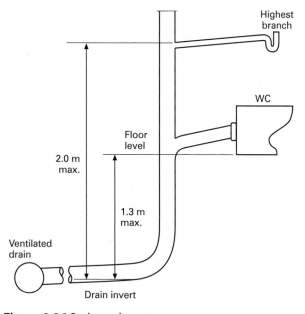

Figure 9.26 Stub stack system

Direct WC connection to drain

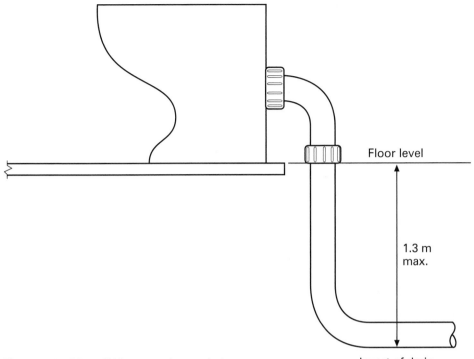

Figure 9.27 Direct WC connection to drain

A WC may be connected directly to the drainage system, provided that the invert of the drain is within 1.3m of the base of the WC.

Causes of trap seal loss

There are a number of ways in which trap seals may be lost:

- evaporation – occurs in warm weather when the trap is not being used, with the water in the seal simply evaporating
- wavering – caused by excessive wind pressure across the top of the vent pipe creating a wave motion in the trap (usually WCs) causing water to wash over the weir of the trap
- momentum – a large volume of water, such as flushing with a bucket, removes the seal of the trap
- capillary attraction – in S-traps caused by a thread of material over-hanging into the trap seal and into the discharge pipe, water is then lost from the seal by capillary attraction
- self-siphonage – this commonly occurs in basins. A partial vacuum is created in the discharge pipe between the water plug and the basin. This negative pressure can siphon the water out of the trap, particularly if the water empties quickly. Self-siphonage can be avoided by ensuring that branch pipes are not too long and are laid to correct falls.

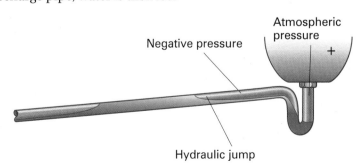

Figure 9.28 Self-siphonage

If it occurs it can be eliminated by fitting ventilating pipework to the appliance, or more commonly by fitting a resealing trap

- induced siphonage – as the water plug flows past the second appliance connection, negative pressure is created between the pipe and appliance, which can siphon the contents of the second trap. This is why care needs to be taken when connecting two appliances into a common discharge pipe with the primary ventilated stack system. The problem can be cured by installing ventilation pipework to the two appliances, or by fitting resealing traps

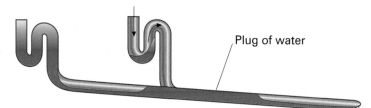
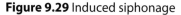

Figure 9.29 Induced siphonage

- compression – as water is discharged into a stack from upper floor levels it creates a compression effect (back pressure) at the base of the stack, which can be sufficient to remove a trap seal. This is why long radius bends must be used at the foot of the stack and branch connections must not occur within 450mm of the invert of the stack for buildings up to three storeys high.

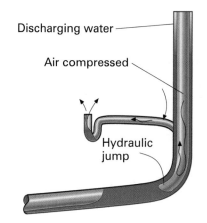

Figure 9.30 Compression

Now review pages 341 to 344 of *Plumbing NVQ and Technical Certificate Level 2*, relating to pipework installation, access and materials.

Soundness testing above-ground discharge systems

The soundness testing of above-ground discharge systems involves a three-stage process:

- visual inspection
- pressure testing
- final system checks.

Visual inspection

This is the process of preparing the system to be tested and will include such things as checking all joints are properly made, all pipes are properly clipped and the system design meets the specification and the requirements of regulations/standards.

Pressure testing

Above-ground discharge systems are usually required to be pressure tested under the Building Regulations using an air test. Figure 9.31 shows the procedures to carry out the air test.

Did you know?

It's possible to test above-ground systems for soundness with smoke. A smoke test should not however be used with plastic pipework, as it can degrade the plastic.

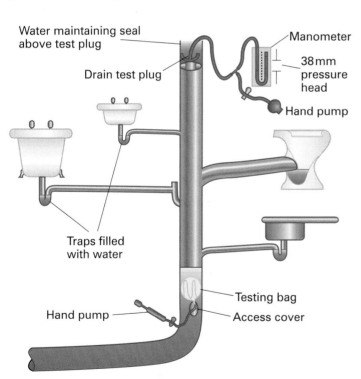

Water maintaining seal above test plug

Drain test plug

Manometer

38 mm pressure head

Hand pump

Traps filled with water

Hand pump

Testing bag

Access cover

Figure 9.31 Air test being carried out

- the system to be tested is sealed with hollow drain plugs (a test bag can be used at the lower end if it proves difficult to use a plug), a test nipple is inserted into the plug where the manometer is to be sited
- all the traps are filled with water and the test plugs covered to eliminate air leakage from them
- using the hand pump, air is pumped into the system to give a water head reading of 38mm on the manometer. The plug cock is turned off and the test continued for a 3-minute period. There should be no visible drop in pressure
- if a pressure drop is found, the source of the leakage should be traced using leak-detection fluid.

Final system checks

Once the system has been pressure tested and proved to be leak free, it should be performance tested. This is carried out by filling all appliances to their overflow level then simultaneously releasing water into the system from them as well as flushing the WC. When all the water has discharged into the system from the appliances, a minimum water seal depth of 25mm must be retained in each trap. The trap seal depth is checked with a dip-stick.

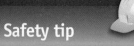

Definition

Manometer – a device used for air testing sanitation systems. It is used to establish the correct test pressures in the system and to indicate whether there is any leakage.

Stick painted matt black

Figure 9.32 Performance testing traps

Maintaining above-ground discharge systems

Before undertaking maintenance and indeed some aspects of installation work on above-ground discharge systems there are a few points that you need to consider:

- hygiene – handling used materials such as sanitary appliances and sanitary pipework needs to be carried out with due care to avoid the spread of serious disease, so it's advisable when working with this type of equipment to wear rubber gloves
- open pipe ends – open pipe ends that are connected to live systems should be properly capped while working on the system to avoid noxious smells entering the building
- drain stoppers – these are an essential item of equipment to have available, particularly when maintaining larger systems, as they prevent the flow of waste materials reaching the point in the system that you are working on
- provision of WCs – for maintenance activities that take a relatively long time to complete (particularly on larger systems such as office blocks), consideration needs to be given to the need to provide temporary WC

Safety tip

Special care needs to be taken when locating the source of blockages in WCs and associated pipework: it has been known for the blockage to be caused by hypodermic syringes discarded by drug users.

and washing facilities. Effective communication with the customer is also vital when arranging to undertake work that will interrupt an essential service.

Routine maintenance

Larger systems may well have a requirement for routine (annual) maintenance to be carried out, key points of the system that may be checked as part of the routine maintenance schedule include:

- effective access to the system, access points are not jammed and can be opened
- undertake a visual inspection of the system for signs of damage and check for conformity with regulations/standards requirements
- check the system for leakage by applying a pressure test
- check for effective discharge from sanitary appliances and performance test for retention of adequate trap seal depth
- check the operation of urinal water-control devices and water levels in WCs.

System faults

Maintenance work is likely to involve communication with the customer, particularly relating to diagnosing the fault and agreeing to the work carried out; companies have different policies relating to the job responsibilities of plumbers, particularly in relation to providing costs for undertaking work. In general terms the following outlines typical job responsibilities:

- plumbing apprentice – limited job responsibility – normally working with someone else who will assist in diagnosing faults, not normally involved in negotiating cost with customers
- Level 2 qualified plumber – will usually have significant responsibility in diagnosing faults but may need to refer back to his/her supervisor deal with costing information/ordering parts and confirming costs with customers
- Level 3 qualified plumber –will usually have complete responsibility for diagnosing faults, ordering parts and confirming costs/orders with customers.

Remember – the golden rule is to always fully communicate to customers the action needed to repair or replace parts, this includes the cost of the work. If this doesn't take place, complaints are likely to occur.

Typical faults that may be encountered:

Noxious smells

Noxious smells entering a room from time to time from the sanitary appliances, a gurgling noise from the appliance trap can often be associated with this problem. The solution is to check for adequate retention of the trap seal after performance testing the system; this should identify a deficiency in the system which will need rectification, it may be possible to rectify by installing a resealing trap, or alternatively in more serious cases (including compression) pipework modifications may be necessary.

Blockage of waste appliances

Blockages of this type may be full or partial blockages. The location of the blockage will usually be either at the trap or in the pipework.

If a full blockage occurs in the trap then it's probably easiest to remove the trap and clean it out, checking to establish that the wrong type of trap has not been installed, e.g. a bottle trap on a kitchen sink. With partial blockages a force cup (plunger) may be used to remove the waste material.

Blockages in pipework can usually be cleared with a force cup and/or a flexible pipe drain cleaner. It's worth checking to establish that the pipework has been laid to the correct gradient as part of the work, as typically pipework laid to too low a gradient is susceptible to blockage and may benefit from modification.

Blockage of WCs

WCs may suffer from full or partial blockage. The blockage may be removed by the use of a disc-type WC plunger. It's also worth checking to establish whether a foreign body such as a detergent block holder has fallen into the WC pan; these can be the source of quite a lot of blockages and may result in the need to remove the pan to retrieve the block.

A blockage may also occur in the drainage system, which will usually require rodding or in more serious cases jetting may be required. Blockage in drainage systems can also be brought about by damage to the drainage system, e.g. tree roots, in which case a section of the pipework will require replacement.

Below-ground drainage systems

Domestic plumbing work does not usually include the installation of the below-ground drainage system. Plumbers do however need to know what the various types of below-ground drainage systems are so that they can avoid discharging foul water into surface water drainage systems, causing serious contamination issues. The primary types of below-ground drainage system are:

Did you know?

A waste pipe connecting to a trapped gulley should discharge below the grating but above the water level in the gulley.

Combined drainage system

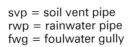

svp = soil vent pipe
rwp = rainwater pipe
fwg = foulwater gully

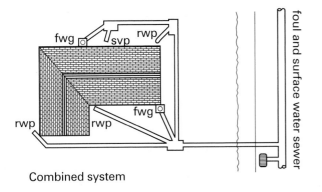

Combined system

Figure 9.33 Combined drainage system

Did you know?

In a combined drainage system the rainwater pipework needs to include trapped gullies at the point of connection between above and below ground, to ensure smells do not come from the pipework.

In this system the water from the sanitary appliances (foul water) and the rainwater (surface water) go into the same sewer.

Separate drainage system

In this system foul water runs into the sewer system and surface water is discharged into a separate system which may ultimately discharge into a local watercourse such as a river or stream.

Rainwater systems

Domestic rainwater systems may be produced from the following materials:

- cast iron
- aluminium
- PVCu (this is the most popular).

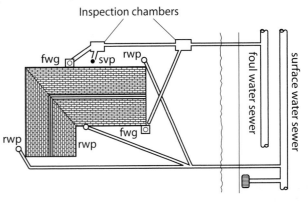

Figure 9.34 Separate drainage system

Gutter systems are available in a number of different profiles (shapes).

 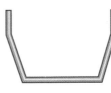 

Standard half round   Square   Ogee

Figure 9.35 Gutter profiles

Gutters are usually fixed to the building using fascia brackets when fitted to fascia boards. Drive-in brackets are used when installing direct to masonry surfaces. The following outlines the key points of installing PVCu gutter and rainwater systems:

- screws used for fixings should be corrosion resistant.
- gutter should usually be laid to a fall of 1 in 600, the process of lining the brackets is carried out using a string line
- the maximum intervals for brackets on the gutter system is usually 1m
- an allowance must be made for thermal movement of plastic gutters (an expansion space is usually marked in fittings or if this is not provided allow 3mm for every metre run)
- the down pipe (fall pipe) is marked out using a plumb line or spirit level and clips should be spaced at 1.5m intervals
- when measuring and cutting the down pipe, allowance must be made for thermal expansion as with the gutter system, typically 6–8mm space is left from the shoulder of fittings
- a swan-neck arrangement is often used to connect the gutter outlet to the down pipe, care must be taken to ensure that the swan-neck bends are the right way up in order to avoid leakage
- the down pipe is connected directly to the drain, or discharges above a grating using a component called a shoe
- on completion the gutter and rainwater pipework should be tested for leakage (soundness) by discharging water at the highest point of the gutter, preferably using a hose pipe.

Typical faults on plastic rainwater systems

There aren't many things that can go wrong with a rainwater system, here are the main points:

- water running over the front edge of the gutter – gutter blocked with leaves, requiring cleaning, or gutter outlet blocked with a ball, or rainwater pipe blocked either above or below ground
- water running between the back edge of the gutter and the fascia board – felt underlay disintegrated and not properly directing water to the gutter system (may need to be referred to a roofing contractor)
- leakage from plastic gutters or rainwater pipe joints – may be by mechanical damage but could also be due to insufficient expansion space provided in fittings, in which case shorten gutter or down pipe lengths and re-make the joints.

Short answer questions

1. Which type of documentation can be used to determine the position of a soil and vent pipe on a new building?

2. What type of tool is required to make a strap-on boss (saddle branch connection) on a section of soil stack?

3. What type of plastic soil pipe component is used to gain access for maintenance purposes in a length of soil pipework?

4. What is the name of the component that is used at the termination of a soil stack?

5. What is the name of the plastic soil pipe fitting in Figure 9.36?

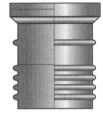

Figure 9.36

6. What is the main danger when replacing lengths of cast-iron soil pipework?

7. A trap seal is being lost by induced siphonage, what modifications could be made to the system to overcome the problem?

8. A trap seal that is lost when a large bucket of water is discharged into the appliance is lost by?

9. Name two types of equipment that may be used to seal pipe ends during an air test on an above-ground system.

10. What type of brackets are used to fix gutters directly to masonry wall surfaces?

Multiple-choice test

1. Which Building Regulations Approved Document details the requirements for sanitary pipework systems?
   a) G   c) J
   b) H   d) L

2. The type of soil pipework fittings to be used on a new-build property will be detailed in:
   a) Building plans   c) Job specification
   b) Site plans   d) Work programme

3. The detailed installation requirements of a sink waste-disposal unit are laid down in:
   a) *Building Regulations*
   b) *Water Regulations*
   c) *BS 6700*
   d) *Manufacturer instructions*

4. Baths may be manufactured from which one of the following materials:
   a) *Enamelled copper*
   b) *Enamelled pressed steel*
   c) *Polybutylene*
   d) *Polythene*

5. A threaded waste to a plastic bath is 'made-in' with what type of sealing material:
   a) *Putty*
   b) *Jointing compound*
   c) *Rubber washer*
   d) *Lead washer*

6. A double-trap siphonic pan uses what type of device to draw air from the void between the two traps as part of the flushing mechanism?
   a) *Pressure-reducing valve*
   b) *Pressure-increasing valve*
   c) *Double-check valve*
   d) *Single-check valve*

7. An alternative to a siphon in a new toilet is to use a:
   a) *Power flusher*
   b) *Drop valve*
   c) *Check valve*
   d) *Anti-siphon valve*

8. To meet Water Regulation requirements a new WC flushing cistern working with a dual flushing mechanism operates on the following flush volumes:
   a) *3-litre short flush & 8-litre long flush*
   b) *4-litre short flush & 6-litre long flush*
   c) *4-litre short flush & 8-litre long flush*
   d) *7.5-litre short flush & 9-litre long flush*

9. The final electrical connection to a macerator WC is made from which of the following electrical connection units:
   a) Unswitched connection unit
   b) Pull-cord switch
   c) Rocker plate switch
   d) 13 amp plug socket

10. An unslotted waste would be used with which one of the following types of sanitary appliance:
    a) Basin without overflow
    b) Basin with overflow
    c) Water closet
    d) Bidet with overflow

11. What type of trap is shown in the following drawing?

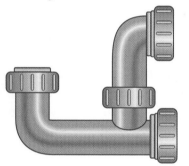

Figure 9.37

   a) S-trap
   b) P-trap
   c) Bottle trap
   d) Low-level bath trap

12. An S-trap is more likely to lose its seal by which of the following:
    a) Wavering
    b) Compression
    c) Induced siphonage
    d) Self-siphonage

13. Which of the following types of trap is not suitable for use on a kitchen sink?
    a) P-trap
    b) Swivel trap
    c) Bottle trap
    d) Tubular resealing trap

14. The minimum depth of seal for a bath trap connected to a soil stack is:
    a) 25mm
    b) 38mm
    c) 50mm
    d) 75mm

15. A waste pipe must not connect to a soil stack in a property up to three storeys high within what distance of the invert level of the drain?
    a) 150mm
    b) 250mm
    c) 450mm
    d) 600mm

16. A soil and waste system that has all the appliances closely grouped around the main stack and does not have branch ventilating pipework is described as a:
    a) System with WC connection direct to the drain
    b) Primary ventilated stack system
    c) Ventilated branch discharge system
    d) Secondary stack system

17. When a vent pipe terminates within 3m of an openable window it should rise to what height above the window?
    a) 600mm
    b) 750mm
    c) 900mm
    d) 1200mm

18. What is the name of the following soil and vent pipe component?

Figure 9.38

   a) Drain connector
   b) Boss adaptor
   c) Concentric waste reducer
   d) Bird cage

19. Which one of the following types of test should not be carried out on plastic pipework?
a) Smoke
b) Air
c) Water
d) Performance

20. Which of the following correctly describes the air test requirements for an above-ground discharge system?
a) Tested at 25mm water gauge for 3 minutes
b) Tested at 38mm water gauge for 1 minute
c) Tested at 38mm water gauge for 3 minutes
d) Tested at 50mm water gauge for 5 minutes

21. When air testing a system:
a) All traps must be sealed with a bung
b) All traps must be properly filled with water
c) Rubber bungs are not covered with water
d) No rubber bungs are required at the main stack

22. Which of the following is likely to be included in a routine maintenance schedule for an above-ground discharge system?
a) Checking and adjusting water levels in WC cisterns
b) Flushing out all soil and waste pipework
c) Removing all sanitaryware to check for damage
d) Replacing all sanitaryware fixings

23. The servicing procedure for a macerator WC is normally laid down in the:
a) Manufacturer instructions
b) Building Regulations
c) Water Regulations
d) BS EN 12056

24. A WC pan has been removed in a property overnight, which of the following is the preferred action to take with the open-ended soil pipe?
a) Blank the end with newspaper
b) Leave a warning notice
c) Advise the customer that smells may occur
d) Cap the pipe end with a bung

25. A below-ground drainage system in which soil and rainwater pipework discharges to the main sewer is said to be a:
a) Separate system
b) Partially separate system
c) Combined system
d) Boosted system

26. The rainwater pipe to a combined system of drainage connects to the drainage system by means of a:
a) Slow radius bend
b) Tight radius bend
c) Trapped gulley
d) Pipe inverter

27. The following shows the profile of which type of gutter system?

Figure 9.39

a) Ogee
b) Half round
c) Square
d) Curved linear

28. The minimum recommended fall for gutters is:
a) 1 in 200   c) 1 in 600
b) 1 in 300   d) 1 in 1000

29. Gutter brackets are laid out to the correct falls using which of the following?
a) Plumb line   c) Water level
b) Spirit level   d) String line

30. Dripping between the gutter and the fascia board is a sign that:
a) Sufficient expansion allowance has not been provided in the gutter unions
b) The gutter fixings have not been properly fixed
c) The gutter fall is too great
d) The felt underlay directing water to the gutter has disintegrated

10 Sheet leadwork

By the end of this chapter you should be able to demonstrate understanding of the following sheet leadwork topics which will assist you in completing knowledge assessment in the Sheet Lead Weathering Unit of the Level 2 Certificate in Basic Plumbing Studies:

- Sources of information:
  - Technical standards
  - Site information
- Properties of sheet lead:
  - Codes and sizes of sheet lead
  - Malleability
  - Thermal movement
  - Other properties of sheet lead
- Safety in the use of sheet lead
- Lead bossing
  - Leadworking tools
- Lead welding:
  - Lead-welding equipment
  - Safety in lead welding
- Fixings to sheet leadwork:
  - Lead wedges
  - Clips for sheet leadwork
- Weatherings to abutments:
  - Abutment step-and-cover flashings for single-lap tiling
  - Abutment with soakers and step flashings
  - Abutment flashing with secret gutter
- Chimney weathering sets:
  - Front apron
  - Back gutter
  - Step flashings
  - Typical faults on chimney weathering sets
- Lead slate.

Sources of information

Technical standards

The following are the key technical standards related to the installation of sheet-lead weatherings:

- Control of Lead at Work Regulations – dealing with lead safety issues
- BS EN 12588 Rolled lead sheet for building purposes – this is the standard specification used for sheet lead on the majority of buildings
- Lead Sheet Association (LSA) Manuals – these detail best practice in the forming/production and installation of sheet lead components.

Site information

On new properties in particular the building (construction) detail plans usually provide information on the technical detail of the sheet-lead weathering work to be carried out; these plans may be supported by a specification for the work. In addition the job may also be supported by a work programme showing the stage(s) of the job where the sheet-lead weathering work should take place.

Properties of sheet lead

Codes and sizes of sheet lead

British Standards identify the colour code of sheet lead that relates to the material's thickness and weight.

BS 12588 Code No	Thickness mm	Weight kg/m²	Colour code
3	1.32	14.97	Green
4	1.80	20.41	Blue
5	2.24	25.45	Red
6	2.65	30.05	Black
7	3.15	35.72	White
8	3.55	40.26	Orange

Figure 10.1 Sheet lead codes and sizes

Sheet lead for general applications is usually available in rolls:

- width – 150mm up to 600mm
- length – 3m up to 6m.

For general applications such as those identified in the plumbing technical certificate, the following codes are used for the type of sheet lead components listed:

- soakers – code 3
- lead-welded components and limited bossing applications such as cover flashing turn-around to chimney front apron – code 4
- main bossed components such as a chimney front apron – code 5.

Malleability

Lead is the softest of metallic plumbing materials in use. It is very malleable (easily worked) and can be used to make joints of the most complex shapes on building surfaces.

Thermal movement

Lead has a relatively high coefficient of linear expansion, due account needs to be taken of this when preparing components for installation:

- limiting the size of components will assist with thermal movement
- including joints that permit expansion will permit thermal movement and minimise possible cracking/breakdown of the sheet lead
- providing fixings that permit thermal movement of the sheet lead.

Other properties of sheet lead

Sheet lead has other properties:

- durability – when it is fitted correctly it is highly durable and will last for years
- corrosion resistant – sheet lead is resistant to most forms of corrosion. However, corrosion can occur in the presence of some mortars and the acid run-off from lichen or moss on a roof surface
- patination – given time, sheet lead develops a strong patina (silver-grey sheen); this helps protect against corrosion. In certain circumstances the patina can be washed off on to other components of the building, resulting in staining. The use of patination oil while the lead is being fitted will prevent this
- fire resistant – lead is incombustible, but does melt at 327°C
- recyclable – old lead is easily recycled to form new lead materials.

Did you know?

Lead bossing

Bossing makes good use of the malleable property of sheet lead to form it into complex shapes to make buildings watertight.

Definition

Creep describes the tendency of metals to slowly stretch over time.

Fatigue is a loss of strength in the lead due to thermal movement; it can eventually lead to cracking.

Did you know?

Lead can be particularly prone to corrosion in seaside locations when in contact with aluminium, due to salt in the atmosphere.

Safety in the use of sheet lead

Care needs to be taken when working with sheet lead, owing to the following:

- lead is a poisonous material, plumbers are therefore at risk when working with lead:
  - through ingestion into the body by bad hygiene practices – eating, drinking or smoking without washing the hands. Protection can be provided against lead being ingested into the body by wearing gloves, and barrier creams can guard against lead getting into the bloodstream through cuts in the hands
  - by inhalation during the lead-welding process, short-term lead welding outdoors will present very little risk to health, whereas long-term lead welding of components indoors will present a higher risk and will require controls such as a local exhaust ventilation system and health surveillance of staff carrying out the work
- lead poisoning may result in kidney/liver disorders and nerve/brain damage
- lead is a heavy material and care needs to be taken in handling it – the use of lifting aids such as a sack trolley is preferable to manual handling; two people may be required to manually handle lead coils if the material cannot be lifted by mechanical means.

Lead bossing

Bossing is the term used for working sheet lead into shape using a range of hand tools.

Leadworking tools

The following shows a range of tools used in the lead-bossing process:

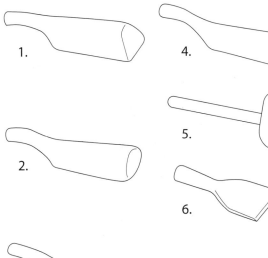
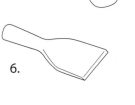

Figure 10.2 Lead-bossing tools

The specialist leadworking tools listed below are used for the following purposes:

1. Dresser – used to make the metal lie flat on a surface (remove any humps)
2. Bossing stick – used with a mallet to boss the lead into shape
3. Bending stick – used with a mallet to boss the lead into shape
4. Setting-in stick – used to reinforce or sharpen folds or angles
5. Mallet – used to boss the lead in conjunction with the other bossing tools
6. Chase wedge – used for setting-in the corner or a fold or crease.

Lead welding

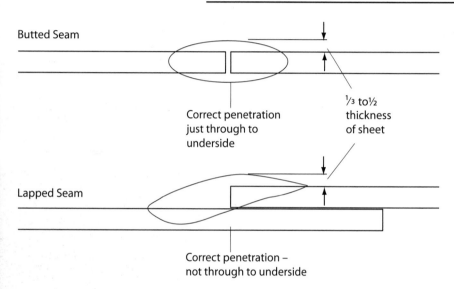

Butted Seam

Correct penetration just through to underside

⅓ to½ thickness of sheet

Lapped Seam

Correct penetration – not through to underside

Figure 10.3 Butted seam and lapped seam

Lead welding is the term used for jointing two pieces of lead by melting together (with heat) the edges of the lead (the parent metal) while adding a filler rod of lead. Two types of lead-welded joint are used, depending on the component being made:

- butted seam
- lapped seam.

The standard width of the weld depends on the lead being used and the seam pattern. When welding code 4 this will usually be a minimum of 10mm.

Incorrect lead-welding procedures can result in undercutting or reducing the thickness of the lead weld as shown below, with possible cracking occurring; this is caused by overheating the metal by leaving the flame too long on its surface.

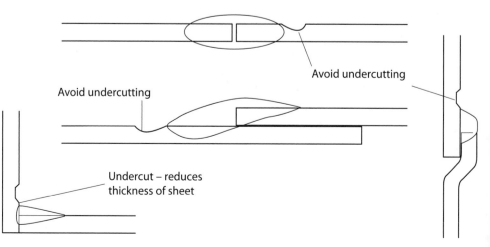

Avoid undercutting

Avoid undercutting

Undercut – reduces thickness of sheet

Figure 10.4 Undercutting

Figure 10.5 shows the production of a lead-welded back gutter; this is produced by adding gussets (additional material) to form the required shape. The gussets are then lead welded using butt joints.

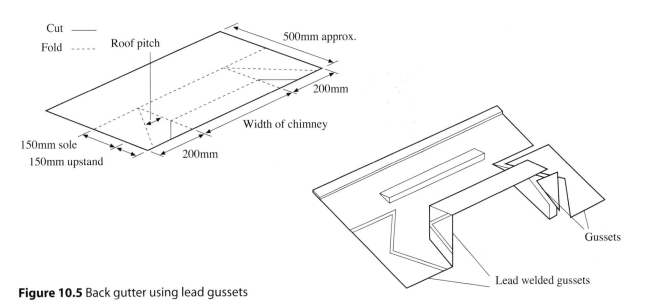

Figure 10.5 Back gutter using lead gussets

Lead-welding equipment

Figure 10.6 shows a typical lead-welding kit.

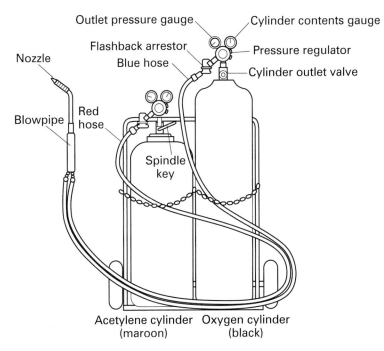

Figure 10.6 Lead-welding kit

Key points of using the kit are:

- lead welding is carried out using oxyacetylene as the heat source; oxygen cylinders are black, acetylene cylinders are maroon (lead welding can also take place using LPG)
- for general applications a lead-welding torch is used, with nozzle sizes 2 and 3 being used for sheet-lead codes 4 and 5 respectively
- eye protection should be used (clear lenses) when lead welding, in order to avoid molten lead splashing into the eyes
- flashback arrestors should be included in the kit, in order to prevent flashback into the cylinders
- the pressure gauges on both the oxygen and acetylene cylinders are set at 0.14 bar
- when lighting, first turn on the acetylene, then light it, then feed in the oxygen
- a neutral flame will achieve the best results for lead welding
- when turning off the welding torch, first turn off the acetylene control, then the oxygen control.

Safety in lead welding

The following is a safety checklist of the procedures that must be observed when lead welding.

1. Gas cylinders should be stored in a ventilated area on a firm base. If possible, store oxygen and acetylene separately. Empty and full bottles should also be stored separately.
2. Acetylene gas bottles should be stored upright to prevent leakage of liquid.
3. Oxygen cylinders are highly pressurised. They should be stored and handled carefully to prevent falling. If the valve is sheared, the bottle will shoot forward with great force.
4. Keep oxygen cylinders away from oil or grease, as these materials will ignite in contact with oxygen under pressure.
5. Check the condition of the hoses and fittings. If they are punctured or damaged, replace them. Do not try to repair or piece them together.
6. Do not allow acetylene to come into contact with copper: this produces an explosive compound.
7. Make sure the area where you are welding is well ventilated.
8. Erect signs or shields to warn and protect people from the process.
9. Always have fire-fighting equipment to hand.
10. Wear protective clothing: gloves, overalls, goggles – clear are fine for lead welding.
11. Make sure that hose check valves are fitted to the blowpipe and flashback arrestors to the regulators. This prevents any possible flashback on the hoses and the cylinders.
12. Allow the acetylene to flow from the nozzle for a few seconds before lighting up.
13. In the event of a serious flashback or fire, plunge the nozzle into water, leaving the oxygen running to avoid water entering the blowpipe.

Fixings to sheet leadwork

Lead wedges

Sheet lead is primarily fixed to masonry walls using lead wedges. The sheet-lead material with a 25mm turn-in to a raked-out mortar joint will be fixed with lead wedges. Lead wedges are made using off-cuts of sheet lead, which are cut into strips approximately 22mm wide, rolled up and squashed so that they are thicker than the gap between the lead turn-in and the brickwork.

Figure 10.7 Abutment fixings with lead wedges

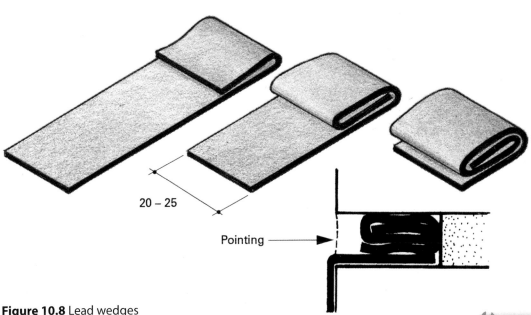

20 – 25

Pointing

Figure 10.8 Lead wedges

Requirements for fixing by lead wedges will depend on the component being fixed. Typically for a straight cover flashing, fixings should be at 300–450mm centres. Once the lead has been fixed, it should be pointed with a flexible sealant such as mastic, a 1 part cement to 4 parts sand mortar mix is sometimes used, however the cement can be corrosive to lead.

Clips for sheet leadwork

Clips are used to secure the 'free edge' of a lead flashing to prevent lifting and distortion in high wind conditions. The method of fixing the clip depends on the material on which the sheet lead is resting. The clips are usually manufactured from copper, tinned copper or stainless steel with a width of approximately 50mm. The thickness of the clips will usually depend on the degree of exposure of the building surface. Clips are usually spaced at intervals of 500mm.

Did you know?

Nails

Large copper-headed nails may be used for sheet-lead fixings.

Did you know?

Screws

Brass or stainless steel screws may be used for sheet-lead fixings.

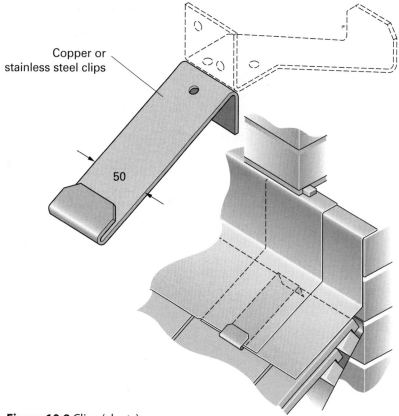

Copper or
stainless steel clips

50

Figure 10.9 Clips (cleats)

Weatherings to abutments

The type of flashing used depends largely on the roofing material used on the building.

Abutment step-and-cover flashings for single-lap tiling

Figure 10.10 shows the type of flashings used for single-lap tiling – no soakers are used with the step-and-cover flashing in one piece of lead.

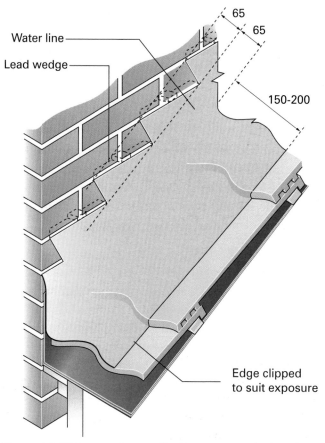

65
65
150-200
Water line
Lead wedge

Edge clipped
to suit exposure

Figure 10.10 Step-and-cover flashing over single-lap tiles

Definition

Abutment flashings

A type of sheet-lead flashing, used where a roof needs weathering against a masonry wall surface.

a. Soakers

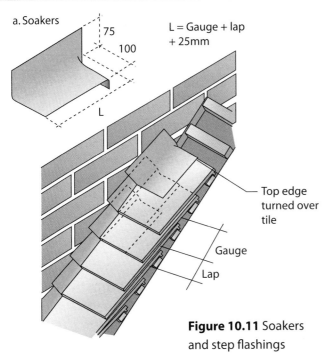

L = Gauge + lap + 25mm

Top edge turned over tile

Gauge

Lap

Figure 10.11 Soakers and step flashings

b. Marking-out step flashing

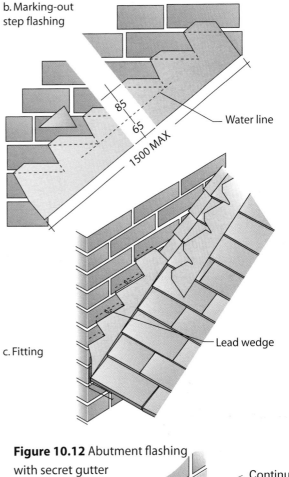

Water line

1500 MAX

Lead wedge

c. Fitting

Abutment with soakers and step flashings

This type of flashing is used with slated or double-lap tiled pitched roofs. The flashing includes a soaker and separate cover flashing arrangement.

- separate soakers are provided based on the tile or slate details. The formula for calculating the length of soaker is Length (L) = Gauge + Lap + 25mm. The minimum soaker width is 175mm with a 75mm upstand and 100mm projection onto the roof
- the top edge of the soaker should be turned over the tile to prevent slippage occurring
- the flashing details should ensure a minimum overlap of 65mm, this is known as the water line measurement and is the minimum height of coverage to guard against capillarity.

Abutment flashing with secret gutter

A secret gutter may be included in the roof design to protect against surcharging of rainwater and the risk of blockage from leaves, it may be used with a single step-and-cover flashing arrangement or a separate soaker and step-flashing arrangement.

Figure 10.12 Abutment flashing with secret gutter

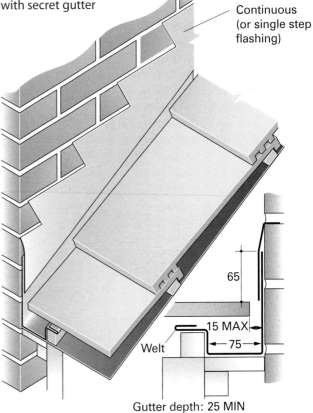

Continuous (or single step flashing)

Welt

Gutter depth: 25 MIN

Chimney weathering sets

The component parts of a chimney weathering set are as shown in Figure 10.13.

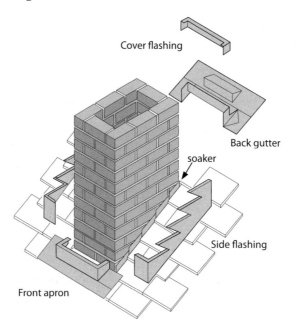

Figure 10.13 Component parts of a chimney weathering set

Soakers are as per the detail provided under 'Weatherings to abutments' (previous page).

Front apron

The front apron to a chimney may be bossed or lead welded. The joint in the brickwork must be a minimum height of 75mm above the surface of the tile or slates. The LSA recommend that the sheet lead used to produce the apron by either bossing or lead welding is a minimum width of 300mm (150mm for the upstand against the chimney and 150mm for the apron over the tiles or slates).

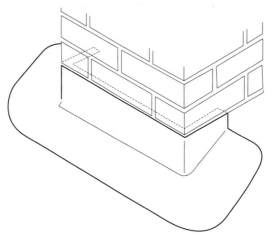

The length of sheet lead required will be the width of the chimney plus 150mm at each side (rising to 200mm at each side with deeply contoured tiles).

Figure 10.14 Front apron

Back gutter

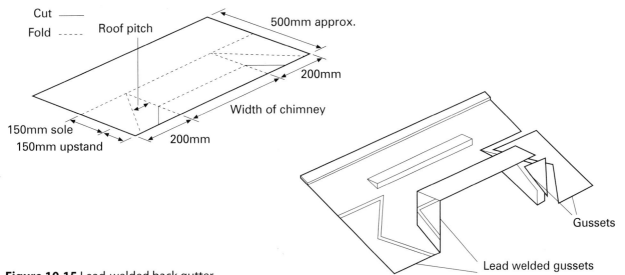

Figure 10.15 Lead-welded back gutter

It is usually preferable to lead weld the back gutter, owing to the complex shape to be covered and the length of time required to produce the back gutter by bossing.

The width of sheet lead required will vary dependent on the chimney and roof material details. Key dimensions are:

- the length of sheet lead required will be the width of the chimney plus 150mm at each side (rising to 200mm with deeply contoured tiles)
- the sheet lead should rise to a minimum height of 100mm above the bottom of the gutter and turn round the chimney side cheeks by a minimum of 100mm.

Step flashings

The step flashing is produced as per the requirements laid down for weatherings to abutments. A minimum of 75mm needs to be added for turning the lead around the front of the chimney and over the apron. A folding ruler is used to mark out the steps on a continuous piece of lead flashing.

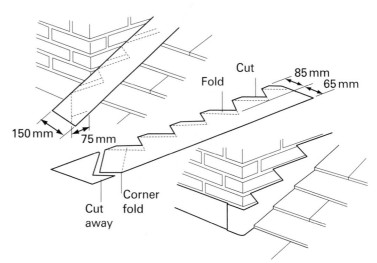

Figure 10.16 Step flashing

Typical faults on chimney weathering sets

Typical faults that can occur with chimney weathering sets include:

- lifting of the sheet leadwork – this normally occurs in windy or exposed conditions and can be cured by fixing clips to secure the leading edge of the leadwork in place
- dripping during heavy rain – a small amount of dripping that occurs during heavy rain is usually caused by poor component design whereby capillary attraction is taking place between the components that are not meeting the minimum 65mm water line measurement. A higher volume of water will usually indicate a fault such as wind lift of the component or slippage.

Lead slate

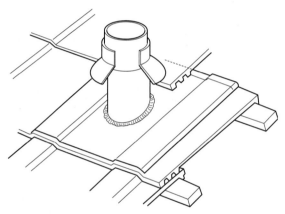

Figure 10.17 Lead slate

Key features of lead slates are:

- the slate is usually manufactured by the lead-welding process, a butt weld is used to joint the two parts of the upstand together, a lap joint is used at the upstand flange connection to the base
- the base of the lead slate should be a minimum of 150mm coverage from the front, rear and sides of the upstand (150mm in all directions); the lead slate should project at the back at least 100m under the tile or slate
- the vertical upstand should be a minimum of 150mm in height at the back of the lead slate and a storm collar should be fixed at the top of the upstand to prevent water penetration between the gap in the slate and the pipe surface
- the formula for calculating the length of material for the upstand is $\pi \times D$ (alternatively $2 \times \pi \times R$) plus 5mm for tolerance.

Short answer questions

1. Which organisation details best practice standards in the production and fixing of sheet-lead components?
2. Prolonged lead welding indoors may require the provision of what type of safety measures?
3. Sheet lead is flattened by using which type of leadworking tool?
4. When turning off an oxyacetylene welding torch, which gas supply should be turned off first?
5. Roof tiles are laid at a gauge of 250mm and have a lap of 125mm; what length of soaker is required for the tile?
6. What is the name of the following sheet-lead component detail?

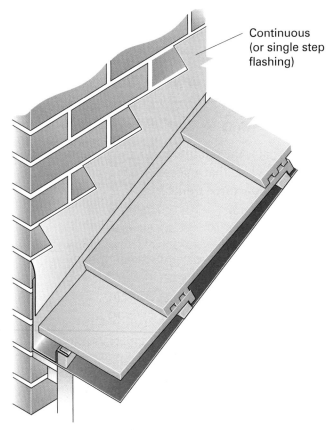

Continuous (or single step flashing)

Figure 10.18

7. What is the minimum sheet-lead code that soakers can be produced from?
8. What material can clips for lead sheeting be manufactured from?

9. Calculate the length of sheet lead required to form the upstand to a lead slate if the diameter of the pipe is 200mm and an allowance of 5mm is to be provided to permit the slate to fit on the pipe.
10. What is the most likely cause of movement of sheet-lead components on a roof?

Multiple-choice test

1. Details of the roofing components to be weathered on a new-build construction site will be found in:
   a) *Manufacturer instructions*
   b) *Building Regulations*
   c) *Work programmes*
   d) *Building plans*

2. Rolled sheet lead for use on buildings is manufactured to:
   a) *BS 5449*
   b) *BS 6700*
   c) *BS EN 12056*
   d) *BS EN 12588*

3. What is the minimum recommended lead sheet code for producing a lead-welded back gutter to a chimney?
   a) *Code 3*
   b) *Code 4*
   c) *Code 5*
   d) *Code 6*

4. What is the minimum recommended lead sheet code for producing a bossed front apron to a chimney?
   a) *Code 3*
   b) *Code 4*
   c) *Code 5*
   d) *Code 6*

5. One of the main reasons that sheet lead is used on buildings as a weathering material is its:
   a) *Ductility*
   b) *Malleability*
   c) *Conductivity*
   d) *Solvency*

6. Which of the following may be the outcome of lead poisoning?
   a) Dermatitis
   b) Nerve damage
   c) Weil's disease
   d) Smithson's disease

7. What is the name of the following lead-working tool?

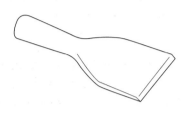

   a) Setting-in stick
   b) Mallet
   c) Bossing stick
   d) Chase wedge

8. Continuous step flashings are set out using which of the following tools:
   a) Folding rule
   b) Tape measure
   c) Bossing stick
   d) Mallet

9. Oxygen bottles for lead welding are colour coded:
   a) Blue   c) Black
   b) Brown   d) Blue

10. The oxygen and acetylene gauges on a portable lead-welding kit should be set at:
   a) 0.05 bar   c) 0.14 bar
   b) 0.1 bar   d) 0.24 bar

11. If the acetylene pressure is set higher than the oxygen pressure on a lead-welding torch the result will be a:
   a) Neutral flame
   b) Oxidising flame
   c) Carburising flame
   d) Mixed flame

12. A gusset to a back-gutter is usually formed using which type of lead-welded joint?
   a) Lapped seam
   b) Butted seam
   c) Standing seam
   d) Lead drip

13. The recommended width of sheet-lead weld to code 4 sheet lead is:
   a) 5mm   c) 15mm
   b) 10mm   d) 20mm

14. Which of the following type of fixings can be used to minimise wind lift to a chimney front apron?
   a) Anodised screw
   b) Masonry nail
   c) Copper clip
   d) Rawl-bolt

15. Which of the following is not a component that forms part of a chimney weathering set?
   a) Back gutter
   b) Front apron
   c) Soakers
   d) Valley gutter

16. What is the minimum recommended width of sheet lead that a bossed front apron should be manufactured from?
   a) 150mm   c) 250mm
   b) 200mm   d) 300mm

17. The minimum recommended upstand at the back of a lead slate is:
   a) 150mm   c) 250mm
   b) 200mm   d) 300mm

18. The minimum recommended vertical gutter back upstand to a chimney is:
   a) 75mm   c) 125mm
   b) 100mm   d) 150mm

19. What is the minimum recommended width of sheet lead to produce a soaker for a slated roof?
   a) 75mm   c) 150mm
   b) 125mm   d) 175mm

20. Which of the following components is fitted immediately above the upstand on a lead slate to prevent water penetration between the lead slate and the pipe?

a) *Bird cage*

b) *Storm collar*

c) *Drain connector*

d) *Rubber grommet*

21. The water line measurement when setting out step flashings is:

a) *25mm*   c) *65mm*

b) *50mm*   d) *75mm*

22. It is recommended that lead wedges to a straight cover flashing be positioned at intervals of:

a) *150–200mm*

b) *200–300mm*

c) *300–450mm*

d) *450–600mm*

23. The preferred sealant between sheet lead and masonry wall joints is:

a) *Sand and cement*

b) *Putty*

c) *Jointing compound*

d) *Mastic*

24. Fatigue in sheet lead is likely to be caused by:

a) *Water penetration*

b) *Expansion/contraction and incorrect fixing*

c) *Undercutting when lead welding*

d) *Using sheet lead that is too thick*

25. Lead should not be used in conjunction with which of the following metals in a marine (salty) environment, owing to corrosive effects?

a) *Aluminium*

b) *Copper*

c) *Zinc*

d) *Plastic*

By the end of this chapter you should be able to demonstrate understanding of the following environmental awareness topics which will assist you in completing knowledge assessment in the Environmental Awareness Unit of the Level 2 Certificate in Basic Plumbing Studies:

- Sources of information:
  - Technical standards
- Types of energy
- The environmentally friendly use of plumbing materials
- Disposal of waste materials
- Commissioning of plumbing systems.

Sources of information

There are a number of information sources that plumbers should know about, relating to environmental awareness.

Technical standards

Did you know?

The hot water outflow and primary pipework to a cylinder must be insulated for at least 1m from the cylinder connections.

Heating and hot water pipework not contributing to the heating of the building must be adequately insulated.

- Building Regulations – these are the main regulations which must be complied with when installing central heating and hot water systems. Approved document L1 – conservation of fuel and power – details the main requirements; this can be freely downloaded from the DCLG website at www.communities.gov.uk. Key features of part L1 of the regulations are:
  - New properties should have a Standard Assessment Procedure (SAP) rating for the energy efficiency of the property, which must meet minimum requirements; this has impact on the amount of insulation in the property and hence the size of heating system and use of fuel
  - Central heating and hot water services are classed as a controlled service or fitting under the Building Regulations, the work must therefore be notified to the local authority or be completed by a company which is a member of an approved competent persons scheme

- Most boilers must meet a minimum SEDBUK (seasonal efficiency) rating, mostly requiring the highest efficiency condensing boilers to be fitted
- There must be independent time control of the hot water and radiator circuits
- There must be independent temperature control of the hot water and radiator circuits
- There must be a boiler interlock (last circuit to close turns off the pump and boiler and prevents system short cycling).

- Water Regulations – these lay down the statutory requirements that must be carried out when installing, commissioning and maintaining water systems. Water Regulations documentation can be freely downloaded from www.defra.gov.uk, who also produce a guidance document to the Water Regulations. The aim of the Water Regulations is to prevent:
  - wastage – long dead-legs on hot water pipework waste water and energy
  - undue consumption – linked to wastage: oversized appliances such as baths waste water
  - contamination – backflow of contaminated water into the supply pipe can be a real health risk
  - misuse – using water for a purpose for which it wasn't intended
  - erroneous measurement – fiddling the water meter.

- Manufacturer instructions – these are provided by appliance or component manufacturers to outline the installation, commissioning and maintenance requirements of their products. Manufacturer instructions usually take precedence over British Standards but should not conflict with Building or Water Regulations, which are statutory (legal) requirements. Manufacturers also provide user instructions, essential guides to the customer on the proper use of the equipment.

Types of energy

Energy conservation has become an important topic as the world's fuel supplies become depleted. Energy types that plumbers may come across are:

- non-renewable energy sources:
  - fossil fuels such as coal
  - oil
  - gas
  - electricity (electrical appliances are highly efficient, however the process of generating electricity is environmentally damaging).

- renewable sources:
  - solar water heating; as the term describes, this energy source is constantly renewed and there is no atmospheric pollution.

Non-renewable sources will eventually run out and they impact on the environment in the form of pollution. The primary concern in relation to heating appliances is the production of carbon dioxide (CO_2).

The environmentally friendly use of plumbing materials

Plumbers can play a real part in conserving energy through the proper use of materials. Here are a few key points:

- repairing components if it is possible can be more environmentally sound than replacing them: the manufacturing process used to make components can expend large amounts of energy
- the proper measurement, cutting and bending of materials conserves a great deal of materials; this saves money and saves the impact on the environment in producing additional materials
- treat screws and fixings, etc. like money: waste them and you're adding to the impact on the environment
- this is more for the system designer – push-fit fittings, etc. minimise environmental impact through not being subject to heating; they also reduce the risk of fire
- when soldering fittings, use solder wire carefully, an auto-ignition torch doesn't waste as much gas as a manual ignition device. Try to solder fittings in groups rather than individually, as this saves on gas and carbon dioxide emissions
- be particularly careful with sanitaryware, as it is easily broken
- take care when lifting floor surfaces – damaged flooring materials will require replacement
- using a renewable product such as a magnetic water conditioner is more environmentally friendly than a water-softening device that requires additives
- do not dispose of large quantities of materials such as oils and disinfectants down the drain; they may discharge to a water course and cause serious contamination
- look to replace lead pipework wherever possible, as it can be a health risk, and remember that when jointing pipework on hot and cold water systems, only lead-free solders must be used.

Disposal of waste materials

Plumbers will be involved in the disposal of waste; there are stringent requirements that must be followed when dealing with waste products:

- plumbing companies disposing of waste (this may include short lengths of copper pipe, sanitaryware, building debris) must have a registered waste carrier's licence issued by the local authority

Did you know?

A more environmentally friendly form of non-renewable fuel is a biomass-type fuel such as pelleted organic waste material, which can be burnt in heating appliances. This fuel does produce pollutants into the atmosphere, but these are usually in smaller quantities than some other non-renewable types.

- under no circumstances must waste materials be 'fly tipped' – it's an offence. Typical arrangements for disposal of materials include by skip, by taking waste to a proper waste disposal site, or for metals, by taking them to a scrap dealer for recycling
- burning of materials on construction sites is not recommended practice; in the event that this takes place, care should be taken not to burn materials that will give off significant quantities of smoke and fumes, such as foam and polystyrene
- plumbers may sometimes come across the need to dispose of refrigerators; these must not be broken down and must be disposed of at a site that is approved to accept them, the release of refrigerants can have a particularly harmful impact on the environment
- if asbestos is encountered then safety comes first; it should normally only be worked on or moved by a licensed contractor who should ensure that it is properly bagged, labelled and disposed of at an approved asbestos waste disposal site. On finding asbestos, your first priority is to report the matter to your company, ceasing work if a risk of possible contamination is present.

Commissioning of plumbing systems

Plumbing and heating systems must be properly commissioned on completion of the work, not only to make sure that they work properly but also to ensure that they don't waste valuable resources such as fuel and water. As part of the commissioning process it is now usually a requirement for commissioning records to be completed to show that the system has been properly checked and tested.

On completion of commissioning the user should be given proper instruction in the operation of the system and the proper use of the controls, this is particularly important with central heating appliances, in order to minimise wastage of fuel and conserve energy. The user should also be provided with any manufacturer instructions to assist with the effective operation of the equipment.

Short answer questions

1. What does the term SAP stand for?
2. Under Approved Document L1 of the Building Regulations what arrangement must be provided to a new central heating system to ensure that the last circuit to turn off, turns off the pump and boiler?
3. Identify three types of fossil fuel.
4. When installing copper pipework, what is the main factor a plumber should consider in minimising impact on the environment?
5. What does the following symbol identify?

6. What are the main actions to take on identifying white asbestos insulating material on pipework in a property?
7. State two methods of effectively disposing of waste materials from a job.
8. Which item of plumbing equipment tends to be the most susceptible to breakage during installation?
9. Whose advice should be sought when disposing of large quantities of disinfectant from a cold water system down a drain?
10. Following the commissioning of a central heating boiler in an owner-occupied property, what is the next action?

Multiple-choice test

1. Under the Building Regulations the installation of central heating and hot water services is classified as:
   a) Water-borne services
   b) Controlled services
   c) Essential services
   d) Essential supplies

2. Under Approved Document L1 of the Building Regulations, pipework to/from a hot water cylinder should be insulated to what distance from the cylinder?
   a) 0.5 metre   c) 1.5 metres
   b) 1.0 metre   d) 2.0 metres

3. Which of the following jointing processes uses a non-renewable fuel?
   a) Push-fit fittings
   b) Solvent welded fittings
   c) Capillary soldered fittings
   d) LCS threaded fittings

4. Harmful environmental emissions are not produced by:
   a) Biomass heated boiler
   b) Gas multipoint water heater
   c) Solar-powered hot water cylinder
   d) Oil fired cooker

5. Which of the following is an acceptable method of jointing to old lead pipework?
   a) Lead to lead wiped joint
   b) Lead to copper wiped joint
   c) Lead to plastic wiped joint
   d) Lead to copper proprietary fitting

6. The efficiency of a hot water system is reduced by including which of the following in the pipework system?

a) *A check valve*   c) *Insulation*

b) *Dead-legs*   d) *Bypass loop*

7. In order to remove waste materials from site, a plumbing company must hold a:

a) *Waste carrier's licence*

b) *Plumbing goods licence*

c) *Waste disposal licence*

d) *Removing goods licence*

8. Which of the following may produce noxious fumes when burnt on a construction site?

a) *Paper*

b) *Timber packing*

c) *Polystyrene*

d) *Cardboard*

9. By legislation, which of the following must not be broken down by plumbing operatives before disposal:

a) *Refrigerator*

b) *Boiler*

c) *Plastic cistern*

d) *Copper cylinder*

10. A plumber can advise the customer on reducing the amount of energy used by:

a) *Properly setting control thermostats*

b) *Increasing the pump pressure in the system*

c) *Changing the fuel supplier*

d) *Fitting a frost thermostat*

12 Customer care

By the end of this chapter you should be able to demonstrate understanding of the following customer care topics which will assist you in completing knowledge assessment in the Improvement of Business Products & Services Unit of the Level 3 Certificate in Domestic Plumbing Studies:

- Presenting a Quality Image of the Plumbing Industry
  - Get to know your customer
  - Personal presentation
  - Communication with the customer
  - Principles of basic customer care
  - Customer care 'on the job'
  - Customer complaints
  - Improving customer care.
- The Customer Service Policy
  - Formal customer service policies
  - Putting a customer service policy into practice.

Presenting a quality image of the plumbing industry

Get to know your customer

Plumbing businesses may encounter a range of customers; here are the main ones:

- private customer – this is an individual who has invited your company to undertake work in their property, often their home. The private customer will often have very little knowledge of plumbing systems and will need explanation of what is happening as various parts of the job are progressed. The private customer will have a number of expectations of the work that you are doing, e.g. that it is going to be carried out in a neat and tidy manner. One of your main actions should be to meet those expectations before you are asked to
- contract work – this could be work for property developers or local authorities. It's a common mistake to believe that you have no customer on this type of job, here you may be working for the contractor's

representative, such as the site agent. Individuals such as the site agent may have an in-depth technical knowledge of the work that you are carrying out, so the way that you communicate and work with them is likely to be different from the private customer

- internally within your own company – plumbing companies are sometimes part of a much larger building services or construction company. Here it's really easy to forget that there is a customer; that would be wrong, as the customer is the parent company representative who you may be working for and typically these days it's possible for the parent company to look for plumbing services elsewhere if customer service is lacking in their own subsidiary company.

Personal presentation

As a Level 3 plumber you'll often be right in the 'firing line' in dealing with customers, and in many cases you will be the individual from your company who meets the customer for the first time, first impressions often count with customers, so here are a few points to put into practice:

- your own personal appearance is vital in presenting a positive image of your company, so clean and tidy overalls are a must, and changing from boots into shoes when entering a carpeted house is good practice
- keeping your company vehicle clean and tidy is important as the customer may use it to judge the way in which you will work in their property.

> **Remember**
>
> Some customers, particularly the elderly, may require you to show ID before you can enter their property, so make sure you have it on you in case you are asked.

Communication with the customer

The following diagram shows the key points in effective communication.

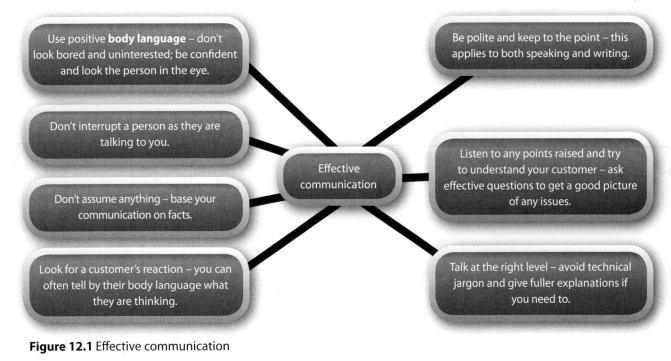

Use positive **body language** – don't look bored and uninterested; be confident and look the person in the eye.

Be polite and keep to the point – this applies to both speaking and writing.

Don't interrupt a person as they are talking to you.

Don't assume anything – base your communication on facts.

Effective communication

Listen to any points raised and try to understand your customer – ask effective questions to get a good picture of any issues.

Look for a customer's reaction – you can often tell by their body language what they are thinking.

Talk at the right level – avoid technical jargon and give fuller explanations if you need to.

Figure 12.1 Effective communication

When communicating with customers the correct communication method must be selected to deal with a specific circumstance:

- verbal communication should be used for less important actions where a permanent record is not required, e.g. establishing the position of a radiator with the customer
- written communication should be used where a written record of the activity is required, e.g. a major variation to the job that has cost implications for the customer.

Here are a few more examples where verbal and written communication are likely to be used:

Use verbal communication for:	Use written communication for:
confirming the location of components before they're installed	giving a job **quotation**
establishing the initial job requirement	confirming the work (this is done by the customer)
things that need to be carried out before you commence the work, e.g. emptying the airing cupboard	major alterations to the original quotation or **specification**
solving simple problems and straightforward complaints.	confirming quotation/specification alterations (this is done by the customer)
	commissioning reports or **job records** (usually kept by the customer for future use)
	dealing with more complicated problems and complaints.

Figure 12.2 Verbal and written communication

Principles of basic customer care

The principles of good customer care start with:

- understanding what the customer's needs are
- respecting the customer's concerns and dealing with problems as they arise
- showing that you are committed to your job.

In undertaking a specialist service such as plumbing for your customer, he/she will expect you to be competent in your job, so you should:

- know your subject – that doesn't mean that you can't refer to manufacturers' instructions to do the job – never guess a job if you don't know
- be positive about your subject – constant complaints about a product that you are fitting may lead the customer to think that it is sub-standard

Remember

Ignoring a problem or a customer concern will usually result in the problem growing and getting out of hand – it's good practice to deal with the issue as soon as possible, employing a 'nip it in the bud' approach usually works best!

- plan the job properly – thorough planning always shows that you're on top of the job.

Having a positive attitude to work will give confidence to your customer in your work:

- always deal with problems, even if it doesn't appear that they'll go away
- develop good work routines and do the job in a logical sequence – turning the water off unnecessarily for long periods on a job will often upset your customer
- do what you say you're going to do – letting customers down is one of the biggest causes of customer complaints
- never set unrealistic targets – you'll lose the credibility that you've built up.

Customer care 'on the job'

One of the most important points to establish when dealing with customers is the extent of your own job responsibility. At Level 3 you may be expected to take full control of the installation phase of a job, though this may vary from company to company. It's therefore important that you establish with your employer/manager what you may be expected to deal with and what should be handed to him/her for action. In a bigger company this may be explained in a customer service policy that you'll be expected to work to.

The work responsibilities that you have may vary considerably based on the type of work carried out by the company:

- service and maintenance – you may be required to provide a customer with costings for parts and labour for a job before the work begins
- installation work – you may be required to plan and co-ordinate the work from start to finish.

It's common in small companies for the employer (your boss) to do the design, surveying and pricing work associated with larger jobs such as a central heating installation. The price for the job will often be in the form of a simple quotation with very little specification of component positions such as pipe runs. So as the plumber taking responsibility for the installation phase of such a project, one of the most important parts of your job is to get a good briefing on essential job details such as pipe runs and radiator/boiler positions. It's also worth confirming these with the customer as a double check before fitting them – it's easier to deal with a change in radiator position before it's fitted than after!

Did you know?

A Level 2 qualified plumber is usually required to work under minimum supervision from others.

A Level 3 qualified plumber will usually work under their own initiative and may take responsibility for the work of other plumbers on jobs.

Remember

Many properties may have a no-smoking policy – so don't just light up.

The following chart shows examples of good and bad practice when dealing with customers on site.

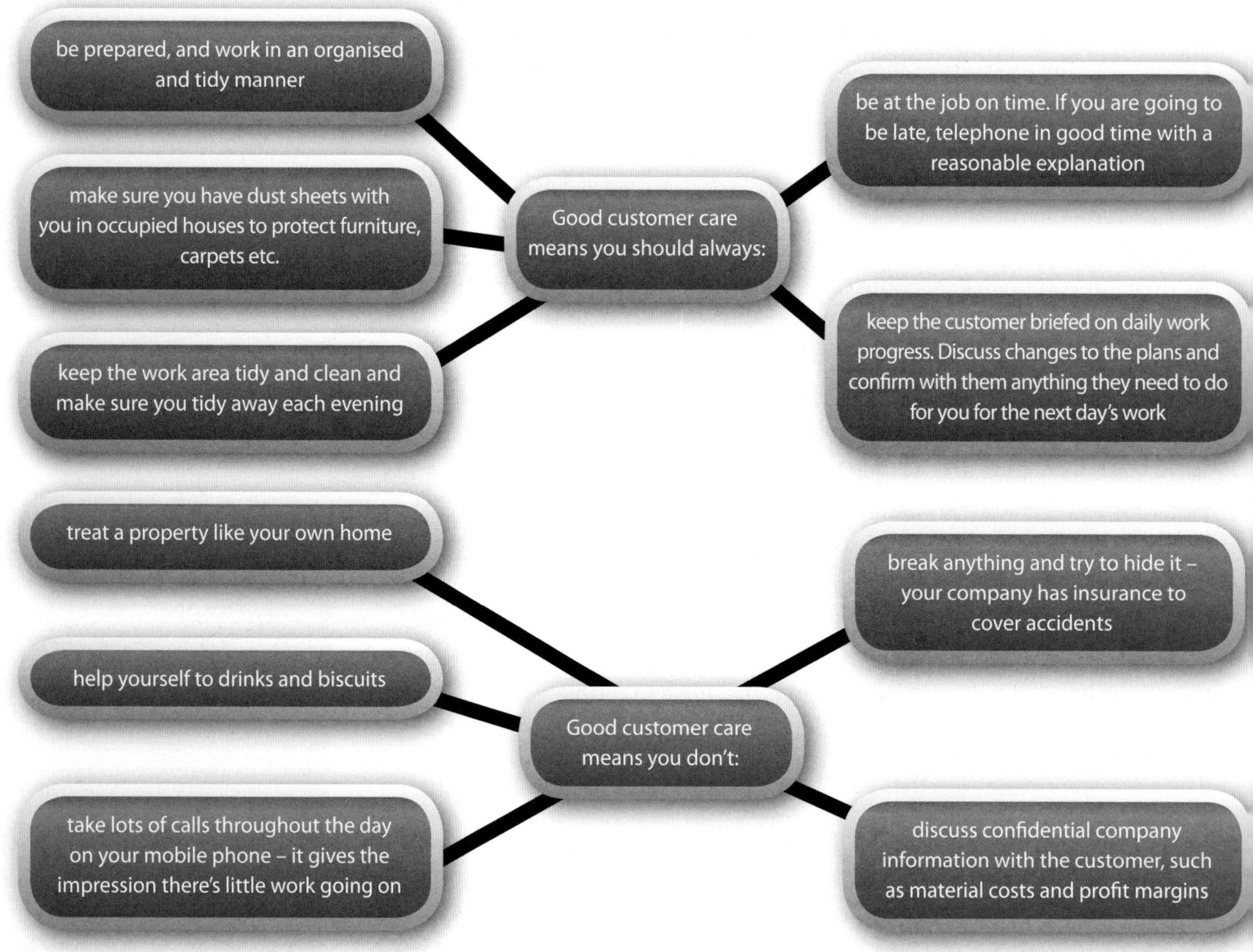

be prepared, and work in an organised and tidy manner

make sure you have dust sheets with you in occupied houses to protect furniture, carpets etc.

Good customer care means you should always:

be at the job on time. If you are going to be late, telephone in good time with a reasonable explanation

keep the customer briefed on daily work progress. Discuss changes to the plans and confirm with them anything they need to do for you for the next day's work

keep the work area tidy and clean and make sure you tidy away each evening

treat a property like your own home

help yourself to drinks and biscuits

Good customer care means you don't:

break anything and try to hide it – your company has insurance to cover accidents

take lots of calls throughout the day on your mobile phone – it gives the impression there's little work going on

discuss confidential company information with the customer, such as material costs and profit margins

Figure 12.3 Good and bad customer care

Don't forget that you may have responsibility for other plumbers on the job, so it may be your responsibility to deal with any problems that they have or may have caused with the customer, you just can't sit down and watch a blazing row between a plumbing apprentice and the customer – it's your job to stop it happening and get it sorted.

Completing the job doesn't just mean you're down the road in the van as soon as possible:

● customer's property should be left as it was found, so be prepared to tidy up after the job is completed, removing any waste materials from site unless otherwise agreed by the customer
● commission the job properly – call-backs leave a bad impression of the company
● provide a demonstration of the completed installation and leave all user/commissioning records
● have the customer complete any satisfaction forms that your company may require.

Customer complaints

Even the best companies do from time to time get customer complaints; the extent to which you get involved with them will depend on your level of job responsibility: as we mentioned before, customer complaints must be handled quickly before they grow.

Here are the top five reasons that customers had cause to complain with companies:

Reasons customers complain	
1.	The customer didn't get what they had been promised.
2.	A company employee was rude.
3.	The service was regarded as poor – the customer felt no one was going out of their way.
4.	Nobody listened to the concerns or issues the customer raised.
5.	The company employees had a 'can't do' or 'couldn't care' approach.

Figure 12.4 Top five reasons for customer complaint

From time to time you may encounter the 'rogue customer'; this is someone:

- whose expectations of a job are far beyond the price that they have agreed to pay, or
- who may be trying to get your company to do the work without intending to pay for it.

As you get more experienced in your job you may see signs of this happening, in which case you should usually refer the matter to your employer/manager for action. It will usually be out of your job responsibility. They in turn will usually act with written communication to deal with the problem, as it will be imperative to use written records as evidence of the problem.

Improving customer care

Most companies will encourage their staff to feed back on areas in the company for improving customer care, there may in fact be a proper mechanism for this, such as a suggestion box. You should therefore look for ways in which customer care may be improved (you never know, you may get a bonus!), but be prepared to feed back in a positive manner, being too negative or critical may just lead you into hot water.

The customer service policy

Customer service policies lay down the company's/staff's commitment to customer care. Policies may be:

- informal – not written down but using many of the principles mentioned earlier in this chapter, companies will often monitor the performance of their staff against an informal policy, even if it's not written down
- formal – the written customer service policy.

Formal customer service policies

The customer service policy is a statement of standards that the company aims to meet in its dealings with customers. The policy statement must be effectively communicated to the company's staff, and will often be provided to the customer. The policy will usually cover such areas as:

- general issues – staff politeness, etc.
- the process for accepting quotations – written acceptance required from the customer
- the timescales for carrying out work
- procedures for agreeing daywork costs
- details of cooling-off periods for orders and the refunds policy
- responsibilities of staff on site while doing the work
- the complaints procedure and timescales for dealing with complaints
- the company's guarantee periods for materials and labour
- standards of follow-up service including any timescales
- the customer care policy may be supported by detailed procedures that staff are required to follow to put the policy into action.

Putting a customer service policy into practice

On completing the development of a customer service policy the most important action is to put it into practice with the staff; this is often done through a series of 'toolbox talks'. Also, remember that many companies have procedures in place for checking on the effectiveness of the customer care that you've provided, by contacting the customer both during and after the job.

Did you know?

A written customer service policy is often given to potential customers as a promotional tool in order to assist in getting the work.

Did you know?

A toolbox talk is a relatively informal training session, often carried out in the workplace.

Short answer questions

1. Identify two areas of personal presentation that positively promote the company.
2. What is your understanding of the term 'private customer' in relation to customer care?
3. What are the two methods usually employed to communicate with customers?
4. What type of communication should be used to provide a quotation for a job?
5. What type of communication should be used to obtain positioning details for a shower tray from the customer?
6. What action is a customer likely to take with your company if they feel they have been treated badly?
7. What is the best action for dealing with an angry customer on the telephone?
8. What type of procedure is used to deal with customer problems relating to work carried out?
9. What type of document must be provided to the customer on completion of the installation of an unvented hot water cylinder?
10. State two examples of a 'rogue customer'.

Multiple-choice test

1. The preferred method of protecting a customer's carpet when servicing a boiler is to:
   a) *Get on with the work with no protection required*
   b) *Sheet the immediate area with dust sheets*
   c) *Protect the whole room and furniture with dust sheets*
   d) *Lift the carpet before the work is carried out*

2. The most appropriate action to take in the event that a plumber cannot attend site is to contact the customer and:
   a) *Apologise and confirm a new time*
   b) *Cancel the job*
   c) *Invoice for the wasted day's work*
   d) *Argue with the customer if they become irate*

3. A good customer care policy will include details on:
   a) *The company's current trading status*
   b) *Customer complaint procedures*
   c) *Staff holiday arrangements*
   d) *The employment terms and conditions of staff*

4. A new shower pump that is not performing to specification should be:
   a) *Left for the customer to deal with*
   b) *Reported to the water undertaker*
   c) *Reported to the manufacturer for action*
   d) *Replaced with a model from a different manufacturer*

5. Which one of the following, on request, may be provided to the customer?
   a) *Detail of the range of work carried out*
   b) *The profit margin the company applies*
   c) *The current price of plumbing components*
   d) *The hourly rate of pay of the plumbing staff*

6. The best method of ensuring good customer care is to:
   a) *Take on as much work as possible*
   b) *Respond to information requests promptly*
   c) *Offer a poor service*
   d) *Ensure that staff do the work as quickly as possible*

7. A customer satisfaction sheet is aimed at:
   a) *Checking that good customer care has been provided to the customer*
   b) *Checking to establish that the work complies with Building Regulations*
   c) *Ensuring payment is made by the customer*
   d) *Dealing with customer complaints as they arise*

8. The customer is more likely to respond positively to the removal of waste materials from site if:
   a) *They are left to dispose of it themselves*
   b) *The plumber burns the materials on site*
   c) *They are left for the bin collection service to remove them*
   d) *They are taken from site and disposed of by the plumber*

9. The usual method for ensuring that companies investigate customer complaints in a consistent manner is to:
   a) *Provide training in personal protection*
   b) *Use a complaints procedure*
   c) *Ignore them wherever possible*
   d) *Forward all complaints to the plumber for action*

10. The most effective way of ensuring that a company's customer service policy is applied by all its staff is to:
    a) *Only provide a copy to customers*
    b) *Train the staff in customer care principles and the policy requirements*
    c) *Sack all staff who infringe on any requirements of the policy*
    d) *Offer a bonus to all who read it*

13 Advanced cold water systems

This chapter builds on the revision completed at Level 2 Chapter 5: Cold water systems. You should therefore read through that chapter and familiarise yourself with its content prior to progressing through this Level 3 chapter.

By the end of this chapter you should be able to demonstrate understanding of the following cold water systems topics which will assist you in completing knowledge assessment in the Cold Water Systems Unit of the Level 3 Certificate in Domestic Plumbing Studies:

- Sources of information:
  - Technical standards
- The Water Supply (Water Fittings) Regulations:
  - Schedules
- Materials and substances in contact with water:
  - Approved materials
  - Prohibited materials
- Requirements of water fittings:
  - Galvanic action
  - Resistance to external forces
  - Ingress of contaminants
  - Frost precautions
  - Permeation or deterioration
  - Pipework support
  - Storage cisterns
  - Concealed water systems
- Design principles, system installation and commissioning:
  - Proximity of drains and sewers
  - Avoiding damage to pipework

- Water temperature in cold water systems
- Stop valves and servicing valves
- Commissioning systems
- Backflow prevention and fluid categories:
  - Fluid risk categories
  - Backflow prevention devices
  - Examples of backflow prevention devices in use
- Prevention of cross connection to unwholesome water
- Cold water services:
  - Cistern inlet controls
  - Warning and overflow pipes
  - Contamination of stored water
- Other appliances:
  - Water closets
  - Flushing urinals
  - Drinking water supplies
- Water for outside use:
  - Animal drinking vessels
  - Ponds, pools and fountains.

Sources of information

There are a number of information sources that plumbers may have to use to obtain the necessary detail to undertake their work.

Technical standards

- Water Regulations – these lay down the statutory requirements that must be carried out when installing, commissioning and maintaining water systems. Responsibility for monitoring compliance with the Water Regulations is given to the local water undertakers. Water Regulations documentation can be freely downloaded from www.defra.gov.uk, who also produce a guidance document to the Water Regulations.
- Water Fittings and Materials Directory – this is produced by the Water Regulations Advisory Scheme (WRAS), and lists approved components and fittings for use in hot and cold water systems in the UK; the guide is freely accessible at www.wras.co.uk.
- British Standards – these support statutory documentation such as the Building Regulations, providing greater detail on installation requirements. Although British Standards are not statutory (legal) documents, they can be used in potential legal action relating to defective systems installation. The main British Standard relating to cold water supply is BS 6700 – Specification for design, installation, testing and maintenance of services supplying water for domestic use within buildings and their curtilages.

The Water Supply (Water Fittings) Regulations

These Regulations came into force on 1 July 1999; they are made up of 14 Regulations, split into three parts and supported by three schedules (the schedules should be treated as though they are part of the Regulations). Here's a brief overview of them:

Regulation 1 – Interpretations

This provides definitions of some common terms used in the Regulations:

Approved contractor:

- a person who has been approved by the water undertaker to undertake work for the area where a fitting is installed or used
- a person who has been certified as an approved contractor by an organisation specified in writing by the regulator, e.g. WIAPS (Water Industry Approved Plumber Scheme), APHC Scheme, IPHE Scheme.

The Regulator:

- in England the Regulator is the Secretary of State
- in Wales it is the National Assembly for Wales.

Material change of use:

A change in how premises are being used, so that after they are changed they are used:

- as a dwelling
- as an institution
- as a public building
- for storage or use of substances that mix with water to make a category 4 or 5 fluid.

Supply pipe:

- the internal pipework in the property under the influence of the water undertaker's main.

> **Did you know?**
>
> A distributing pipe is a pipe conveying water from a storage cistern or a cylinder fed with water from a cistern where the pipework is under pressure from that cistern.

Regulation 2 – Application

Regulation 2 details the circumstances in which the regulations apply.

The Water Supply (Water Fittings) Regulations 1999	
Do apply to:	**Do not apply to:**
Every water fitting installed or used where the water is supplied by the water undertaker.	Water fittings installed or used for any purpose not related to domestic or food production, so long as: • the water is metered • the supply does not exceed 1 month (3, with written consent) and • no water is returned to any pipe vested in a water undertaker • water fittings that are not connected to water supplied by a water undertaker • lawful installations used before 1 July 1999 (these do not have to be replaced).

Figure 13.1 Application of the Regulations

Regulation 3 – Restriction on installation

This regulation identifies that the water fitting itself, or the work carried out on it, must not lead to:

- waste
- misuse
- contamination
- undue consumption
- erroneous measurement of the water supplied by the water undertaker.

> **Did you know?**
>
> Erroneous measurement is 'fiddling' or bypassing the water meter.

Regulation 4 – Requirements for water fittings

This Regulation identifies that the water fittings installed must be of an appropriate quality, i.e. approved and fit for purpose, and the fittings must be installed in a workmanlike manner.

Regulation 5 – Notification

This Regulation requires a person who proposes to install certain water fittings to notify the water undertaker, and not to undertake that work without the undertaker's consent. The water undertaker then has ten days within which a reply to the notice should be provided; the response could be one of the following:

- unconditional approval
- approval with conditions, e.g. a change in proposed system type
- refusal to progress the work.

The installation of the following water fittings requires notice to be given to the water undertaker, except those shown in bold below if the work is carried out by a recognised approved contractor:

- the erection of a building or other structure, not being a swimming pool or pond (any new-build property)
- **the extension or alteration of any water system in a building other than a house**
- a material change of use of any premises
- the installation of:
    - a bath having a capacity of more than 230 litres
    - **a bidet with ascending spray or flexible hose**
    - a pump or booster pump drawing more than 12 litres a minute
    - a unit that incorporates reverse osmosis
    - a water-treatment unit that uses water for regeneration or cleaning
    - **an RPZ valve assembly or other mechanical device for backflow protection from fluid category 4 or 5**
    - a garden watering system, unless designed to be operated by hand
    - any water system laid outside a building less than 750mm or more than 1350mm underground.

Regulation 6 – Certificates

This Regulation requires that if work on a water fitting (including alteration or disconnection) is carried out by an approved contractor, the contractor must provide a compliance certificate confirming that the work complies with the Regulations to the person who commissioned the work. Additionally, if the work is the subject of notification then a copy of the compliance certificate must be forwarded to the water undertaker.

Part 3 – this deals with enforcement actions

Regulation number	Content of Regulation
7 & 8	Provide for a fine not exceeding level 3 on the standard scale for contravening the Regulations. **It is a defence to show that the work on a water fitting was done by or under the direction of an Approved Contractor, and that the contractor certified that it complied with the Regulations.** This defence is extended to the offences of contaminating, wasting and misusing water under section 73 of the Water Industry Act 1991 (reg 8).
9	Enables water undertakers and local authorities to enter premises to carry out inspections, measurements and tests for the purposes of the Regulations.
10	Requires the water undertaker to enforce the Regulations (this is done by the Regulator or the Director General of Water Services).
11	Enables the Regulator to relax the requirements of the Regulations on the application of the water undertaker.
12	Requires the Regulator to consult water undertakers and organisations representing water users before giving an approval for the purpose of the Regulations, and to publicise approvals.
13	Provides for disputes arising under the Regulations between a water undertaker and a person who has installed or proposes to install a water fitting to be referred to arbitration.
14	Revokes the existing Water Byelaws made by water undertakers under section 17 of the Water Act 1945.

Figure 13.2 Part 3 – Enforcement actions

Schedules

Schedule 1 defines the water fluid categories.

Schedule 2 lays down the requirements for water fittings, including the quality of the fitting and how it must be installed.

Schedule 3 revokes the old Water Byelaws that were in place before the Regulations were introduced.

Materials and substances in contact with water

Schedule 2 to the Regulations identifies that no water fitting by virtue of its quality or its installation should give rise to contamination of the water supply if the water is being used for domestic or food production purposes, e.g. drinking, washing, etc.

This requirement does not apply to a water fitting:

- installed downstream of the supply, where wholesome water is not required, e.g. in an industrial process, and
- a suitable backflow prevention device has been fitted to protect the supply.

An example of what this means is shown in Figure 13.3.

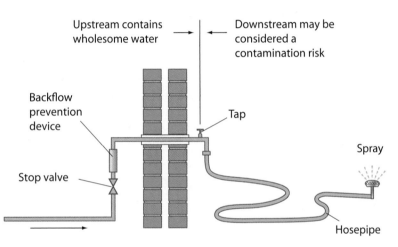

Figure 13.3 Preventing contamination

There are two potential risks here:

- backflow – the water in the hosepipe, or more seriously anything the spray outlet is dipped in, being siphoned back into the supply pipework
- contamination – the material that the hose is manufactured from is not approved for use to convey water in a water installation, as the rubber material will taint the supply. In fact materials such as overflow pipes, flushing cisterns and f&e cisterns aren't permitted to convey wholesome water because they are not approved for the purpose and can contaminate the supply.

Figure 13.4 Manufacturer's product marking

Approved materials

All water fittings should be approved showing compliance with a recognised standard such as that shown in Figure 13.4.

The range of common symbols used for approving products in the UK is shown in Figure 13.5.

WBS teardrop symbol still shown on certain products tested before July 1999.

The WRAS approved product symbol shows that the product has been tested for approval and is listed in the Fittings and Materials Directory.

The CE mark indicates that the product has been tested to EN standards and may legally be placed on the market.

The BSI Kitemark, along with the BS number, shows that the product has been fully tested under the BSI quality testing scheme.

Figure 13.5 Common plumbing materials approval symbols

Prohibited materials

There are two materials specifically forbidden from use in wholesome water systems owing to the health hazards they present:

- lead – this also includes lead solder (wholesome water supplies must be made with lead-free solders)
- bituminous coatings made from coal tar.

Requirements of water fittings

Galvanic action

The Regulations require that water fittings need to be immune or protected from galvanic action. The further apart metals are in the electromotive series, the more likely it is that galvanic action (corrosion) will take place.

Metal	Chemical symbol	Electrode potential (volts)	
Silver	Ag	0.80 +	cathode
Copper	Cu	0.35 +	noble end
Lead	Pb	0.12 –	anodic
Tin	Sn	0.14 –	base end
Nickel	Ni	0.23 –	
Iron	Fe	0.44 –	
Chromium	Cr	0.56 –	
Zinc	Zn	0.76 –	
Aluminium	Al	1.00 –	
Magnesium	Mg	2.00 –	
Sodium	Na	2.71 –	

Did you know?

A connection to old lead pipe must be made in such a way that it will not lead to further contamination, i.e. using a proprietary fitting such as a 'leadloc' joint – joint wiping is not now acceptable.

Definition

Galvanic action is the corrosion that takes place when two dissimilar metals are brought together in the presence of an electrolyte (a solution such as water).

Figure 13.6 The electromotive series

From the table in Figure 13.6 it can be seen that copper and zinc are relatively dissimilar metals: zinc is the metal that will corrode, this is why it is bad practice to mix galvanised steel (zinc-coated) tube and copper tube in an installation.

It is possible in certain cases to apply cathodic protection to guard against galvanic action, e.g. a sacrificial anode can be sited inside a hot water storage cylinder: the anode will corrode protecting the cylinder itself from corrosion.

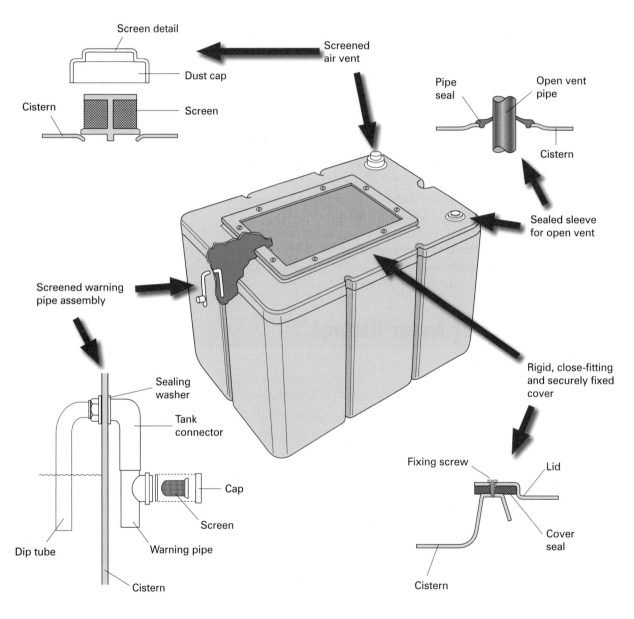

Figure 13.7 Protected cistern guarding against the ingress of contaminants

Resistance to external forces

A water fitting is required to resist damage from:

- external load or settlement – an example could be the point at which a supply pipe enters a building; it is protected by a sleeve to minimise the effect of the load of the building on the pipe
- vibration – caused by loose pipework or faulty fittings
- stress or temperature changes – hot water pipes in particular must be installed so that thermal movement is permitted when the pipe heats up, otherwise undue stress can be created in the pipe
- pressure surges – these may occur in the main from time to time, creating a higher than normal supply pressure which the water fittings should be capable of withstanding.

Ingress of contaminants

Every water fitting must be constructed and installed in order to prevent the ingress of contaminants such as chemicals, insects, etc. The most vulnerable parts of the system are fittings that include air gaps, such as storage cisterns.

The storage cistern supplying wholesome water as shown in Figure 13.7 is required to have a rigid, close-fitting lid, screened overflow and vent to prevent insects and dust entering it. In addition, a cistern must not be installed in a position (without protection) where it may become flooded, i.e. below ground.

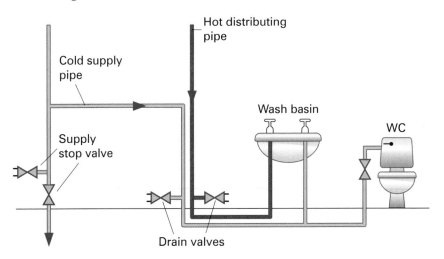

Figure 13.8 Drain valve location with solid-floor installation

Drain valves present the possibility of contaminant ingress, so in a solid-floor installation as shown in Figure 13.8 they must be sited above floor level. This means there is no likelihood of them becoming submerged and they are accessible for maintenance.

Frost precautions

Frost protection needs to be considered before any installation of pipework. When designing a system the first priority should not be to consider pipework insulation but to consider designing the system to avoid potential areas of freezing, such as:

- known draughty areas
- on the outside of buildings
- unheated parts of the building – garages, roofspaces, etc.
- on cold surfaces such as external walls.

If these areas can't be avoided then insulation will need to be considered.

Underground pipework

Underground pipework (external to the building) should be installed at a depth of between 750mm and 1350mm. This depth provides protection against freezing and mechanical damage through activities such as digging. Pipework located deeper than 1350mm makes accessibility difficult for maintenance or repair.

External above-ground pipework

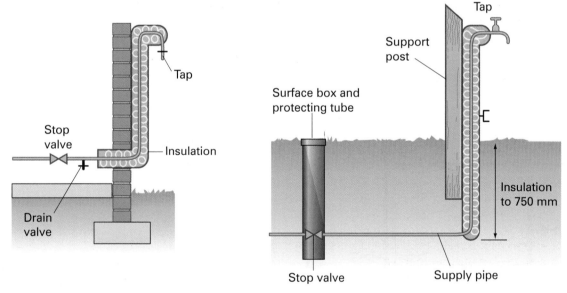

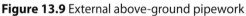

Figure 13.9 External above-ground pipework

If at all possible this should be avoided. In certain circumstances however, it may be necessary, such as the supply to an outside tap or the connection to an animal drinking trough, in which case the supply pipe must be insulated with waterproof material down to a depth of 750mm and the above-ground pipework must be protected from mechanical damage.

Supply pipework entering buildings

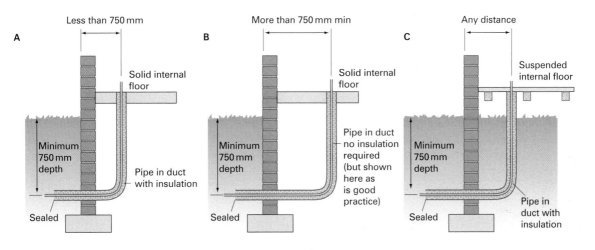

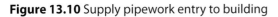

Figure 13.10 Supply pipework entry to building

Where a supply pipe enters a building it should:

- be laid in a duct
- pass through or under the building at a minimum depth of 750mm
- rise vertically into the building at least 750mm from the external wall (as shown in B). If less than 750mm then the vertical section of the pipe below ground must be insulated (as shown in A)
- where the pipe rises vertically through a suspended timber floor then the vertical section of pipe must be insulated to a depth of 750mm below ground (as shown in C).

Cold surfaces and unheated spaces

Pipes must not be chased or ducted into external walls. Pipes that are run on external walls must be clipped using spacer clips or be sited on a timber baseboard.

Water fittings in roof spaces

In a cold roof such as that shown, the loft insulation must not run below the cistern. This is to assist in preventing the cistern from freezing during winter months. Don't forget that where a cistern is sited in a warm room it may also need insulating to protect

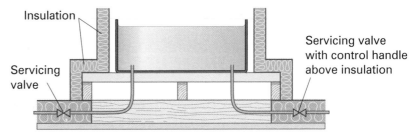

Figure 13.11 Water cistern insulation

against undue warming. The Water Regulations require plumbers to ensure that the temperature of cold water in any water fittings cannot reach 25°C, in order to avoid the growth of legionella bacteria.

Thermal insulation

The Regulations state the conditions in which pipes must be thermally insulated to guard against freezing; potential freezing locations are classified as normal or extreme. Figure 13.12 shows examples of where these conditions apply.

	Normal conditions	Extreme conditions
Applies to:	Domestic accommodation and other types of premises where habitable rooms are normally heated for up to 12 hours each day (even though they are within the envelope of the heated accommodation, water fittings in unheated rooms need to be protected against freezing)	Water fittings: • installed externally to a building • inside any building or part of a building that is unheated, or only marginally heated, for fewer than 12 hours each day • inside a building but located outside the thermal envelope
Examples:	Water fittings in: • cloakrooms • store rooms • utility rooms • roof spaces located below the ceiling insulation etc.	Water fittings: • located under suspended ground floors • above the level of ceiling insulation in a roof space • in a communal staircase or corridor on flats • in domestic garages or other buildings • external above ground installations

Figure 13.12 Requirements for thermal insulation

Thermal insulation of insulation material at 0°C					
Watts per metre degrees Kelvin	0.02 W/(m.K)	0.025 W/(m.K)	0.03 W/(m.K)	0.035 W/(m.K)	0.04 W/(m.K)
15	20	30	25	25	32
22	15	15	19	19	25
28	15	15	13	19	22
25	15	15	9	9	13
42 & over	15	15	9	9	9

Figure 13.13 Pipework insulation for normal conditions

Guidance should be sought from the manufacturer on the required thickness of insulating material to protect against extreme conditions. Figure 13.13 shows the table from BS 5422 that identifies required thicknesses for insulating material based on pipe size and thermal properties of the insulating material.

Permeation or deterioration

Materials such as plastics can be susceptible to permeation, this is where gases/fumes that come in contact with the plastic permeate through the pipe wall and into the water supply, introducing a smell or taste to it. Examples of where this may occur are:

- petrol station forecourts, where petrol may permeate into the pipework
- brownfield building sites – building on industrial land that may have been previously contaminated.

Pipework support

Pipework must be adequately supported to minimise the effects of noise, vibration and the weight of unclipped pipework causing undue pressure at joints. Any pipe brackets used, however, must be capable of permitting thermal movement of the pipework. Figure 13.14 shows the recommended clip spacing requirements for common pipe materials.

Pipe size		Copper (m)		Low Carbon Steel (LCS) (m)		Plastic (m)	
mm	in	horizontal	vertical	horizontal	vertical	horizontal	vertical
15	½	1.2	1.8	1.8	2.4	0.6	1.2
22	¾	1.8	2.4	2.4	3.0	0.7	1.4
28	1	1.8	2.4	2.4	3.0	0.8	1.5
35	1¼	2.4	3.0	2.7	3.0	0.8	1.7
42	1½	2.4	3.0	3.0	3.6	0.9	1.8
54	2	2.7	3.0	3.0	3.6	1.0	2.1

Figure 13.14 Minimum clip spacing requirements for common pipe materials

Storage cisterns

Cold water storage cisterns put a great deal of weight on a building structure. When sited in roof spaces their weight must be spread across as many rafters as possible and preferably be sited across a load-bearing wall. Figure 13.15 outlines key requirements for cistern support.

Flexible cisterns	Rigid cisterns
• Continuous support is required over the whole base area of the cistern. • Cisterns must not be supported on chipboard or composite board that may be weakened by dampness. • No connections should be made to the base of plastic cisterns.	• The weight should be distributed over two or more timber joists (depending on the size of the cistern). • Continuous support of the base is not required for galvanised steel cisterns.

Figure 13.15 Storage cistern support requirements

Concealed water fittings

A concealed fitting is defined as:

- a fitting installed below ground
- a fitting passing though or under any wall, footing or foundation
- a fitting enclosed in any chase or duct
- a fitting in any position which is inaccessible or renders access difficult.

Figures 13.16 and 13.17 show examples of correct methods for locating pipework in concealed locations.

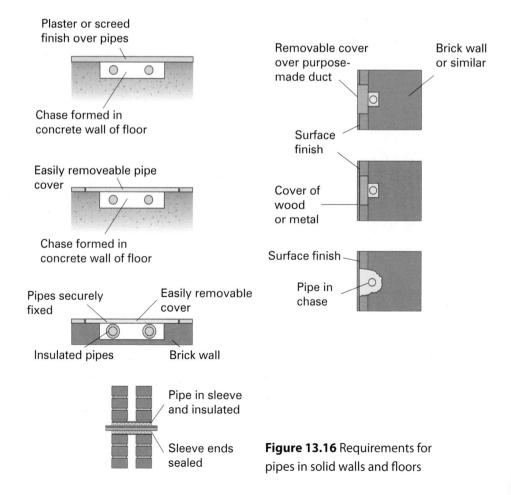

Figure 13.16 Requirements for pipes in solid walls and floors

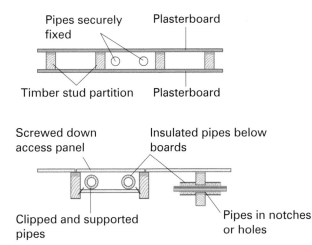

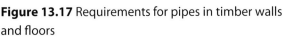

Figure 13.17 Requirements for pipes in timber walls and floors

Design principles, system installation and commissioning

Proximity of drains and sewers

Pipes should be properly located so that they avoid becoming contaminated. Water pipes should therefore be located in a position where they are not going to come into contact with:

- foul soil
- refuse or a refuse chute
- ashpits
- a sewer, drain or inspection chamber.

Figure 13.18 shows an example of pipework routed around an inspection chamber, not run through it.

Avoiding damage to pipework

Particular care needs to be taken to avoid damage to pipework, the following precautions apply:

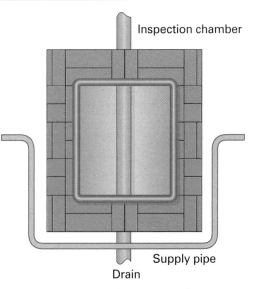

Figure 13.18 Pipework routing in the vicinity of an inspection chamber

- below-ground pipework should be installed at a minimum depth of 750mm
- pipes passing through walls should be sleeved and protected against ground settlement
- pipes passing through walls or embedded in solid walls or floors should be wrapped or protected from contact with corrosive material such as cement
- pipes in channels or ducts must be arranged so that they are accessible for maintenance or repair.

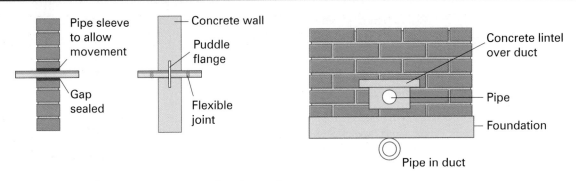

Figure 13.19 Sleeving arrangements for pipework

Water temperature in cold water systems

The Regulations require that any cold water system pipework or fittings should be installed to ensure that the water temperature in the pipework at no time reaches a temperature above 25°C. Ways in which this can be met are:

- avoid siting pipework and fittings in warm (hot) parts of the building
- insulate pipework and fittings in circumstances where they may be heated, e.g. in loft spaces
- site cold pipes below hot pipes in a pipe run (the hot pipe will not be able to heat the cold one by air circulation), and don't permit them to touch each other.

Stop valves and servicing valves

Every supply pipe supplying water to premises must be fitted with a valve located to enable the supply to be shut off to those premises without shutting off the supply to any other premises. There must be a stop valve sited at the boundary of the property (the supplier's stop valve) and a stop valve must be sited immediately as the supply enters the premises. The internal stop valve must be located:

- above floor level
- as close as possible to the point of entry.

Figure 13.20 shows the position of stop valves in a block of flats where each flat has its own dedicated supply pipe.

Figure 13.21 shows the position of stop valves in a block of flats fed by a communal supply pipe. Note the stop valve sited externally to the property (this is so that the individual supply to the flat can be isolated from outside the flat if the occupants are away from home); it is also good practice to include a valve sited in each flat as well.

Definition

Stop valve – a valve used for shutting off the flow of water in a pipe.

Servicing valve – a valve used for shutting off the flow of water to a fitting for the purposes of maintenance or repair.

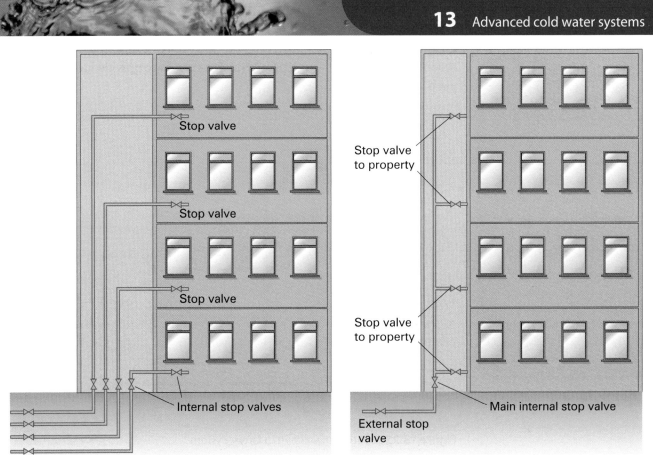

Figure 13.20 Flats fed by individual supply pipes

Figure 13.21 Flats fed by common supply pipework

The Regulations require that a water system should be capable of being drained down without wasting water. Servicing and drain valves must be fitted at appropriate points in the system. Figure 13.22 shows the minimum locations at which service valves should be fitted.

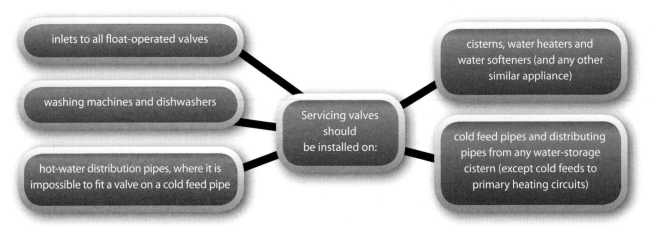

Figure 13.22 Where to install servicing valves

Figure 13.23 shows the location of the various valves in a larger system. Note that with the larger system separate service valves are provided to isolate each bathroom.

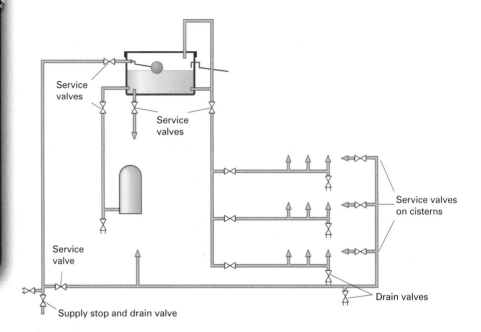

Figure 13.23 Location of valves in a larger system

Commissioning systems

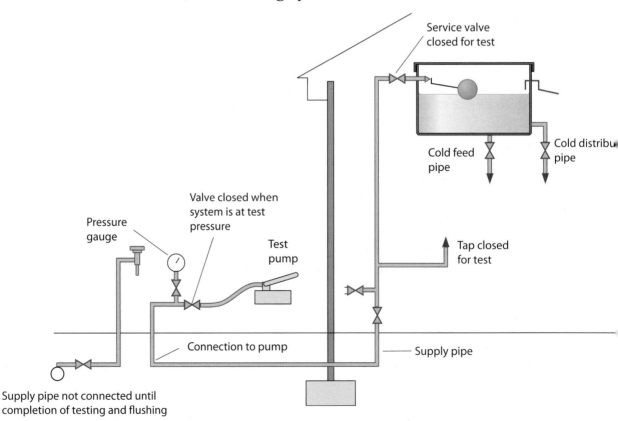

Figure 13.24 Soundness testing the supply pipework

The commissioning of a water system includes:

- visual inspection, e.g. checking that joints have been properly made
- soundness testing
- flushing and disinfection
- performance testing – checking the flow rate and pressure at fittings
- final checks and the handover to the customer.

Soundness testing

The Regulations require that new installations or major modifications in any type of property (including dwellings) are subject to a soundness test to make sure they are properly watertight. The Regulations refer to differing test procedures for systems:

- containing metallic pipework, e.g. copper
- containing non-metallic pipework, e.g. plastics.

Metallic pipework

- once the system has been filled, it should be allowed to stand for 30 minutes to allow the water temperature to stabilise
- the system should be pressurised using hydraulic testing equipment to a pressure of 1.5 times the system working pressure
- leave to stand for 1 hour
- check for visible leakage and loss of pressure. If sound, the test has been satisfactorily completed
- if not sound, repeat the test after locating and repairing any leaks.

Plastic pipework

BS 6700 has two test procedures for plastic pipes – procedures A and B. See Water Regulations for more details.

Test A procedure:

- apply test pressure (1.5 times maximum working pressure) and maintain by pumping for a period of 30 minutes, and visually inspect for leakage
- reduce pressure by bleeding water from the system to 0.33 times maximum working pressure. Close the bleed valve
- visually check and monitor for 90 minutes. If the pressure remains at or above 0.33 times working pressure, the system can be regarded as satisfactory.

Test B procedure:

- apply test pressure (1.5 times maximum working pressure) and maintain by pumping for a period of 30 minutes
- note the pressure and inspect visually for leakage.

Note the pressure after a further 30 minutes. If the pressure drop is less than 60 kPa (0.6 bar), the system can be considered to have no obvious leakage; then visually check and monitor for 120 minutes. If the pressure drop is less than 20 kPa (0.2 bar), the system can be regarded as satisfactory.

System flushing

Every new installation or major modification to an existing system must be the subject of thorough flushing before the system is put into use. Flushing involves running a relatively large quantity of water through the system to make sure that any foreign matter such as flux is completely removed from the system.

System disinfection

The following identifies the range of work on hot and cold water systems that requires disinfection:

- new installations, except private dwellings occupied by a single family
- major extensions or alterations, except private dwellings occupied by a single family
- underground pipework, except localised repairs or insertion of junctions
- where contamination may be suspected, e.g. fouling by sewage, drainage, animals, insects and vermin
- after physical entry by personnel for interior inspection, painting or repairs, e.g. large storage cisterns
- where a system has not been in regular use and not regularly flushed. Regular use means periods of up to 30 days without use, depending on the characteristics of the water.

Disinfection procedure

The following outlines the procedure from BS 6700 for carrying out disinfection with a chlorine-based material:

- thoroughly flush the system prior to disinfection
- introduce a disinfection agent at specified concentrations into the system, filling systematically to ensure a total saturation. If using chlorine, use initial concentrations of 50 mg per litre (50 ppm)
- leave the system for a contact period of one hour. If using chlorine, check the free residual chlorine levels at the end of the contact period. If this is less than 30 mg per litre, then the procedure requires repeating
- immediately following successful disinfection, the system should be drained and thoroughly flushed with clean water until the residual chlorine level is at the same level as the drinking water supplied.

Did you know?

Great care must be taken when disinfecting systems – building users must not be allowed to use the system whilst the disinfection is progress, hand contact with the disinfectant should be avoided and the discharge of large amounts of disinfectant from a system into the drain may have to be notified to the local authority.

Backflow prevention and fluid categories

One of the major requirements under the Water Regulations is that systems should be deigned so that backflow in a system cannot occur, resulting in a potentially serious contamination of the supply pipework in the property and the water undertaker's main. Backflow can be by:

- back-pressure – the reversal of flow in a pipe caused by an increase in pressure in the system
- back-siphonage – siphonage from a cistern or appliance back into the pipe that feeds it.

Fluid risk categories

In order to prevent backflow an initial assessment of the risk presented by a particular fluid needs to be carried out, i.e. the water coming through the water undertaker's main presents no risk as it is wholesome water, whereas the water contained in a WC pan presents a significant risk to health and is regarded as fluid category 5 – a serious hazard to health. Figures 13.25 and 13.26 classify fluids into the various risk that they present.

Fluid category	Description	Application
1	Wholesome water supplied by a water undertaker complying with the Requirements of the Regulations made under Schedule 67 of the Water Industry Act 1991	
2	Water that would be classed as fluid category 1 except for odour, appearance or temperature. These changes in water quality are aesthetic changes only and the water is not considered a hazard to human health	(a) water heated in a hot-water secondary system (b) mixtures of fluids from categories 1 and 2 discharged from combination taps or showers (c) water that has been softened by a domestic common salt regeneration process

Figure 13.25 Fluid risk categories

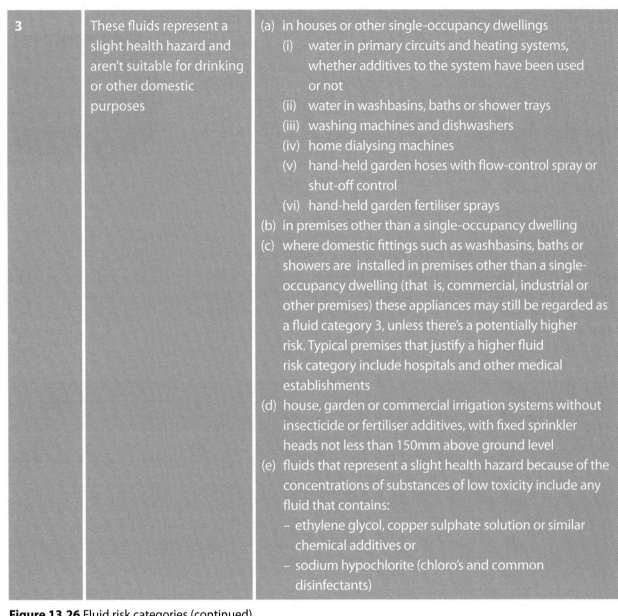

| 3 | These fluids represent a slight health hazard and aren't suitable for drinking or other domestic purposes | (a) in houses or other single-occupancy dwellings
   (i) water in primary circuits and heating systems, whether additives to the system have been used or not
   (ii) water in washbasins, baths or shower trays
   (iii) washing machines and dishwashers
   (iv) home dialysing machines
   (v) hand-held garden hoses with flow-control spray or shut-off control
   (vi) hand-held garden fertiliser sprays
(b) in premises other than a single-occupancy dwelling
(c) where domestic fittings such as washbasins, baths or showers are installed in premises other than a single-occupancy dwelling (that is, commercial, industrial or other premises) these appliances may still be regarded as a fluid category 3, unless there's a potentially higher risk. Typical premises that justify a higher fluid risk category include hospitals and other medical establishments
(d) house, garden or commercial irrigation systems without insecticide or fertiliser additives, with fixed sprinkler heads not less than 150mm above ground level
(e) fluids that represent a slight health hazard because of the concentrations of substances of low toxicity include any fluid that contains:
   – ethylene glycol, copper sulphate solution or similar chemical additives or
   – sodium hypochlorite (chloro's and common disinfectants) |

Figure 13.26 Fluid risk categories (continued)

4	These fluids represent a significant health hazard and aren't suitable for drinking or other domestic purposes. They contain concentrations of toxic substances, and include:	(a) water containing chemical carcinogenic substances or pesticides (b) water containing environmental organisms of potential health significance (micro-organisms, bacteria, viruses and parasites of significance for human health which can occur and survive in the general environment) (c) water in primary circuits and heating systems other than in a house, irrespective of whether additives have been used or not (d) water treatment or softeners using other than salt (e) water used in washing machines and dishwashing machines for other than domestic use (f) water used in mini-irrigation systems in a house garden without fertiliser or insecticide applications such as pop-up sprinklers, permeable hoses or fixed or rotating sprinkler heads fixed less than 150mm above ground level
5	Fluids representing a serious health risk because of the concentration of **pathogenic organisms**, radioactive or very toxic substances, including any fluid which contains: (a) faecal material or other human waste, or (b) butchery or other animal waste, or (c) pathogens from any other source	(a) sinks, urinals, WC pans and bidets in any location (b) permeable pipes or hoses in other than domestic gardens, laid below ground or at ground level with or without chemical additives (c) grey-water recycling systems (d) washing machines and dishwashers in high-risk premises (e) appliances and supplies in medical establishments

Figure 13.26 Fluid risk categories (continued)

Backflow prevention devices

Once the fluid categories have been established, a suitable backflow prevention device can be chosen to guard against the risk presented by the fluid. Backflow prevention devices fall into:

- non-mechanical devices, primarily air gaps of which there are 10 devices
- mechanical devices – of which there are 14 devices.

Figure 13.27 shows the types of non-mechanical device detailing the fluid risk categories that the device can protect against.

Did you know?

The difference between mechanical and non-mechanical devices is that mechanical devices have moving parts, whereas non-mechanical devices are air-gap-based with no moving parts.

Type	Description of backflow prevention arrangements and devices	Fluid category for which suited	
		Back-pressure	Back-siphonage
AA	Air gap with unrestricted discharge above spillover level	5	5
AB	Air gap with weir overflow	5	5
AC	Air gap with vented submerged inlet	3	3
AD	Air gap with injector	5	5
AF	Air gap with circular overflow	4	4
AG	Air gap with minimum size circular overflow determined by measure or vacuum test	3	3
AUK1	Air gap with interposed cistern (e.g. a WC suite)	3	5
AUK2	Air gaps for taps and combination fittings (tap gaps) discharging over domestic sanitary appliances such as a washbasin, bidet, bath or shower tray shall be not less than the following –	x	3
AUK3	Size of tap or combination fitting Distance of tap outlet above appliance spillover level Not exceeding G½ Exceeding G½ but not 20 mm exceeding G¾ 25 mm Exceeding G¾ 70 mm Air gaps for taps or combination fittings (tap gaps) discharging over any higher risk domestic sanitary appliances where a fluid risk category 4 or 5 is present, such as (a) Any domestic or non-domestic sink (b) Any appliance in premises where a higher level of protection is required such as some appliances in hospitals or other health care premises The air gap shall be not less than 20 mm or twice the diameter of the inlet pipe to the fitting, whichever is the greater	x	5
DC	Pipe interrupter with permanent atmospheric vent	x	5

Notes:

1   X indicates that the backflow prevention arrangement or device is not applicable or not acceptable for protection against back pressure for any fluid category within water installations in the UK.

2   Arrangements incorporating type DC devices shall have no control valves on the outlet side of the device, they shall be fitted not less than 300 mm above the spillover level of a WC pan, or 150 mm above the sparge pipe outlet of a urinal, and discharge vertically downward.

3   Overflows and warning pipes shall discharge through, or terminate with, an air gap, the dimension of which should satisfy a Type AA air gap.

Figure 13.27 Non-mechanical backflow prevention devices

Figure 13.28 shows the type of mechanical device detailing the fluid risk category that it can protect against.

Type	Description of backflow prevention arrangements and devices	Fluid category for which suited	
		Back-pressure	Back-siphonage
BA	Verifiable backflow preventer with reduced pressure zone (RPZ valve)	4	4
CA	Non-verifiable disconnector with difference between pressure zones not greater than 10%	3	3
DA	Anti-vacuum valve (or vacuum breaker)	x	3
DB	Pipe interrupter with atmospheric vent and moving element	x	4
DUK1	Anti-vacuum valve combined with verifiable check valve	2	3
EA	Verifiable single check valve	2	2
EB	Non-verifiable single check valve	2	2
EC	Verifiable double check valve	3	3
ED	Non-verifiable double check valve	3	3
HA	Hose union backflow preventor. Only permitted on existing hose union taps in house installations	2	3
HC	Diverter with automatic return (normally integral with domestic appliance applications only)	x	3
HUK1	Hose union tap which incorporates a verifiable double check valve. Only permitted for replacement of existing hose union taps in house installations	3	3
LA	Pressurised air inlet valve	x	2
LB	Pressurised air inlet valve with check valve downstream	2	3

Notes:
1. X indicates that backflow prevention device is not acceptable for protection against back-pressure for any fluid category within water installations in the UK.
2. Arrangements incorporating a type BD device shall be fitted not less than 300mm above the spill-over level of the appliance and discharge vertically downwards.
3. Types DA and DUK1 shall have no control valves on the outlet of the device and be fitted on a minimum 300mm type A upstand.
4. Relief outlet ports from types BA and CA backflow prevention devices shall terminate with a type AA air gap.

Figure 13.28 Mechanical backflow prevention devices

In the UK we apply point of use backflow protection, that is, a backflow device is fitted to each water fitting/appliance to prevent backflow occurring. Point of use protection prevents contaminated water getting into other parts of the system as well as the undertaker's main. There are circumstances in which additional protection in the form of whole site or zone protection must be applied:

- when a supply or distributing pipe feeds water to two or more separately occupied premises
- when a supply pipe feeds water to premises that are required to provide more than 24 hours' water storage for ordinary use.

Figure 13.29 shows a zone protection device applied to a common supply pipe, isolating an industrial process from a domestic water system. In this case the zone protection is likely to be a break cistern with a Type AA air gap guarding against a fluid category 5 risk.

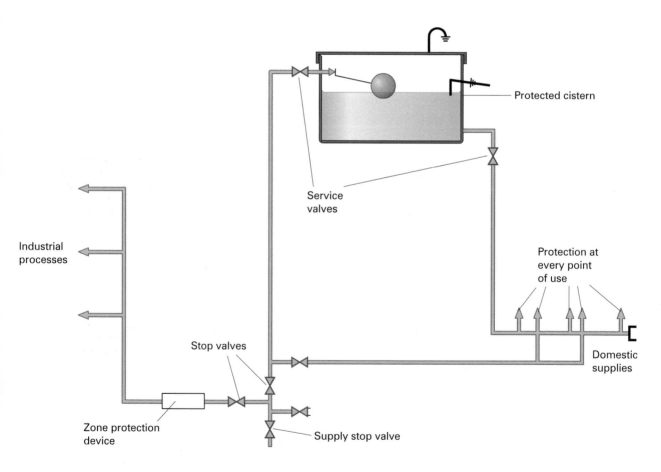

Figure 13.29 Zone protection

Examples of backflow prevention devices in use

WCs and urinals

WC pans and urinals are a fluid category 5 risk. The backflow prevention device for a standard WC supplied from a cistern is a Type AUK1 device – interposed cistern. Note the minimum dimensions.

A pressure-flushing valve may be used in non-domestic properties to flush WCs and urinals, provided that a type DC pipe interrupter with permanent atmospheric device is used to guard against a fluid category 5 risk.

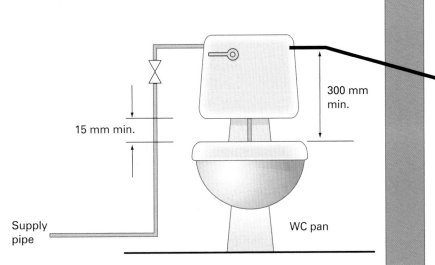

300 mm min.

15 mm min.

Supply pipe

WC pan

Figure 13.30 WC with type AUK1 device

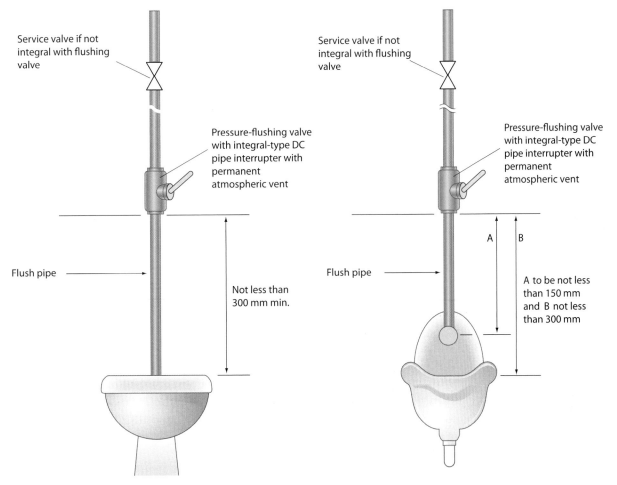

Service valve if not integral with flushing valve

Pressure-flushing valve with integral-type DC pipe interrupter with permanent atmospheric vent

Flush pipe

Not less than 300 mm min.

Service valve if not integral with flushing valve

Pressure-flushing valve with integral-type DC pipe interrupter with permanent atmospheric vent

Flush pipe

A   B

A to be not less than 150 mm and B not less than 300 mm

Figure 13.31 Pipe interrupter to WC and urinal bowl

Contaminated fluid storage

Certain contaminated types of fluid or unknown types of fluid are regarded as a fluid category 5 risk, e.g. reserve water for fire-fighting purposes, in which case the suitable device is a type AA air gap with a minimum air-gap distance of 20mm or twice the diameter of the inlet pipe, whichever is the greater. The air gap is measured above the spillover level of the cistern, not any overflowing level.

Fill method for fluid category 5 risk

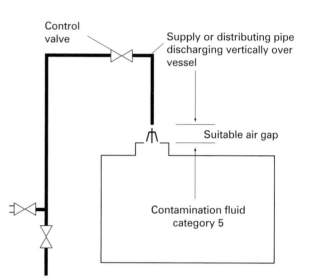

Figure 13.32 Fluid category 5 risk with type AA air gap

Bidets

Bidets present a high risk of contamination, they can be divided into two groups:

- over-the-rim type fed by taps – these can be fed from the supply pipework, provided a Type AUK2 tap gap is maintained
- ascending-spray type or over-the-rim type with spray hose – these must not be fitted to the supply pipe as there is no backflow protection device available to protect against the fluid category 5 risk they present.

Connection of ascending-spray bidets

Ascending-spray bidets and over-the-rim bidets with spray hoses must be connected from storage, in particular independent hot and cold pipework should be used to ensure that water cannot be siphoned in a backflow condition from the bidet to another appliance. Figure 13.33 shows a method of taking independent supplies to a bidet.

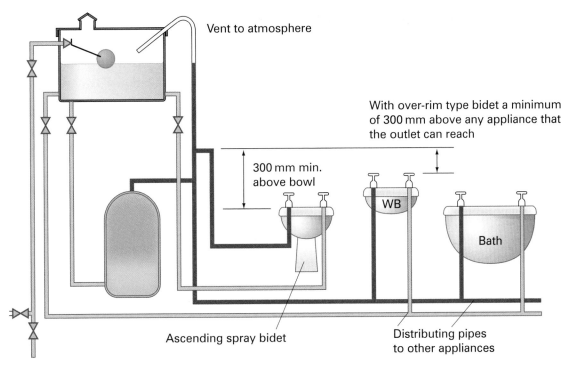

Vent to atmosphere

With over-rim type bidet a minimum of 300 mm above any appliance that the outlet can reach

300 mm min. above bowl

WB

Bath

Ascending spray bidet

Distributing pipes to other appliances

Figure 13.33 Independent supplies to bidet

Taps

- Taps to washbasins, baths and bidets in domestic properties should be protected against a fluid category 3 risk and include a Type AUK2 tap gap.
- Taps to domestic and non-domestic sinks and sanitary appliances in high-risk applications, e.g. medical uses, should be protected by a Type AUK3 tap gap.

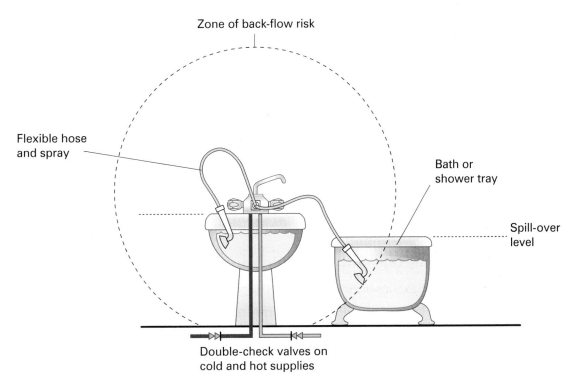

Zone of back-flow risk

Flexible hose and spray

Bath or shower tray

Spill-over level

Double-check valves on cold and hot supplies

Figure 13.34 Category 3 risk created by flexible hose

Appliances with hoses

Figure 13.34 shows a basin with a spray hose; the hose may be dipped in the basin or bath and therefore the supply/distributing pipework needs to be protected against a fluid category 3 risk by the installation of two type EC or ED double-check valves.

Figure 13.35 shows a flexible hose that may fall into a bidet or WC, creating a fluid category 5 risk, in this case the only method of protection is for the supplies to the bath to be fed from independent dedicated distributing pipes from a higher level storage cistern.

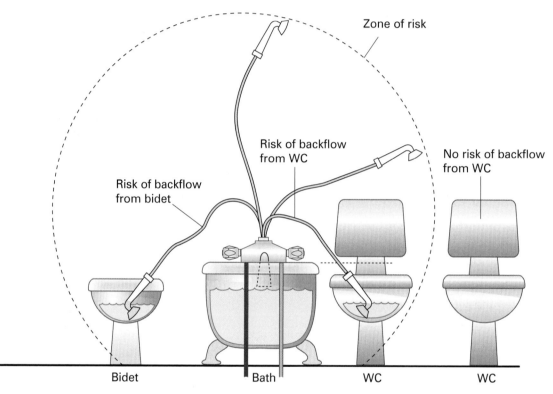

Figure 13.35 Category 5 risk created by flexible hose

Washing machines

Standard washing machines for domestic use include a type EC or ED double-check valve to guard against a fluid category 3 risk. Non-domestic washing machines for use in locations such as healthcare premises can include a type AD device – air gap with injector; this protects against a fluid category 5 risk.

Outside taps with hose union attachment

Hand-held hoses for use in domestic gardens must be fitted with a self-closing mechanism to promote water conservation. In addition new outside tap installations must be:

- fitted with a double-check valve sited inside the property
- positioned where they will not be subject to freezing.

Existing garden taps can be dealt with in a slightly different manner:

- the preferred option is to fit a Type EC or EC double-check valve inside the property, as for new installations
- alternatively, either of the following can be used for existing installations:
  - a type HUK1 device – hose union tap with in-built double-check valve, or
  - a type HA backflow preventer that screws on to the tap.

Porous hose in a domestic garden

A porous hose system in a domestic garden presents a fluid category 4 risk owing to the possibility of contaminants getting into the low-level hose. The type of device to use for this application is a type DB pipe interrupter with moving element.

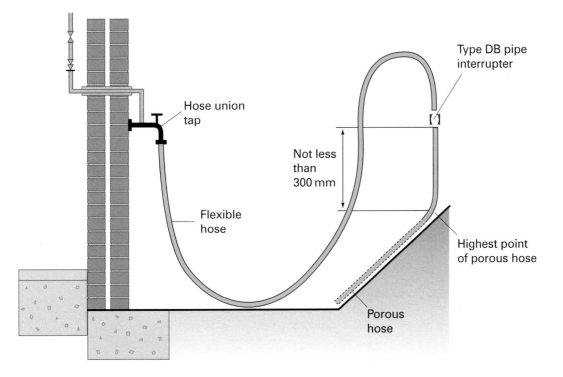

Figure 13.36 Domestic garden with porous hose

Animal drinking troughs

Appliances in agricultural usage are classed as fluid category 5 risks and must therefore be protected by an appropriate air gap arrangement. Figure 13.37 shows a cattle trough installation that includes a Type AA air gap to protect against the fluid category 5 risk, permitting the trough to be fed from the supply pipe.

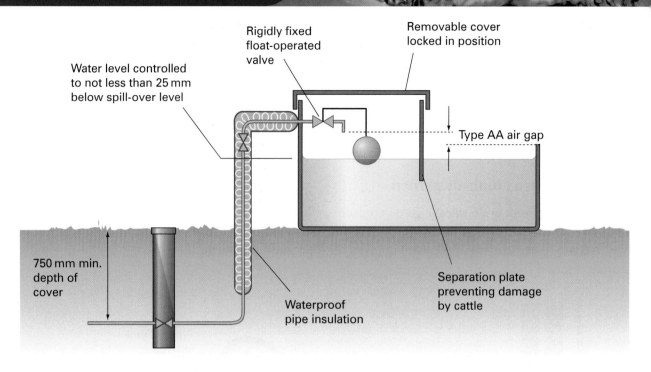

Figure 13.37 Cattle trough with type AA air gap

Fire protection systems

A sprinkler system, such as that shown in Figure 13.38, which has no additives and which is connected direct to the supply pipe presents a fluid category 2 risk which can be protected by a type EA or EB single-check valve.

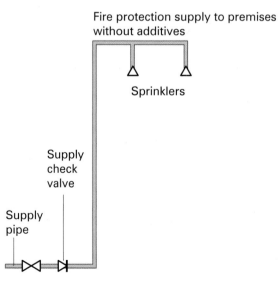

Figure 13.38 Sprinkler system with no additives

Figure 13.39 shows a pressurised fire protection system with a pumping set and hydro-pneumatic pressure vessel, this presents a fluid category 4 risk which can be protected by an RPZ valve or an appropriate break cistern and air gap arrangement.

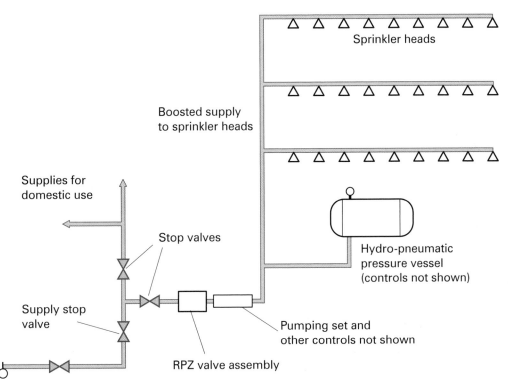

Sprinkler heads

Boosted supply to sprinkler heads

Supplies for domestic use

Stop valves

Hydro-pneumatic pressure vessel (controls not shown)

Supply stop valve

Pumping set and other controls not shown

RPZ valve assembly

Figure 13.39 Pressurised fire protection system with hydro-pneumatic pressure vessel

Prevention of cross connection to unwholesome water

Pipes located in buildings above ground should be colour coded to BS 1710 so that they can be distinguished from one another. Usually this only applies to industrial/commercial buildings, however in domestic properties that use water other than wholesome water, e.g. a grey-water recycling system, then the colour coding of pipes will be required.

The following shows the colour codes used:

With most new installations accurate as installed pipe layouts are required to be provided to the customer on completion of the installation.

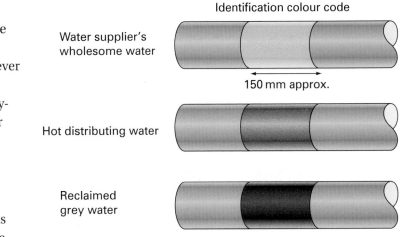

Identification colour code

Water supplier's wholesome water

150 mm approx.

Hot distributing water

Reclaimed grey water

Figure 13.40 Pipework colour codes

Any taps or outlets supplying water that is not considered to be wholesome should be clearly labelled as 'water not for drinking'. Figure 13.41 shows examples of installations where cross connection of supply is considered to be an issue.

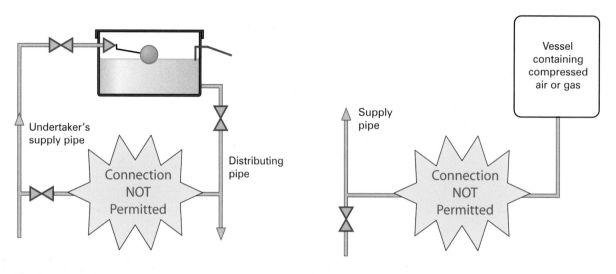

Figure 13.41 Cross connection examples

Cold water services

The Regulations lay down the requirements for installing storage cisterns supplying wholesome water, identifying that they should be:

- fitted with an effective inlet-control device to maintain the correct water level
- fitted with servicing valves on inlet and outlet pipes
- fitted with a screened warning/overflow pipe to warn against impending overflow
- supported to avoid damage or distortion that might cause them to leak
- installed so that any risk of contamination is minimised, and arranged so that water can circulate and stagnation will not take place
- covered to exclude light or insects and insulated to prevent heat losses and undue warming
- corrosion-resistant and watertight and must not deform unduly, shatter or fragment when in use
- unobstructed and have space above them of not less than 350mm for servicing purposes.

Cistern inlet controls

Every storage cistern requires an inlet shut-off valve. The following valves are the various types used in domestic properties:

- BS 1212 Part 1 – Portsmouth type (this valve is now only suitable for replacement of old valves, not on new installations)

- BS 1212 Part 2 – diaphragm type (brass) and Part 3 – diaphragm type (plastic) – usually sited in new cold water storage cisterns
- BS 1212 Part 4 – compact type – usually used in WC cisterns.

Valves above 50mm fall outside the scope of BS 1212 and should be chosen from the list detailed in the Water Fittings and Materials Directory at www.wras.co.uk.

A servicing valve must be fitted to the inlet of all float-operated valves to permit service and maintenance without full system isolation.

The outlet pipework from all cisterns should contain a servicing valve, usually in the form of a gate valve, to permit service or maintenance. The exception to this requirement is the cold feed pipe from an f&e cistern, which must not be valved: for isolation purposes f&e cisterns are controlled from the inlet service valve to the float-operated valve.

Warning and overflow pipes

- Cisterns up to 1000 litre capacity require only a single overflow/warning pipe. The pipe must have an internal diameter of not less than 19mm, with the pipe capable of taking the full flow of water if the inlet control valve fails.
- Cisterns between 1000 and 5000 litres capacity must have separate warning and overflow pipes.
- Cisterns over 5000 litre capacity should be provided with an overflow that operates when the water level reaches 50mm above its normal operating level. A water-level indicator with an audible alarm may be used as an alternative to a warning pipe, operating when the water level reaches 25mm above its normal operating level.

> ### Definition
>
> A **warning pipe** gives warning that an impending overflow is about to take place.
>
> An **overflow pipe** is a pipe from a cistern in which water flows only when the water level in the cistern exceeds a predetermined level.

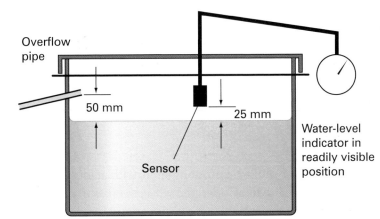

Figure 13.42 Larger cistern with water-level indicator

Key requirements of overflow/warning pipes:

- the overflow/warning pipe must be capable of removing the excess water from the cistern without the inlet device becoming submerged

- warning pipes are to discharge in a conspicuous position, preferably in an external location
- warning/overflow pipes must fall continuously from the cistern to the point of discharge
- feed and expansion cisterns must have separate warning pipes from those serving cold water cisterns
- warning pipes and overflow pipes must be fitted with some means of preventing the ingress of insects etc. (usually in the form of screens or filters)
- when the installation consists of two or more cisterns, the warning or overflow pipe must be arranged so that the cistern can't discharge one into the other.

Contamination of stored water

Cisterns must be installed so as to minimise the risk of contamination, this is partly achieved by protecting the cistern against the ingress of contaminates; other factors to be considered include:

- the cistern must be properly sized, over-sized cisterns present a contamination risk
- cistern outlets must be sited as low as possible in the cistern to prevent sediment build-up, bottom-entry connections are preferred, as shown in figure 13.43

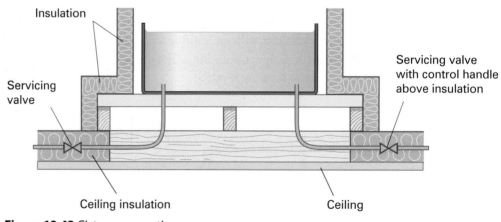

Figure 13.43 Cistern connections

- cistern outlet connections must be properly sited, with at least one outlet at the opposite end from the float-operated valve, to ensure that water is properly drawn across the entire length of the cistern, preventing stagnation
- linked cisterns, as shown in Figure 13.44, should be installed so that a proper throughput of water is maintained from both cisterns, minimising the possibility of stagnation.

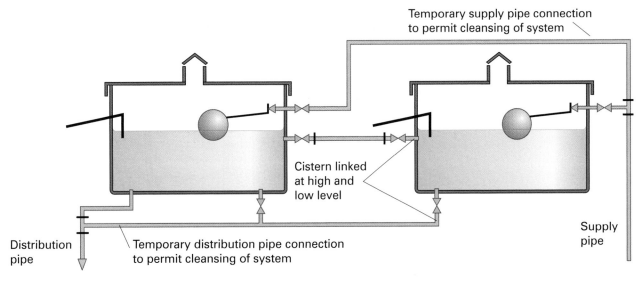

Temporary supply pipe connection to permit cleansing of system

Cistern linked at high and low level

Supply pipe

Distribution pipe

Temporary distribution pipe connection to permit cleansing of system

Figure 13.44 Linked cisterns

Other appliances

Water closets

WCs may be flushed by using either a flushing cistern or a pressure-flushing valve (non-domestic properties only). The key requirement is that the flushing device must clear the contents of the bowl effectively using a single flush of water.

Flushing cisterns may be either single flush or dual flush, flushing capacities must not exceed:

- single flush – 6 litres
- dual flush – 6 litres long flush and 4 litres short flush.

With dual-flush cisterns there must be clear signage to indicate which is the short and long flush.

There are two types of flushing device that can be used in the WC cistern, as shown in Figures 13.45 and 13.46.

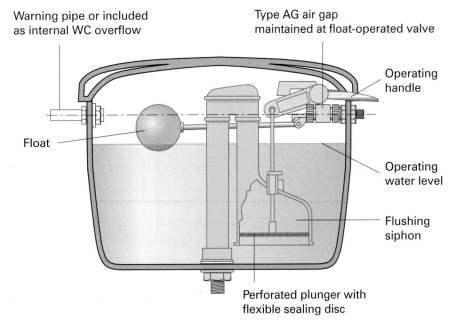

Warning pipe or included as internal WC overflow

Type AG air gap maintained at float-operated valve

Operating handle

Float

Operating water level

Flushing siphon

Perforated plunger with flexible sealing disc

Figure 13.45 Siphon flushing device

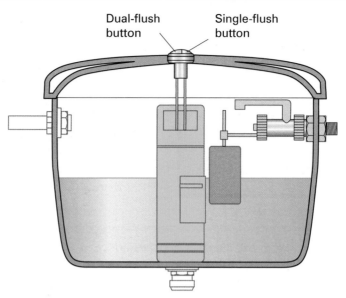

Figure 13.46 Drop-valve flushing device

The alternative to the pressure-flushing cistern is the pressure-flushing valve, a diagram of this valve is shown on page 239. For the valve to operate successfully it must be supplied with water at a flow rate of 1.2 litres per second.

a diagram of this valve is shown on page 239.

Did you know?

An internal overflow to a WC discharges its waste water directly into the WC pan.

Warning pipes to WCs

The internal overflow is now commonly supplied with most WC cisterns, removing the need for a separate overflow pipe to the WC. More obsolete overflow routing methods are still permissible, as shown in Figure 13.47.

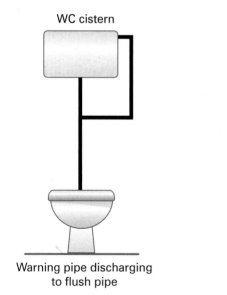

Warning pipe discharging to flush pipe

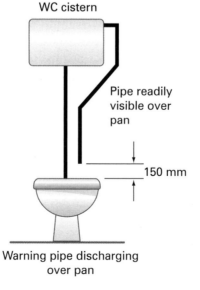

Pipe readily visible over pan

150 mm

Warning pipe discharging over pan

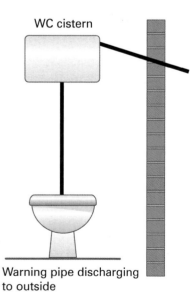

Warning pipe discharging to outside

Figure 13.47 Obsolete overflow arrangements

Flushing urinals

Flushing devices for urinals should be designed so that they do not use more water than is necessary. Acceptable flushing mechanisms are:

- flushing cistern – manual or automatic operation – flushing no more than 10 litres per hour for a single urinal bowl, or 7.5 litres per hour per urinal position if serving multiple bowls, stalls or per 700mm slab position
- flushing valve – manual or automatic operation – an example of this is shown on page 239; these should provide a maximum flush volume of 1.5 litres each time the valve is operated.

Water-saving valves

A water-conservation device must be fitted to urinal cisterns in buildings during periods when they are not occupied (not applicable to buildings occupied 24 hours a day, e.g. motorway services). Devices include:

- a time-operated switch operating a solenoid valve as shown in Figure 13.48

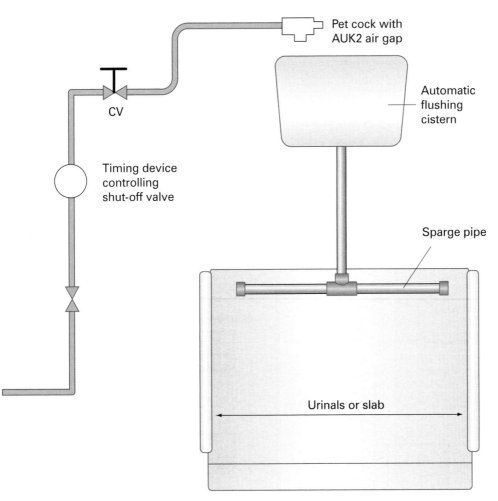

Figure 13.48 Cistern with timing device

- a hydraulic valve that allows water to pass to a urinal cistern when other appliances are used
- by proximity sensing devices (infra-red).

Drinking water supplies

The Regulations state that all premises supplied with water for domestic purposes should have at least one tap conveniently located for the drawing of drinking water; that tap could be supplied from:

- a supply pipe
- a pump delivery pipe drawing water from a supply pipe
- a distributing pipe drawing water exclusively from a cistern storing wholesome water.

Figure 13.49 Boosted water from a break cistern

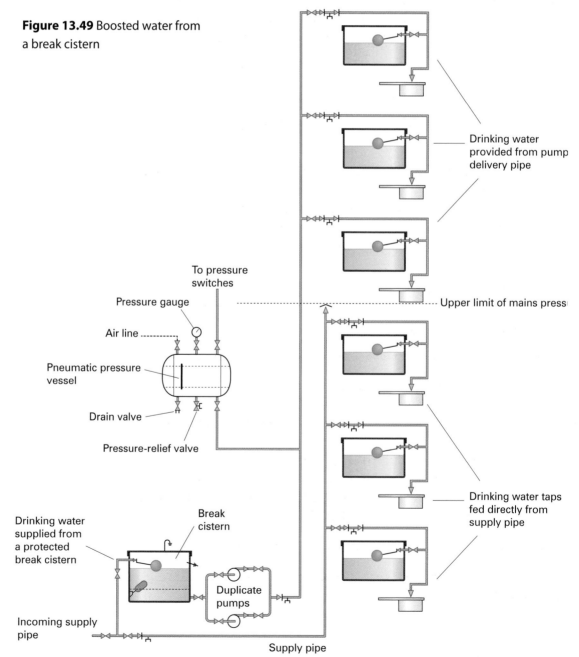

In high-rise buildings it may not be possible to take water directly from the supply pipe, in which case it may be necessary to install a pump or booster system. Figure 13.49 shows the lower flats supplied from the supply pipe, whereas the higher flats are fed from a break cistern feeding a pumping set. The operation of the pumps is controlled by a high- and low-pressure switch sited in a pneumatic pressure vessel; the vessel has a large capacity of water to stop the pump operating for short time periods.

The break cistern is subject to the controls mentioned earlier for systems containing wholesome water. An alternative to the automatic pressure vessel is to use a high-level drinking water header.

Outlets from sanitary appliances

The Regulations identify that every bath, basin, sink or similar appliance should be fitted with a watertight plug to conserve water. There are exceptions to this, such as basins fitted with spray taps, shower trays, drinking fountains etc.

Washing machines and dishwashers

The Regulations lay down the maximum consumption requirements for domestic appliances:

- domestic washing machines – 27 litres per kg of wash load for a standard 60°C cotton cycle
- domestic washer-driers – 48 litres per kg of wash load for a standard 60°C cotton cycle
- domestic dishwashers – 4.5 litres per place setting.

Water for outside use

Animal drinking vessels

Key requirements for animal drinking troughs as shown on page 244 are:

- an inlet control device must be provided to ensure water conservation in use and they must be protected from damage and contamination
- a fluid category 5 backflow device must be included, typically a Type AA air gap
- there must be a servicing valve to the appliance
- the pipework to the trough must be protected by waterproof insulation down to a depth of 750mm and the pipework above ground level must be protected from mechanical damage (boxed-in).

There are two types of single-bowl animal drinking vessel available:

- drinking bowl with type AA air gap – these can be fitted directly to the supply pipe

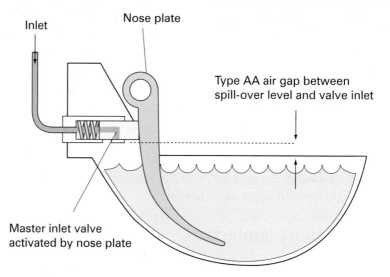

Figure 13.50 Drinking bowl with type AA air gap

- the other type of drinking bowl has a submerged inlet and must only be supplied from a dedicated storage cistern that only supplies similar appliances.

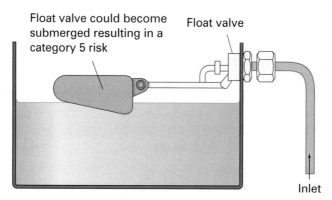

Figure 13.51 Drinking bowl with submerged inlet

Ponds, pools and fountains

Ponds, pools and fountains must contain an impervious lining in order to avoid significant loss of water; in most cases they should not be directly connected to a supply or distributing pipe. If they are connected to a supply pipe, as in the case of a swimming pool, then a backflow device capable of guarding against a fluid category 5 risk must be provided, if the pool contains over 10,000 litres of water and it is replenished automatically, notification must be obtained from the water undertaker prior to the work taking place.

Short answer questions

1. What is the statutory item of legislation governing the installation of cold water supply pipework?
2. What three responses could be provided by the water undertaker to the notification to install a water fitting?
3. On completion of the installation of a new water system, what document must be provided by an approved contractor to the person who commissioned the work?
4. At what stage in the construction process would the sleeve for a cold water supply into a new property be installed?
5. What type of joint should be used to make a copper pipe connection to a lead pipe?
6. What tests should be carried out when performance testing a cold water system?
7. When commissioning a cold water system in an industrial/commercial property, what activity must be carried out in addition to flushing the system?
8. The supply pipework to a cistern containing reserve water for fire-fighting purposes must be protected from the cistern contents by means of what type of backflow-prevention device?
9. The supply to non-domestic sink taps should be protected by means of what type of backflow-prevention device?
10. What two safeguards must be applied to protect the cold water pipework rising above ground to feed an animal drinking trough?

Multiple-choice test

1. The WRAS Approved Contractor Scheme is known as:
   a) IPHE
   b) APHC
   c) WIAPS
   d) WASD

2. On a new commercial development, which of the following can issue a compliance certificate to establish that the cold water system meets the requirements of the Water Regulations?
   a) Architect
   b) Site agent
   c) Approved contractor
   d) Clerk of works

3. Which of the following materials is prohibited from use in water supplies?
   a) Unleaded solder
   b) Bitumen
   c) Brass
   d) Galvanised steel

4. Underground pipework should be sited at a minimum depth below ground of:
   a) 250mm   c) 750mm
   b) 500mm   d) 1000mm

5. The following symbol on a plumbing product is an example of:

Figure 13.52

   a) CE marking
   b) BSI kitemark
   c) WRAS approved product
   d) ISO marking

6. The insulation below a cold water storage cistern in a cold roof should be:
   a) Twice the thickness of the insulation in the rest of the loft
   b) Removed before completing the job
   c) Soaked with water before installation
   d) Four times the thickness of the insulation in the rest of the loft

7. The base of a plastic cold water storage cistern should be supported:
   a) Fully across its base
   b) Across a minimum of 2 rafters
   c) Across a minimum of 3 rafters
   d) Sited on standard chipboard

8. Cold water pipework in external solid walls must:
   a) Be fitted in a purpose-made duct
   b) Be chased to a depth including 10mm for coverage
   c) Only be in plastic materials
   d) Not be sited in this location

9. Where an underground cold water service pipe meets an inspection chamber it:
   a) *May pass through the chamber in a sleeve*
   b) *Should be laid under the chamber in a sleeve*
   c) *Should be routed through the chamber in copper*
   d) *Must be laid around the outside of the chamber*

10. In a domestic property, which is the most likely type of service valve to be used on the inlet to a float-operated valve fed from a supply pipe?
    a) *Spherical plug valve*
    b) *Screwdown stop valve*
    c) *Gate valve*
    d) *Non-return valve*

11. When testing copper pipework the water in the pipework should be allowed to temperature stabilise for what period of time prior to the test taking place?
    a) *15 minutes*   c) *60 minutes*
    b) *30 minutes*   d) *90 minutes*

12. The initial soundness test pressure for plastic pipework (type A test) is:
    a) *0.5 times the maximum operating pressure*
    b) *The maximum operating pressure*
    c) *1.5 times the maximum operating pressure*
    d) *Twice the maximum operating pressure*

13. When disinfecting a cold water system using chlorine, what must the free residual chlorine reading be at the end of the one-hour contact period?
    a) *10PPM*   c) *30PPM*
    b) *20PPM*   d) *50PPM*

14. Under the Water Regulations, which type of pipework must be colour coded to distinguish it from the rest?
    a) *Central heating pipework*
    b) *Supply pipework*
    c) *Distributing pipework*
    d) *Grey-water recycling pipework*

15. The following diagram shows which type of backflow protection device?

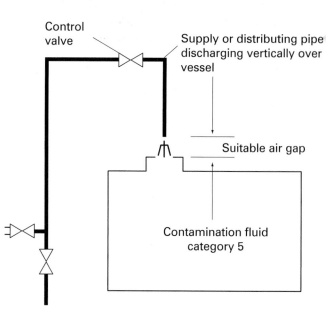

Figure 13.53

    a) *Type AA air gap*
    b) *Type AG air gap*
    c) *Type AUK1 air gap*
    d) *Type AUK3 air gap*

16. Water in the bowl of a bidet is classed as what fluid category risk?
    a) *2*   c) *4*
    b) *3*   d) *5*

17. A fluid category 3 risk is described as:
    a) *Wholesome water*
    b) *Slight health risk*
    c) *Significant health risk*
    d) *Serious health risk*

18. Backflow from a flexible shower hose and spray resting in a shower tray is prevented by using which of the following devices?
    a) *Type EA single-check valve*
    b) *Type ED double-check valve*
    c) *RPZ valve*
    d) *Type AA air gap*

19. A type DC pipe interrupter should be sited at what minimum height above a urinal bowl when a pressure flushing valve is used?

a) 50mm   *c) 150mm*

b) 100mm   *d) 300mm*

20. Which of the following will usually require access to cold water system commissioning manuals on a large job?

a) Customer

b) Architect

c) Site agent

d) Plumber

This chapter builds on the revision completed at Level 2, Chapter 6: Hot water systems; you should therefore read through that chapter and familiarise yourself with its content prior to progressing through this Level 3 chapter. You should also read through Chapter 13: Advanced cold water systems, from the section on Water Regulations (page 214), through to and including the section on prevention of cross connection of unwholesome water supplies (page 246); these sections have common application to this chapter.

By the end of this chapter you should be able to demonstrate understanding of the following hot water systems topics which will assist you in completing knowledge assessment in the Hot Water Systems Unit of the Level 3 Certificate in Domestic Plumbing Studies:

- Sources of information:
  - Technical standards
- Water Regulation Requirements:
  - Expansion in vented systems
- Temperatures in hot water systems:
  - Hot water distribution temperatures
  - Temperature of hot water supplies at taps and on surfaces of hot water pipes
  - What is a thermostatic mixing valve?
  - Energy conservation
  - Secondary hot water systems
- Performance testing hot water systems.

Sources of information

There are a number of information sources that plumbers may have to use to obtain the necessary detail to undertake their work.

Technical standards

- Water Regulations – these lay down the statutory requirements that must be carried out when installing, commissioning and maintaining water systems. Responsibility for monitoring compliance with the Water Regulations is given to the local water undertakers. Water Regulations documentation can be freely downloaded from www.defra.gov.uk, who also produce a guidance document to the Water Regulations.
- Water Fittings & Materials Directory – this is produced by the Water Regulations Advisory Scheme (WRAS). It lists approved components and fittings for use in hot and cold water systems in the UK, and is freely accessible at www.wras.co.uk.
- British Standards – these support statutory documentation such as the Building Regulations, providing greater detail on installation requirements. Although British Standards are not statutory (legal) documents, they can be used in potential legal action relating to defective systems installation. The main British Standard relating to hot water supply is BS 6700 – Specification for design, installation, testing and maintenance of services supplying water for domestic use within buildings and their curtilages.

Water Regulation Requirements

The Regulations lay down the following requirements:

- a vented system should be provided with an appropriate temperature control and an open vent pipe to prevent the temperature of the hot water at any time exceeding 100°C
- no vent pipe over a primary circuit shall terminate over a storage cistern containing water for domestic supply
- no vent pipe from a secondary circuit shall terminate over any f&e cistern connecting to a primary circuit.

Figure 14.1 shows the proper method of termination of the vent pipes above their appropriate cisterns.

Remember

The minimum size of vent pipe for a primary and secondary system is 19mm (internal diameter).

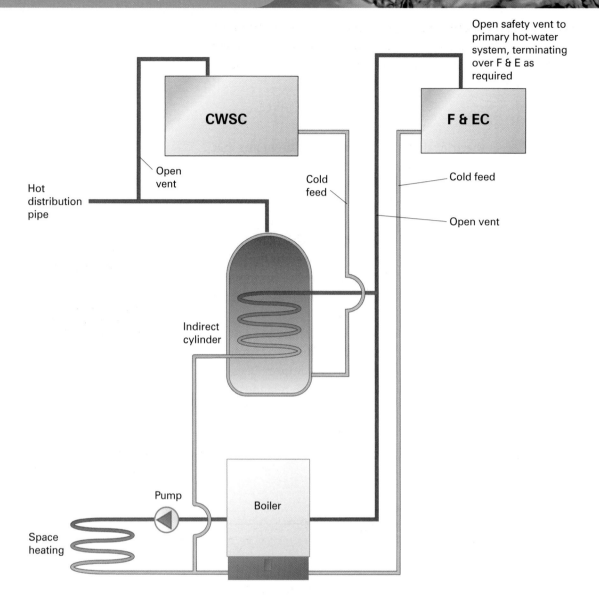

Figure 14.1 Vent pipe termination

- there should be thermostatic control provided to control the water temperature in the hot water storage vessel, this is usually set at 60–65°C.

Expansion in vented systems

When water is heated in both the primary and secondary hot water systems, the volume of water in either system increases by approximately 4%. In an open vented system this water is taken up in:

- secondary system – cold water storage cistern
- primary system – f&e cistern.

The result will be an increase in the water level in the cistern. Care must be taken when setting the water level in the cistern, as there must be a minimum air gap of 25mm between the finished (heated) water level in the cistern and the invert level of the cistern overflow.

Figure 14.2 shows an example of the float valve setting to accommodate the required dimension. Also shown is the minimum dimension that the float-operated valve must terminate over either the overflow or the float-operated valve.

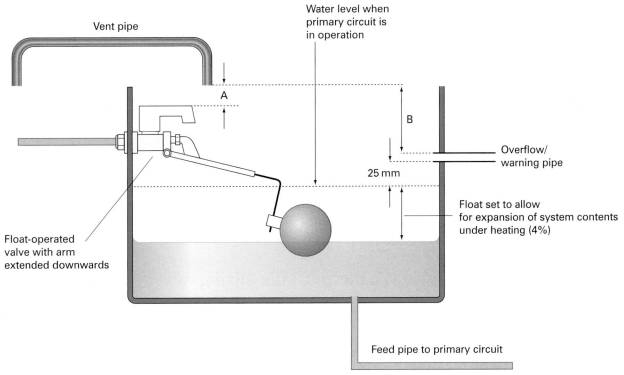

Figure 14.2 f&e cistern requirements

Temperatures in hot water systems

Hot water distribution temperatures

Hot water should be stored at a temperature of not less than 60°C and distributed at a temperature of not less than 55°C, these temperatures are important in minimising the growth of legionella bacteria. This water-distribution temperature may not be achievable where hot water is provided by instantaneous or combination boilers.

The maintenance of acceptable water temperatures may be achieved by efficient routing of pipes, reducing the lengths of pipes serving individual appliances and the application of good insulation practices to minimise freezing of cold water pipes and to promote energy conservation for hot water pipes.

Temperature of hot water supplies at taps and on surfaces of hot water pipes

Where practical, the hot water distribution system should be designed and installed to provide the required flow of water at terminal fittings to sanitary and other appliances at a water temperature of not less than 50°C and within 30 seconds after fully opening the tap. This criteria may not be achievable where hot water is provided by instantaneous or combination boilers.

Terminal fittings for communal showers in schools or public buildings, and in other facilities used by the public, should be supplied with water through thermostatic mixing valves so that the temperature of the water discharged at the outlets does not exceed 43°C.

The temperature of water discharged from terminal fittings and the surface temperature of any fittings in health-care premises should not exceed the temperatures recommended in HS(G)104 – Safe hot water and surface temperatures.

What is a thermostatic mixing valve?

Figure 14.3 Thermostatic mixing valve

Quite simply, it's a mixing valve (similar to a shower mixer valve) sited close to the point of use of higher-risk sanitary appliances – baths in particular. The valve takes a hot and cold supply and accurately blends the water temperature to a safe level for use. The manufacturer specification should be checked to establish the difference in pressure that the valve will work to (hot and cold) if the supply pressures are unequal – from supply pipe cold and distributing pipe hot. If a fault occurs in the system then the valve will only pass cold water, preventing scalding occurring. The valve will need to be set and adjusted to achieve the desired temperature on commissioning.

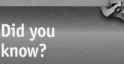

Did you know?

A terminal fitting is the technical name for hot and cold water outlets, such as taps and shower roses.

Did you know?

It is now considered good practice to install thermostatic mixing valves to control the water temperature in most secondary hot water systems fed from storage systems, particularly in properties where the very young, elderly or infirm live.

Did you know?

A thermostatic mixing valve should not be sited a long distance from the appliance(s) it is serving, as the mixed water temperature (around 40°C) is ideal for the proliferation of legionella bacteria.

Energy conservation

All water fittings forming part of a primary or secondary hot water circulation system and all pipes carrying hot water to a tap that are longer than the maximum length given in the table below should be thermally insulated in accordance with BS 5422.

Maximum recommended lengths of uninsulated hot water pipes	
Outside diameter of pipe in millimetres	Maximum length in metres
12	20
Over 12 and up to and including 22	12
Over 22 and up to and including 28	8
Over 28	3

Secondary hot water systems

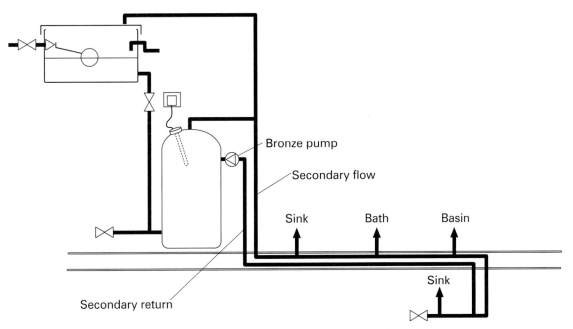

Figure 14.4 Secondary circulation system

The secondary circulation system as shown in Figure 14.4 may be used in a system with long dead-legs to overcome the problems associated with excessive wastage of hot water drawn off each time the tap is used. Key features of the system are:

- the system is usually pumped in the form of a loop
- all flow and return pipework must be insulated to minimise heat loss and the wastage of energy

- where there is more than one return leg (appliances) connecting back to the pump, the system will require balancing rather like a central heating system – this is also important in ensuring that water temperatures aren't low enough to promote the growth of legionella bacteria
- there must be a time control on the system to conserve energy if the building is not in 24-hour use.

Performance testing hot water systems

On completion of soundness testing of a hot water system, the installation needs to be performance tested. This includes:

- checking to ensure that the flow rate is correct at the various outlets – this can be checked using a device such as a weir cup shown in Figure 14.5; the flow rate should be checked against the requirements of the job specification/manufacturer instructions. The Water Regulations also include a table recommending minimum flow rates for appliances

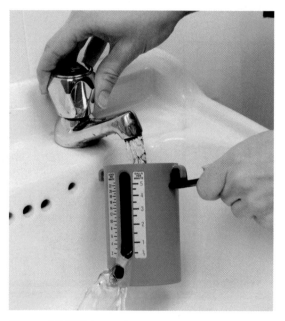

Figure 14.5 Weir cup in use

- checking to ensure that the water temperature at various points in the system meets design requirements:
  - cylinder storage minimum of 60°C
  - hot water pipework distribution temperature minimum of 55°C
  - hot water secondary return temperature of 50°C
  - water temperature at outlets (dependent on whether a mixing valve is installed) 40 to 50°C.

Water temperature is usually checked using a differential digital thermometer with immersion probes (immersed into hot water) and contact probes (to strap onto pipework).

Recommended design flow rates of cold and hot water to sanitary appliances

Outlet fitting or appliance	Rate of flow - litres/second	
	Design rate	Min. rate
WC cistern (to fill in 2 minutes)	0.13	0.05
WC pressure flushing valve (DN 20)	1.5	1
WC flushing trough (per WC served)	0.15	0.1
Urinal cistern (each position served)	0.004	0.002
Urinal flushing valve	0.3	0.15
Washbasin (pillar or mixer taps)	0.15	0.1
Handbasin (pillar or mixer taps)	0.1	0.07
Handbasin (spray or spray mixer taps)	0.05	0.03
Bidet	0.2	0.1
Bath (G ¾)	0.3	0.2
Bath (G 1)	0.6	0.4
Shower head	0.2	0.1
Kitchen sink (G ½)	0.2	0.1
Kitchen sink (G ¾)	0.3	0.2
Kitchen sink (G 1)	0.6	0.4
Washing machine	0.2	0.15
Dish-washing machine	0.15	0.1

1. Flow rates required for washing and dish-washing machines for other than single dwellings should be obtained from the manufacturer.
2. Mixer fittings or combination tap assemblies deliver less flow than two separate taps; it is suggested that 70 % of the above flow rates may be sufficient.
3. The rate of flow required to shower heads will depend on the type fitted; the advice of the shower manufacturer should be sought.
4. The above rates of flow to appliances are applicable where hot water centralised storage systems are installed. Where hot water systems incorporate instantaneous heaters or combination boilers the rates of flow shown in the Table may not be achievable and the system should be designed accordingly.

Figure 14.6 Recommended minimum hot and cold water flow rates

Short answer questions

1. What is the maximum temperature for stored hot water recommended by BS 6700?
2. What item of legislation details the requirements for the insulation of hot water storage cylinders?
3. When should hot water pipework that is to be concealed be tested for soundness?
4. Mixing of hot and cold water in a mixer valve is regarded as what fluid category risk under the Water Regulations?
5. What device should be installed in a secondary return pipework system to prevent reverse circulation when hot water is drawn off?
6. Does extension work on a hot water system in industrial premises require notification to the local water undertaker?
7. What type of device is used to control the operation of a shower pump if the shower rose is sited above the water level in the cold water storage cistern?
8. A hot water tap discharges water at 8 litres per minute. What is the flow rate in litres/second?
9. What is the recommended hot water temperature at the inlet to a mixing valve?
10. The vent pipe from a secondary hot water system should discharge over which cistern?

Multiple-choice test

1. A vent pipe is a safety feature in a hot water system designed to prevent water reaching what temperature?
   a) 50°C
   b) 60°C
   c) 65°C
   d) 100°C

2. Which of the following devices is installed in a secondary circulation system in a large domestic property as an economy measure?
   a) Check valve
   b) Mixing valve
   c) Time clock
   d) Temperature relief valve

3. Which of the following should be carried out immediately before performance testing a hot water system in a dwelling?
   a) System flushing
   b) System disinfection
   c) Soundness testing
   d) Visual inspection

4. What concentration of chlorine should be applied at the beginning of the disinfection process on a hot water system?
   a) 30PPM
   b) 50PPM
   c) 75PPM
   d) 100PPM

5. What type of device controls the temperature at hot water outlets?
   a) Pressure-reducing valve
   b) Check valve
   c) Mixing valve
   d) Temperature relief valve

6. Details of the commissioning requirements of a single-point water heater will be found in:
   a) Manufacturer's catalogue
   b) Site drawings
   c) Installation instructions
   d) Work programme

7. The performance testing of hot water taps will include as a minimum tests for:
   a) pH value and temperature
   b) Flow rate and pH value
   c) Temperature and flow rate
   d) Flow rate and velocity

8. In which type of water-heating device could the temperature of water be described as being inversely proportional to the flow rate?
   a) Instantaneous water heater
   b) Indirect cylinder
   c) Direct cylinder
   d) Electric shower

9. What type of backflow protection should be provided to an ascending-spray bidet fed from a supply pipe?
   a) Type AA air gap
   b) Type ED check valve
   c) RPZ valve
   d) The installation is not allowed

10. What type of device may have to be fitted to a high-pressure hot water pipeline to a basin fitted with lever-operated taps, to guard against damage to the taps, if the pipeline contains a single-check valve?
    a) *Pressure relief valve*
    b) *Mixing valve*
    c) *Shock arrestor*
    d) *Thermostat*

11. What is the maximum recommended uninsulated length of draw-off for a 22mm pipe in a hot water system?
    a) *5m*   c) *10m*
    b) *7m*   d) *12m*

12. Which of the following provides a constant flow of water in an instantaneous water heater?
    a) *Governor*
    b) *Expansion valve*
    c) *Temperature relief valve*
    d) *Solenoid valve*

13. A device fitted to an immersion heater to guard against failure of the control thermostat is called a:
    a) *Temperature relief valve*
    b) *Solenoid*
    c) *Energy cut-out device*
    d) *Residual current device*

14. What is the minimum distance between the finished (heated) water level and the invert level of the warning pipe in an f&e cistern?
    a) *10mm*   c) *50mm*
    b) *25mm*   d) *100mm*

15. Which of the following may need to be advised when commissioning a hot water system in an occupied dwelling?
    a) *Water inspector*
    b) *Building control officer*
    c) *Architect*
    d) *Customer*

By the end of this chapter you should be able to demonstrate understanding of the following unvented hot water systems topics which will assist you in completing knowledge assessment in the Complex Domestic Hot Water Systems Unit of the Level 3 Certificate in Domestic Plumbing Studies:

- Sources of information:
  - Technical standards
- Types of unvented hot water system
- The components of an unvented hot water storage system:
  - Storage cylinders
  - System controls and devices
  - Other controls
- Key Building Regulation Requirements:
  - Specification of the unvented system
  - Specific requirements of direct systems
  - Specific requirements of indirect systems
  - Competence of installers
  - System notification requirements
  - Discharge pipe requirements
- Key unvented system installation requirements:
  - Incoming water supply pressure and flow rate
  - Unvented hot water system component sizes
  - Unvented hot water systems and uncontrollable heat sources
  - Balanced or unbalanced supply
  - Control system application
- Commissioning unvented hot water systems
- Service and maintenance of unvented hot water systems:
  - Servicing requirements
  - Typical faults on unvented systems.

Sources of information

There are a number of information sources that lay down the requirements for the installation and maintenance of unvented hot water systems.

Technical standards

- Building Regulations – these lay down the statutory requirements that must be carried out when dealing with the installation of unvented hot water systems. Copies of the Building Regulations can be freely downloaded from the website of the Department of Communities and Local Government – www.communities.gov.uk. The installation of all unvented hot water systems needs to be notified to the local authority prior to installation, or the work needs to be undertaken by a firm who is a member of a competent persons scheme.
- Water Regulations – these lay down the statutory requirements that must be followed when installing, commissioning and maintaining unvented hot water systems. In unvented hot water systems terms they lay down the requirements of functional controls aimed at water conservation, undue consumption and contamination of the supply pipework. Responsibility for monitoring compliance with the Water Regulations is given to the local water undertakers. Water Regulations documentation can be freely downloaded from www. defra.gov.uk, who also produce a guidance document to the Water Regulations outlining requirements for unvented hot water systems.
- Manufacturer instructions – these are provided by appliance or component manufacturers to outline the installation, commissioning and maintenance requirements of their products. Manufacturer instructions usually take precedence over British Standards but should not conflict with Building or Water Regulations, which are statutory (legal) requirements.

Types of unvented hot water system

The Building Regulations Part G3 apply to unvented hot water storage systems with a storage capacity of more than 15 litres. For the purposes of the Building Regulations the following systems are not categorised as unvented hot water systems:

- storage systems with vessels with a storage capacity of 15 litres or less
- systems providing space heating only
- systems providing water to industrial process plants.

Under the Building Regulations stringent safety control devices are in place for any system storing more than 15 litres. Systems with a storage capacity of less than 15 litres are subject to less stringent requirements and the safety control devices in these systems are as specified by the manufacturer. Systems with vessels of 15 litres or less capacity are usually:

- instantaneous water heaters, e.g. combination boilers, or
- small, single-point under-sink heaters, e.g. displacement heater.

Key fact

Key Building Regulations
Part G of the regulations deals with safety issues relating to unvented hot water systems.

Part L of the of the regulations deals with the energy conservation of systems.

Definition
Under the Building Regulations an unvented hot water storage system is defined as a hot water storage system incorporating a storage vessel that does not have an open vent to the atmosphere.

Note:

Some high-flow combination boilers (often classified as instantaneous water heaters) store more than 15 litres of water and are therefore unvented hot water storage systems, they must by law include the full range of unvented system control components required in the Building/Water Regulations.

Figure 15.1 shows the most popular types of unvented hot water storage system.

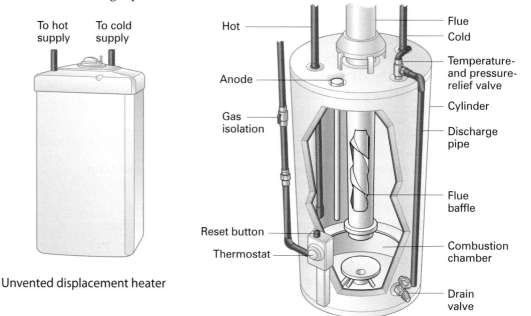

Unvented displacement heater

Gas fired unvented storage heater

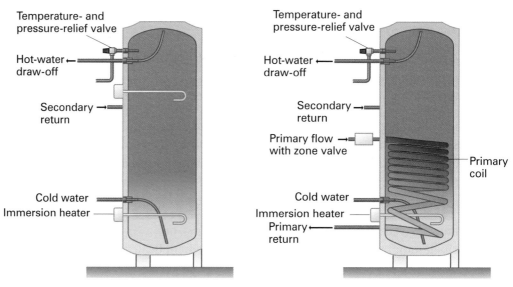

Directed unvented cylinder

Indirect unvented cylinder

Figure 15.1 Types of unvented hot water system

The components of an unvented hot water storage system

Storage cylinders

Storage cylinders must be capable of meeting the requirements of Approved Document L of the Building Regulations relating to energy conservation. The Regulations stipulate that cylinders should be manufactured to BS 7206 – Specification for unvented hot water storage units and packages – which includes minimum requirements for the insulation of the cylinder and the surface area of the heating coil in an indirect system. Cylinders for unvented systems are usually manufactured from:

- copper – this was used in the earliest systems to the UK market but does not now tend to be used owing to the thickness of copper required to withstand the required water pressures. These early systems were typically restricted to a maximum operating water pressure of 2 bar to make the thickness of copper economical in manufacture. These cylinders may have also included a sacrificial anode to protect against some water corrosive effects
- mild-steel lined – these cylinders are manufactured from mild steel coated with a lining material, usually either glass or polythene. They were relatively common when unvented systems were first introduced to the UK, however, there are not many new cylinders manufactured from these materials. A magnesium rod sacrificial anode was essential with this type of cylinder material because there could be the possibility of slight imperfections in the surface of the lining or coating material to the cylinder
- stainless steel – most modern cylinders are manufactured from stainless steel, in most cases a sacrificial anode will not be required with this type of material.

Mild-steel lined and stainless-steel cylinders are suited to higher system-operating pressures than their copper counterparts, typically 3 to 3.5 bar pressure.

System controls and devices

An unvented hot water system contains a series of control devices, classified either as:

- safety devices – to protect the user and the property against the possible effects of overheating/excessive temperatures in the system (see Figure 15.3), or
- functional devices – protecting the water supply (see Figure 15.4).

Figure 15.2 Indirect unvented hot water storage system

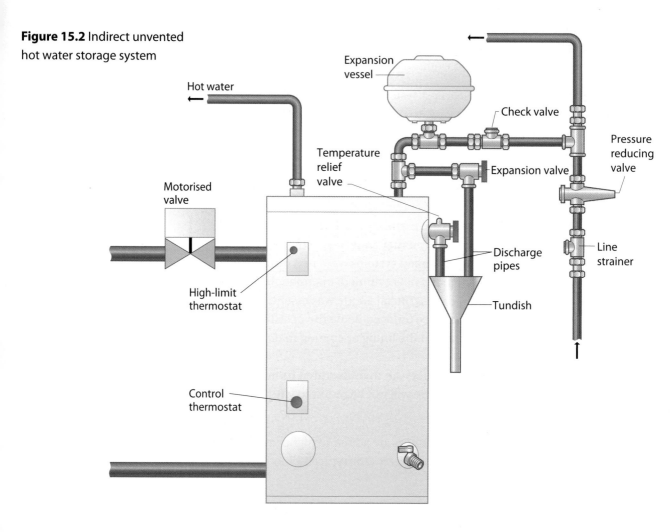

Safety controls

A three-tier level of safety protection is provided to ensure that overheating does not take place:

- the control thermostat (linked to the motorised valve) is set by the user to achieve the desired water temperature in the cylinder
- the high-limit thermostat (permanently set at a fixed temperature higher than the control thermostat and linked to the motorised valve) closes the motorised valve at a fixed water temperature if the control thermostat fails
- the temperature-relief valve activates at a fixed water temperature in the event that both the other temperature control devices fail.

Safety controls

Safety item 1	Control thermostat	Controls the water temperature in the cylinder to between 60 and 65°C
Safety item 2	High limit thermostat (energy cut-out device)	A non-self-resetting device that isolates the heat source at a temperature of around 80–85°C
Safety item 3	Temperature-relief valve	Discharges water from the cylinder at a temperature of 90–95°C (water is dumped from the system and replaced by cooler water to prevent boiling)

Figure 15.3 Safety controls

Functional controls

Line strainer	Prevents grit and debris entering the system from the water supply (causing the controls to malfunction)
Pressure-reducing valve (on older systems may be pressure-limiting valve)	Establishes a fixed maximum operating pressure in the system. The valve is pre-set by the manufacturer (not adjustable by the installer) usually at a pressure in modern systems of between 3 to 3.5 bar
Single check valve	Stops expanded hot water from entering the cold water supply pipe (a fluid category 2 contamination risk)
Expansion vessel or cylinder air gap	Takes up the increased volume of water in the system from the heating process
Expansion valve	Operates if the pressure in the system rises above the design limits of the expansion device (i.e. the cylinder air gap or expansion vessel fails). The expansion valve is not adjustable by the installer and will usually be set at a pressure of around 6 bar in modern systems
Isolating (stop) valve (not shown)	Isolates the water supply from the system (for maintenance purposes)

Figure 15.4 Functional controls

Other controls

Tundish

The temperature-relief and expansion valves discharge water to waste via connecting discharge pipes if a fault occurs in the system. The discharge pipes must be fitted with a tundish in order that:

- an air break is formed to guard against potential blockage in the discharge pipework which could prevent the temperature-relief or expansion valves working correctly. In the event that the discharge pipe becomes blocked, water would discharge at the tundish, resulting in a possible flood, the system would however be safe
- water discharging from the system under fault conditions may be visible at the air gap, showing that the system needs to be repaired.

Figure 15.5 Tundish

Composite valves

Modern unvented hot water storage systems tend to be supplied with composite control valves. This type of valve contains a number of control functions in the one unit, in the case of the valve shown in Figure 15.6 – pressure-reducing valve, line strainer, expansion valve and single-check valve.

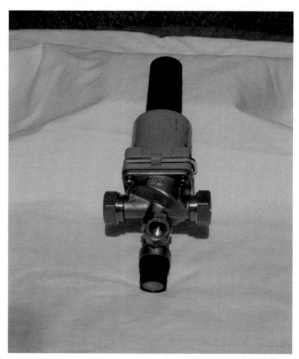

Figure 15.6 Composite valve

Expansion vessels and possible water contamination

A standard single-entry expansion vessel such as that shown in Figure 15.7 can act as a dead leg in the system, resulting in the water in it changing little. In certain conditions the water can stagnate and bacteria grows on the surface of the flexible diaphragm of the vessel, presenting a water-contamination risk. This problem can be overcome in one of two ways:

- by using a throughflow expansion vessel – the cold water supply flows directly through the inlet and outlet connections of the vessel, preventing possible stagnation
- by providing an anti-legionella valve – fitted to the inlet of a single-entry vessel, the valve uses a venturi effect to maintain circulation in the vessel under normal flow conditions and so prevent stagnation taking place.

Figure 15.7 Single-entry expansion vessel

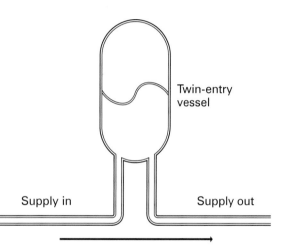

Figure 15.8 Throughflow expansion vessel

Key Building Regulation Requirements

The following outlines the key requirements of unvented hot water systems as outlined in the Building Regulations, aimed at ensuring the safe installation of the system.

The key aims of the Regulations are:

- to ensure that precautions are in place to at any time prevent the temperature of stored water from reaching **100°C**
- To ensure that in a faulted system hot water is **safely** discharged to waste.

Specification of the unvented system

The Building Regulations require that an unvented system is supplied in either a **package** or a **unit** form, i.e. in a kit form provided by the manufacturer. All the components of the system must be tested and approved to ensure that they will work effectively together, therefore it is not acceptable for the plumber to self-build a system with a range of components, the design of which is devised by him/herself.

A unit or package that is installed must be fully approved, approvals include:

- a member of the European Organisation for Technical Approvals (EOTA), e.g. in the UK the BBA or WRAS
- a certification body approved by the United Kingdom Accreditation Service (UKAS) and testing to the requirements of an accepted standard such as BS 7206
- independent assessment clearly showing equivalent performance to those above.

The unvented package

Most modern systems are supplied as packages. Figure 15.9 shows the items that are factory assembled and those that are supplied by the manufacturer to be assembled by the installer.

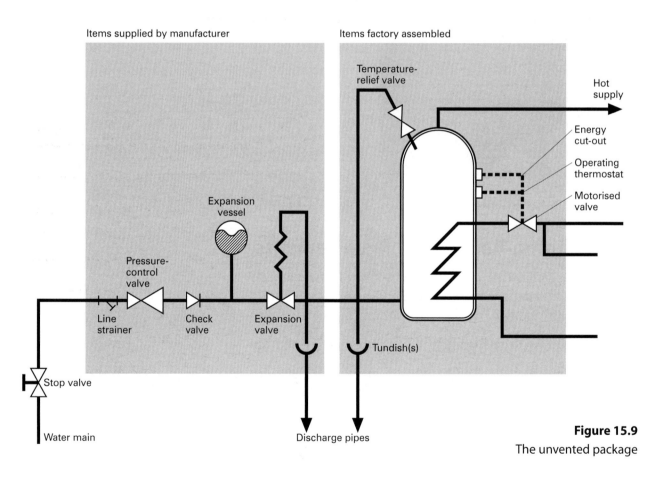

Figure 15.9
The unvented package

Factory-fitted parts:

- temperature-relief valve
- high-limit thermostat
- cylinder thermostat.

Parts that are supplied by the manufacturer and fitted by the installer:

- line strainer
- cylinder primary motorised valve (indirect unit)
- pressure-reducing valve
- single-check valve
- tundish
- expansion vessel
- expansion valve.

The unvented unit

Here all the control devices are factory assembled by the manufacturer. Early unvented systems to the UK market were supplied as units, however most now are packages.

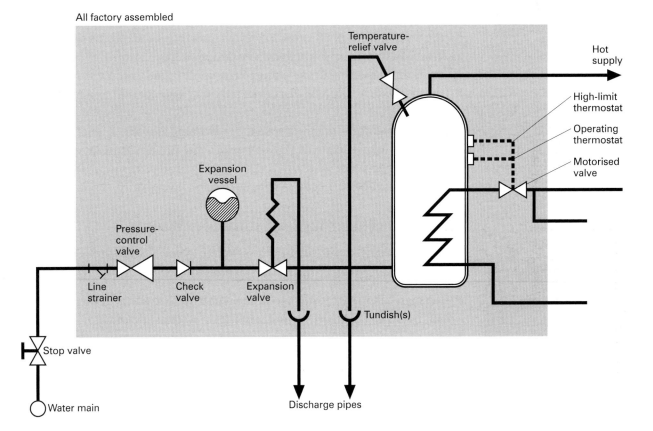

Figure 15.10 The unvented unit

All the safety devices and functional controls are factory-fitted by the manufacturer:

- line strainer
- pressure-reducing valve
- single-check valve
- tundish
- expansion vessel
- expansion valve
- temperature-relief valve
- high-limit thermostat and cylinder primary motorised valve (indirect unit).

Specific requirements of direct systems

Building Regulations Approved Document G3 says that in addition to the user control (cylinder thermostat) there should be a minimum of two temperature-activated safety devices operating in sequence:

- a non-self-resetting thermal cut-out device (high-limit thermostat), and
- one or more temperature-relief valves.

In all cases:

- the temperature-relief valve should be directly located on the storage vessel so that it can sense the water temperature
- the temperature-relief valve must be properly sized to suit the system
- the valves should not be disconnected other than for maintenance or repair
- each temperature-relief valve should discharge via a short length of metal pipe (referred to as D1) and be of a size not less than the outlet size of the temperature relief valve, discharging through an air break over a tundish located vertically as near as possible to the valve.

Specific requirements of indirect systems

Indirect systems require the same controls as direct systems and in addition:

- the high-limit thermostat should be wired up to a mortised valve to cut off the water flow to the cylinder in the event of overheating
- if the system includes a boiler then the thermal cut-out (high limit thermostat) may be on the boiler. Some manufacturers produce unvented cylinder and boiler kits that must be fitted together – these can take advantage of minimising the number of thermostats by having one energy cut-out on the boiler, i.e. in an overheat situation the boiler is de-activated when its water temperature reaches 85°C, removing the need for an additional thermostat on the cylinder
- the temperature-relief valve and discharge pipe requirements are as per the direct system

Remember

An unvented system must incorporate a three-tier level of temperature protection designed to prevent 100°C being reached.

Remember

A key check when maintaining unvented hot water systems is to check that any immersion heater contains two thermostats and that they are properly wired; electricians have been known to 'bridge' the cut-out device, resulting in an unsafe situation.

- where an indirect system has an alternative (back-up) direct method of heating such as an immersion heater fitted, then a thermal cut-out device must be provided on the back-up device as well.

Competence of installers

Under the Building Regulations the unvented hot water storage system must be installed by a competent person. Competency is identified as an operative holding a registered operative identity card issued by one of the following:

- Construction Industry Training Board (CITB)
- Institute of Plumbing and Heating Engineering (IPHE)
- Association of Installers of Unvented Hot Water Systems (Scotland and Northern Ireland)
- individuals on the list of approved installers published by the BBA up to 31 December 1991
- an equivalent body – newer bodies such as BPEC, NIC Certification and Logic Certification offer unvented certification following the introduction of the current Part G in 1992.

System notification requirements

An unvented hot water system must either:

- be notified (for a fee) to the local building control office prior to the installation taking place (notification includes the completion of forms primarily detailing the competence of the installer and detailing that the unvented unit or package has been fully tested and approved by a recognised body), or
- be installed by a firm that is a member of a Department of Communities and Local Government (DCLG) approved Competent Persons Scheme.

If the notification route is chosen then the work must not take place until it has been approved by the local authority and a decision will be made by the authority as to whether to inspect the work or not.

Did you know?

Competent-persons schemes were introduced in plumbing and heating in April 2006 as an alternative to notification for certain types of work including unvented hot water system installation.

Discharge pipe requirements

One of the most important points to consider when siting an unvented hot water storage system is the routing of the discharge pipework so that in a fault situation water can safely discharge to waste.

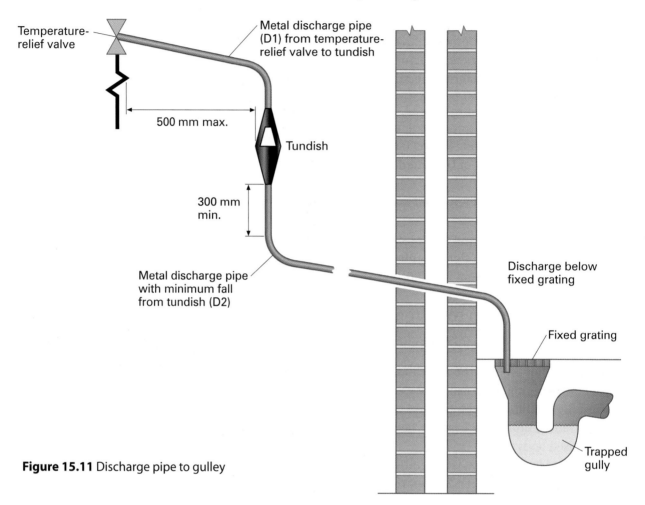

Figure 15.11 Discharge pipe to gulley

Discharge pipework from an unvented hot water system is split into two sections:

- the pipework section from the temperature-relief valve to the tundish (D1), and
- the pipework from the tundish to the discharge point (D2).

D1 Pipe Requirements

The Regulations regarding D1 state that:

- the tundish should be vertical and located in the same space as the storage cylinder. The tundish must be sited within 500mm maximum distance of the temperature-relief valve
- the D1 pipe size must be at least the same size as the outlet from the temperature-relief valve.

It is now common for the D1 pipe to contain the outlet pipework from the expansion valve as well as the temperature-relief valve as shown in Figure 15.12.

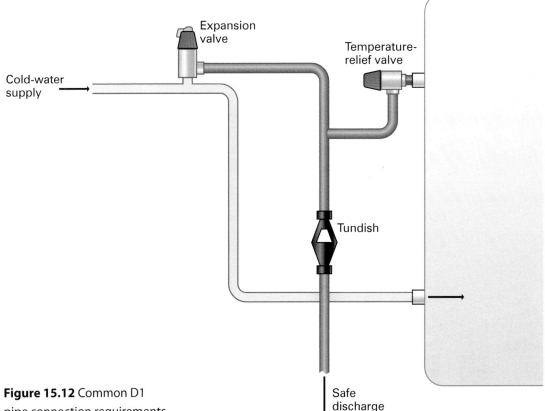

Figure 15.12 Common D1 pipe connection requirements

When connecting both pipes together the maximum distance of 500mm between the temperature-relief valve outlet and the tundish still applies. Care needs to be taken to ensure that the pipework falls continuously from both valves to the tundish, so the position of the cold water pipework will need to be considered in order that the expansion valve can be properly sited to ensure its outlet pipework falls to the tundish.

D2 Pipe Requirements

Requirements for the D2 pipe section are:

- it should fall continuously from the tundish outlet to its discharge point and discharge in a safe place where there is no risk to persons in the vicinity
- it should be of metal; plastics that can cope with high temperature applications are now sometimes used
- it should be at least one pipe size larger that the outlet size of the temperature-relief valve; unless its total hydraulic resistance exceeds 9m in length, discharge pipework with a total hydraulic resistance of between 9m and 18m in length should be at least two pipe sizes larger than the temperature-relief valve outlet, between 18m and 27m total

Did you know?

Plastic D2 pipework is now sometimes used. When the Regulations were introduced in 1992, plastics were not readily available for this purpose, but they are now.

hydraulic resistance at least three sizes larger, and so on. Bends are included in the total hydraulic resistance calculation

- there must be a vertical section of pipe at least 300mm in length below the tundish to the first bend or elbow
- it should be visible at both its inlet and outlet; where this is difficult there must be clear visibility at a minimum of one of these points
- where a common D2 pipe is to be used, say in a block of flats, there should be no more than six systems connecting to the common discharge pipe and the common discharge pipe should be at least one pipe size larger than the largest individual discharge pipe connecting to it
- if discharge pipework is installed in properties such as those occupied by blind people, then consideration should be given to the installation of an electronically operated device to give warning when a fault is occurring.

Discharge pipes may be terminated as follows:

- **low level into a gulley** – as shown in Figure 15.11 this tends to be the preferred and safest option for terminating a discharge pipe

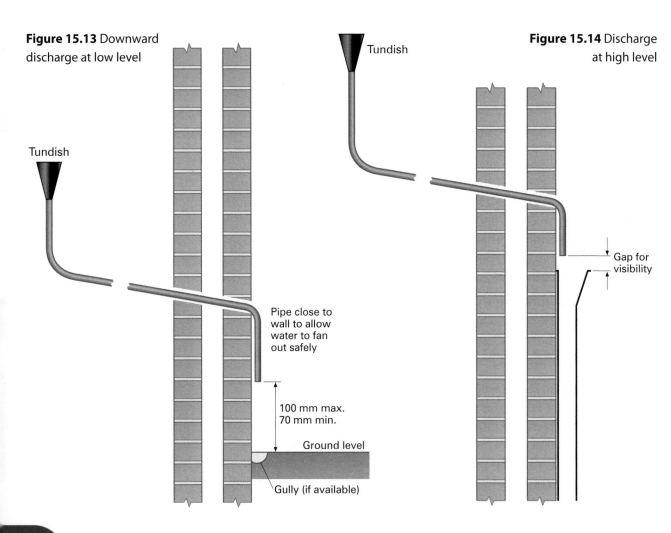

Figure 15.13 Downward discharge at low level

Tundish

Pipe close to wall to allow water to fan out safely

100 mm max.
70 mm min.

Ground level

Gully (if available)

Figure 15.14 Discharge at high level

Tundish

Gap for visibility

- downward discharge at low level – discharge must be within a vertical height of 100mm of a hard standing, grassed area, etc. If children are likely to come into contact with the pipe end, a wire cage or similar guard must be used

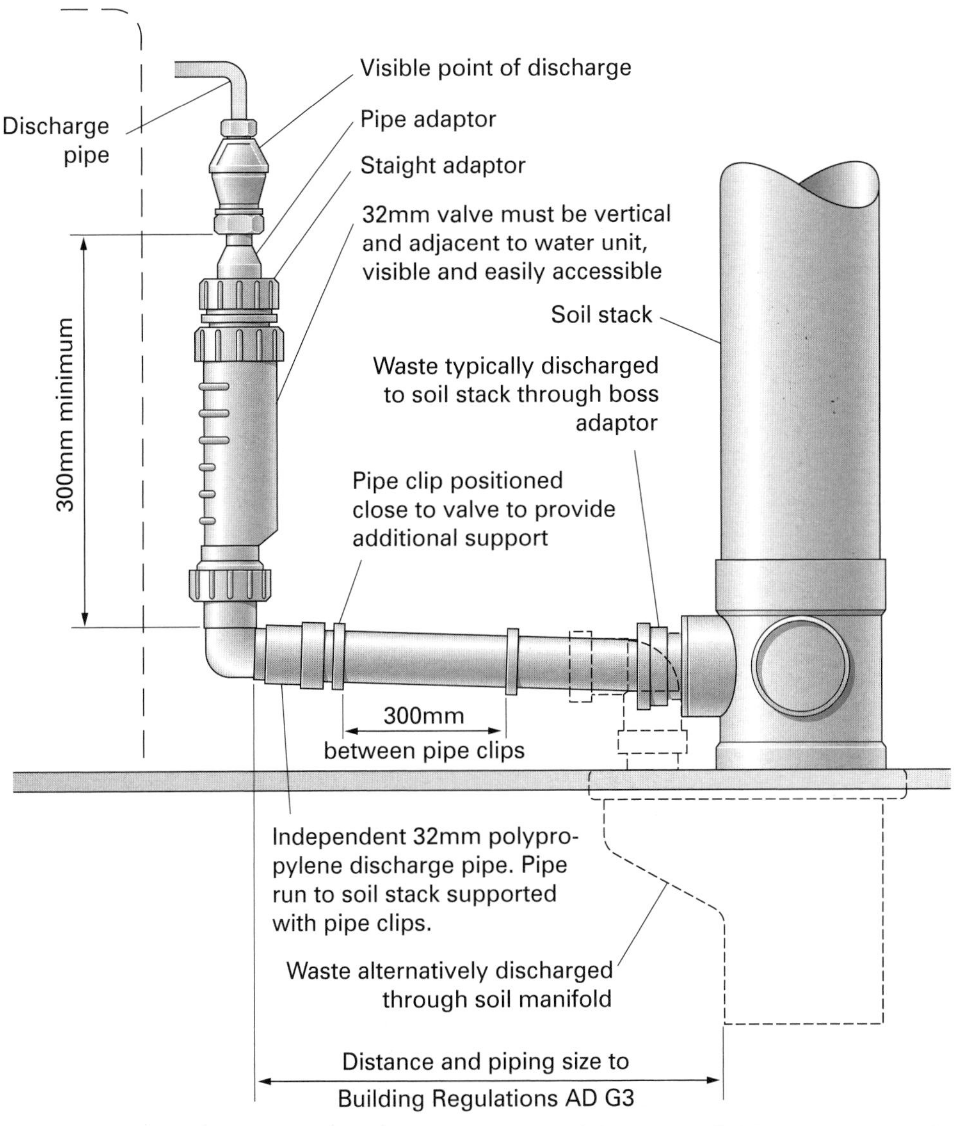

Figure 15.15 Discharge via HEPvO valve to soil system

Discharge pipe

Visible point of discharge

Pipe adaptor

Staight adaptor

32mm valve must be vertical and adjacent to water unit, visible and easily accessible

Soil stack

Waste typically discharged to soil stack through boss adaptor

Pipe clip positioned close to valve to provide additional support

300mm minimum

300mm between pipe clips

Independent 32mm polypro-pylene discharge pipe. Pipe run to soil stack supported with pipe clips.

Waste alternatively discharged through soil manifold

Distance and piping size to Building Regulations AD G3

- **discharge at high level** – discharge may be made to a high-level metal hopper or onto a roof capable of standing high-temperature discharges with at least 3m distance before the water reaches any plastic guttering that may melt

- **discharge via HEPvO valve to soil system** – this is a relatively new method of connecting a discharge pipe, usually in a block of flats where it can be extremely difficult to terminate the pipework in a safe place. Key features are that the soil and waste pipework must be in a material capable of withstanding high water temperatures (most plastic waste systems are) and the remaining requirements of the D2 pipework must be met

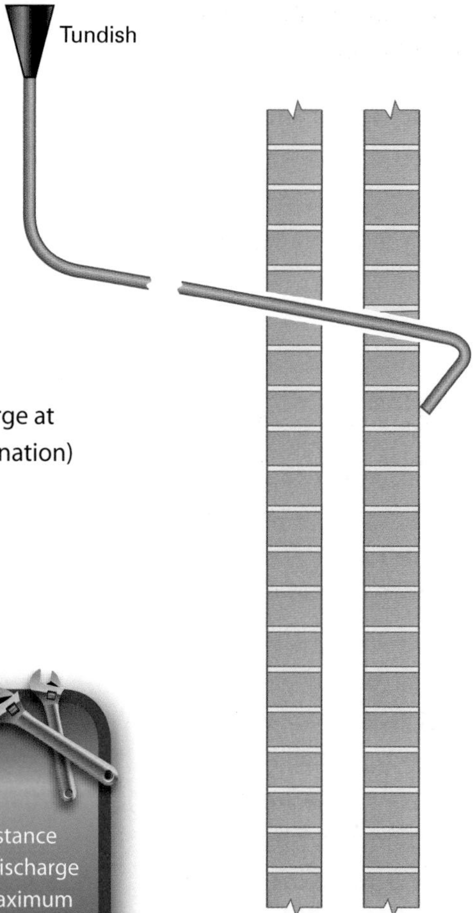

Tundish

Figure 15.16 Discharge at high level (wall termination)

- **discharge at high level (wall termination)** – as a last resort it may be possible to discharge the outlet at high level, provided it is terminated in such a way as to direct the flow of water against the external wall surface using the wall surface to cool the water – so no splashing is allowed. A minimum height must be achieved between the pipe outlet and the highest point on the wall that may be in the reach of anyone coming into contact with it, i.e. the water must be well below a scalding temperature by the time it can be touched.

Sizing the D2 pipe

We mentioned earlier that the D2 pipe needed sizing, the following chart is used in this process.

An example of using the table is shown below.

Valve outlet size	Minimum size of discharge pipe D1	Minimum size of discharge pipe D2 from tundish	Maximum resistance allowed, expressed as a length of straight pipe (i.e. no elbows or bends	Resistance created by each elbow or bend
G1/2	15 mm	22 mm	Up to 9 m	0.8 m
		28 mm	Up to 18 m	1.0 m
		35 mm	Up to 27 m	1.4 m
G3/4	22 mm	28 mm	Up to 9 m	1.0 m
		35 mm	Up to 18 m	1.4 m
		42 mm	Up to 27 m	1.7 m
G1	28 mm	35 mm	Up to 9 m	1.4 m
		42 mm	Up to 18 m	1.7 m
		54 mm	Up to 27 m	2.3 m

Figure 15.17 Discharge pipe size table

What is the required D2 pipe size for a G½ temperature-relief valve if the proposed discharge pipe length is 7m and includes four elbows?

From the table, 22mm is the smallest D2 pipe size with a maximum permitted run of 9m (including any elbows or bends):

- the resistance created by four elbows at 0.8m loss each = 3.2m
- the maximum permitted straight length of pipe in this case is 9.0m less 3.2m for the fittings = 5.8m
- 5.8m is less than the actual length of 7m, therefore 22mm is unacceptable.

The next pipe size up is 28mm with a maximum permitted pipe run of 18m:

- the resistance created by 4 elbows at 1.0m loss each = 4.0m
- the maximum permitted straight length of pipe in this case is 18.0m less 4.0m for the fittings = 14.0m
- 14.0m is greater than the actual length of 7m, therefore 22mm is acceptable.

Key unvented system installation requirements

There are a number of key issues to resolve relating to the installation of unvented systems.

Incoming water supply pressure and flow rate

There must be sufficient incoming water supply pressure and flow rate in order to permit an unvented hot water system to operate correctly and avoid customer complaint. There are two key issues to be checked at the design stage prior to the installation taking place:

- is there significant fluctuation in the supply over a 24-hour period? Some mains supply pipework may be old and under-sized, resulting in the water pressure and flow rate dropping to unacceptable levels at periods of peak draw-off in the area. This can be checked by speaking to the customer at the pricing stage, or by contacting the local water undertaker who may be able to provide advice. An unvented hot water system is not likely to be a good choice of system in circumstances where the supply pressure and flow dip below the minimum recommended by the manufacturer for significant periods of the day
- to establish that the supply pressure and flow rate meet the minimum requirements as laid down by the manufacturer of the appliance, details will usually be provided in the installation instructions, as a rule of thumb this will typically be a minimum of 1.5 bar pressure and 20 litres per minute flow rate.

Remember

An unvented hot water system is designed to exploit the benefits achieved through good water supply pressures and flow rates.

Did you know?

Water pressure is usually measured by taking a standing pressure test at an outlet in the system.

Flow rate is usually measured using a flow-measuring device such as a weir cup (gauge).

Unvented hot water system component sizes

Unvented hot water systems should be properly sized to ensure that they provide a desired performance. The key standard to which the system should be designed is BS 6700 – Specification for design, installation, testing and maintenance of services supplying water for domestic use within buildings and their curtilages. There are however a number of rules of thumb that may be applied to component sizing in the smaller system:

Unvented cylinder size

Most manufacturers produce a simple chart as shown in Figure 15.18, with recommendations on a minimum cylinder size to suit various circumstances.

Property type and plumbing supply requirements	Indirect (l)	Direct (l)
1-bedroom apartment, 1 shower	125	145
2-bedroom house, 1 bath, 1 shower	142	185
3-bedroom house, 1 bath, 1 shower	185	210
2/3 bedroom house, 2 baths, 1 shower/ en suite	210	250
4/5 bedroom house, 2 baths, 1 shower/ en suite	250	300
Larger houses	300	300

Figure 15.18 Cylinder size table

Pipework size

Plumbers sometimes make a mistake in thinking that because the unvented system works off the mains supply pipework, the pipe sizes will in the main be smaller than a vented system. This is not usually true, for the following reasons:

- the flow rate demands on a pipe supplying a domestic property with an unvented hot water system will be higher than a vented system, as all outlets (hot and cold) are drawing off that pipe rather than just the cold and cistern feeds
- the flow rate after the pressure-reducing valve is usually reduced due to the need to limit the incoming pressure
- outlets higher than the pressure-reducing valve are subject to a 0.1 bar reduction in head per metre above the valve.

As a result a domestic property with a single bathroom will typically require hot and cold mains pipework to be sized at 22mm, with branches to individual appliances reduced to 15mm in the case of baths, or possibly less with basins. With the larger system and pipe sizing there is no option other than to go back to basics and size the pipework correctly.

Unvented hot water systems and uncontrollable heat sources

Unvented hot water systems should not normally be supplied from uncontrollable heat sources such as solid-fuel boilers or solar water-heating circuits, this is because it is difficult to rapidly isolate the heat supply in an overheat situation; their installation is therefore not normally permitted under the Building Regulations.

Balanced or unbalanced supply

The position of the pressure-reducing valve can have a significant effect on pressures throughout the system at the various outlets. It is always advisable to endeavour to achieve a **balanced pressure system** (as shown below) in which both hot and cold water outlets are operating at the same supply pressure. In fact this can be essential in ensuring that mixer taps in high-pressure water systems work and can be adjusted correctly by the user.

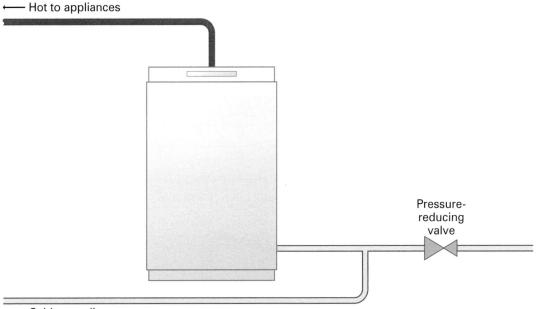

← Hot to appliances

Pressure-reducing valve

← Cold to appliances

Figure 15.19 Balanced supply pressure

The alternative to the balanced supply is the **unbalanced supply** in which one or more of the cold water supplies are taken off before the pressure-reducing valve creating an unbalanced supply at appliance hot and cold outlets. An unbalanced supply is undesirable in a system containing mixer valves. Composite valves tend to present a problem in terms of achieving a balanced supply in a system, because the composite valve must usually be sited in the airing cupboard near to the cylinder, and this may mean installing additional piping to take the cold supply direct up to the valve in the airing cupboard, then feeding back to all cold water outlets in the property from the pressure-reducing valve.

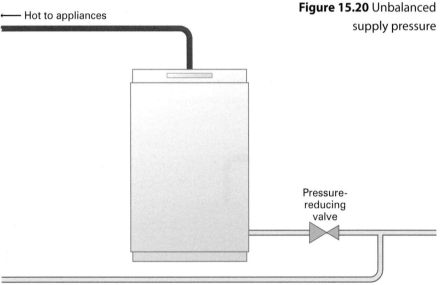

Figure 15.20 Unbalanced supply pressure

← Hot to appliances

Pressure-reducing valve

← Cold to appliances

If an unbalanced supply is unavoidable then care needs to be taken with mixer taps that permit the mixing of hot and cold water in the valve body.

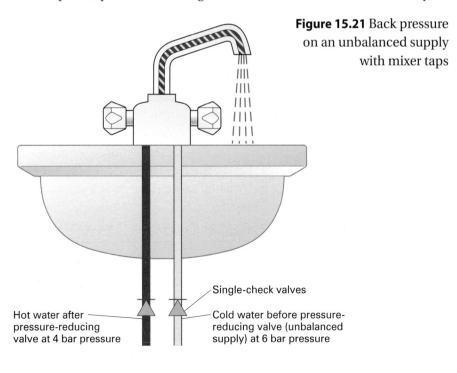

Figure 15.21 Back pressure on an unbalanced supply with mixer taps

Single-check valves

Hot water after pressure-reducing valve at 4 bar pressure

Cold water before pressure-reducing valve (unbalanced supply) at 6 bar pressure

With both taps open the unbalanced cold water supply can back pressurise the system through the hot water supply pipework, causing the expansion valve to nuisance discharge and waste water as a likely result. To overcome this problem, single-check valves must be fitted to the pipework connecting each mixer tap in which mixing in the valve body can take place, as shown in Figure 15.21.

Control system application

Unvented hot water systems are only suited to installation in a fully pumped system, as they require positive isolation of the primary heating circuit in the event of an overheat situation occurring. Control systems that are suitable include:

- 2 x two-port valve arrangement (S plan)
- mid-position valve arrangement (Y plan).

The mid-position valve arrangement does not however provide full isolation of the hot water circuit in all operating conditions and therefore an additional two-port valve must be fitted to the hot water circuit to provide positive isolation. This may require the installation of an additional wiring relay to ensure that the three-port and two-port valve can work together.

Commissioning unvented hot water systems

The following outlines a typical commissioning procedure for an unvented hot water system.

1. When commissioning a system that you haven't installed, the first check is to establish that all items supplied are those supplied by the manufacturer as part of the system.
2. All system component connections should be checked for tightness, especially those made at the factory (they may have come loose in transit).
3. Check that the operating thermostat setting is 60°C to 65°C.
4. Before filling the system, check that the expansion vessel pre-charge pressure is according to manufacturer's instructions. The pressure point is usually on the top of the vessel, under a plastic cap. Vessels are normally supplied with the correct charge pressure. Note: Vessel pre-charge details will be found stamped on the expansion vessel or included in the manufacturer's instructions. For bubble tops, the air gap will be established on filling the system.
5. Make sure the drain valve is closed, then open the highest hot and cold water taps and other fittings.
6. As part of the initial filling procedure it is important to ensure that the system is thoroughly flushed. The flushing procedure should be undertaken in two stages:

Did you know?

The Benchmark Logbook for unvented hot water systems is regarded as a standard method of recording commissioning details for systems as required by the plumbing and heating industry under the Building Regulations.

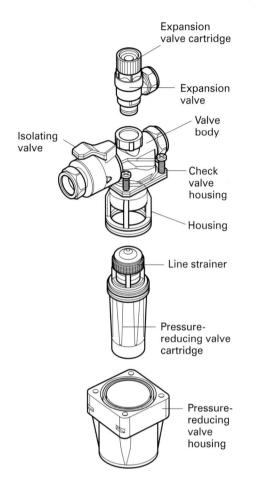

Expansion valve cartridge

Expansion valve

Valve body

Isolating valve

Check valve housing

Housing

Line strainer

Pressure-reducing valve cartridge

Pressure-reducing valve housing

Figure 15.22 Composite pressure-reducing valve assembly

Stage 1 – line strainer (usually part of the pressure-reducing valve)

The line strainer should be removed and water flushed through to ensure that any debris is removed from the pipework up to the strainer. The strainer should then be reassembled.

Stage 2 – open cold water supply stop valve and allow the cylinder to fill with water.

Continue to fill until water issues from the taps. Shut these off, then check again for leaks.

7. If there are no visible leaks the system can now be pressure tested. For copper pipework to a test pressure of 1.5 times the maximum operating pressure for a period of 60 minutes, or for plastic pipework using either of the two test procedures highlighted in previous hot and cold water chapters. If the pressure test proves successful then the entire system should be thoroughly flushed through.

8. Manually operate the test device on both relief valves to allow water to flow for a period of 30 seconds to remove any residue that may have collected on the valve seats. Ensure that water is discharged from the valves and that it runs freely down the discharge pipes. Ensure that the relief valves completely shut on testing.

9. The cylinder should be run up to temperature, confirming operation of control thermostats and that the expansion and temperature relief valves do not discharge water under normal operating conditions.

10. Check the flow rate and pressure at the outlets (taps) and confirm that design requirements are being met.

11. Instruct the user in the operation of the system, complete any commissioning records and leave the manufacturer's instructions on site.

Service and maintenance of unvented hot water systems

Servicing requirements

Unvented hot water systems are relatively trouble free, they do, however, require to be serviced on a 12-monthly basis, primarily to ensure the proper operation of the safety components.

A key feature of the customer handover procedure on commissioning is to advise of the servicing periods and to ensure that the customer is informed of the need to report discharges from the temperature-relief and expansion valves indicating that there is a faulted condition.

The following shows a typical servicing procedure for an unvented system, more detailed advice may be provided in specific manufacturer instructions:

1. Check that all approved components are still fitted and are unobstructed. Check to see if all valves are still in position and all thermostats are properly wired.
2. Check for evidence of recent water discharge from the relief valves, visually and by questioning the customer if possible.
3. Manually check the temperature-relief valve – lift the gear or twist the top on the integral test device on the relief valve for about 30 seconds to remove any residue that may have collected on the valve seat. Check that it reseats and reseals, if not it may need to be replaced.
4. Manually check the expansion valve – lift gear or twist top on the integral test device on the relief valve for about 30 seconds to remove any residue that may have collected on the valve seat. Check that it reseats – and reseals, if not it may need to be replaced.
5. Check discharge pipes from both expansion and temperature-relief valves for obstruction and that their termination points have not been obstructed or had building work carried out around them.
6. Check the cylinder operating thermostat setting, e.g. 60–65°C.
7. Isolate gas and electrical supplies to the heating appliance, turn off water supply and relieve water pressure by opening taps:
   (a) Drain inlet pipework where necessary to check, clean or replace the line strainer filter.
   (b) Check pressure in expansion vessel and top up as necessary while the system is empty or uncharged. If the cylinder includes an air gap as the expansion device, reinstate the air gap as part of the procedure in line with the manufacturer's instructions.
8. Reinstate water, electricity and gas supply. Run the system up to temperature and ensure that control thermostats are working effectively and relief valves are not discharging water.
9. Complete any maintenance records for the system.

Typical faults on unvented systems

There aren't many faults that can occur in unvented hot water systems. Most manufacturers provide a simple flow chart as a guide to identifying faults in systems, here we'll take a look at the main ones.

As with all fault-finding procedures, the first check is always to look for the simple things first, so:

- the first check if the pressure in the system has reduced is to identify that no valves have been fully or partially closed, or
- in the case of the cylinder failing to heat up, is there a problem with the boiler electrical supply etc.? This is before you delve too far into faults with the system components.

Here are some of the more common faults:

Cylinder fails to heat up – primary circuit with no fault

- check to see if the high-limit thermostat has not tripped or developed a fault – this may be a sign that the control thermostat has failed or the high-limit thermostat is defective
- the control thermostat is defective
- the motorised valve is defective.

Discharge from the expansion valve at a relatively high flow rate

- this is usually a sign that the pressure-reducing valve is defective or the expansion valve itself is defective. Checking the working pressure in the system will establish which is at fault.

Nuisance dripping from the expansion valve when the system is heated – low flow rate

- this fault is usually associated with a problem with the expansion space in the system:
  - if the fault has occurred since installation it could mean that the expansion volume is too small, provided that the expansion vessel has been properly charged
  - if the fault has only recently occurred then it may mean that the expansion vessel needs re-charging, or replacing if the membrane has failed, or in the case of a bubble-top cylinder, the air gap may need reinstating
  - the fault could also be due to a defective expansion valve, a key check to establish this will be the working pressure in the system; if it's relatively low then it's the expansion valve; if it's about the pressure setting on the expansion valve then it's a problem with the expansion space.

Discharge from the temperature-relief valve

- the most likely cause of this is failure of the valve itself
- other faults could be failure of the two thermostats in the system (this is most unlikely). It's important as part of the fault-finding procedure with this fault that if it is suspected that thermostat failure has occurred to make sure that both thermostats are properly installed and correctly wired – it's most unusual for two thermostats to have failed.

Short answer questions

1. Which two Regulations lay down the requirements for the installation of unvented hot water storage systems?
2. What is the definition of an unvented hot water storage system under key regulations?
3. Which control device operates in the event of over-pressurisation in the unvented system?
4. What are the three types of materials from which unvented hot water storage cylinders may be manufactured?
5. What are the two methods of accommodating expansion of hot water in an unvented hot water system?
6. What is the maximum distance between the outlet of a temperature-relief valve and the inlet of a tundish in an unvented hot water storage system?
7. What type of discharge pipe termination is particularly suited to a flat with no available external wall?
8. Using the discharge pipe size table on page 284, calculate the size of discharge pipe required serving a G¾ temperature relief valve with a proposed length of 11m and including three elbows.
9. What are the two likely faults associated with a discharging temperature-relief valve?
10. What is the most likely solution to intermittent discharge from the expansion valve of a bubble-top type cylinder?

Multiple-choice test

For questions 1 to 10 please refer to Figure 15.23.

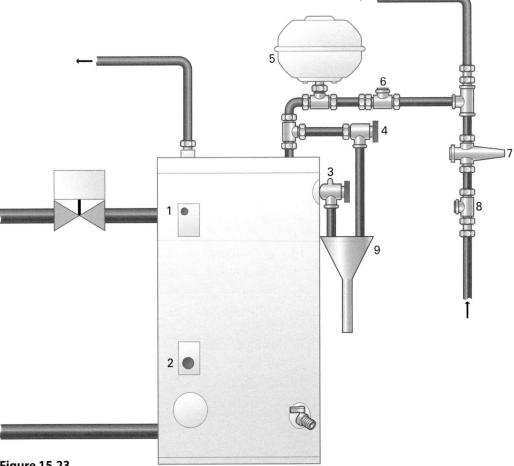

Figure 15.23

1. The tundish is shown at:
a) *Component 1*
b) *Component 3*
c) *Component 5*
d) *Component 9*

2. The expansion valve is shown at:
a) *Component 1*
b) *Component 3*
c) *Component 4*
d) *Component 8*

3. The control thermostat is shown at:
a) *Component 1*
b) *Component 2*
c) *Component 3*
d) *Component 4*

4. The expansion vessel is shown at:
a) *Component 4*
b) *Component 5*
c) *Component 6*
d) *Component 7*

5. The pressure-reducing valve is shown at:
a) *Component 5*
b) *Component 6*
c) *Component 7*
d) *Component 8*

6. The high-limit thermostat is shown at:
a) *Component 1*
b) *Component 3*
c) *Component 6*
d) *Component 9*

7. The line strainer is shown at:
a) *Component 2*
b) *Component 4*
c) *Component 6*
d) *Component 8*

8. The check valve is shown at:
a) *Component 2*
b) *Component 4*
c) *Component 6*
d) *Component 8*

9. The temperature-relief valve is shown at:
a) *Component 2*
b) *Component 3*
c) *Component 7*
d) *Component 8*

10. Which three components together provide a three-tier level of safety protection?
a) *Components 1–2–3*
b) *Components 1–2–7*
c) *Components 3–4–5*
d) *Components 4–6–7*

11. Which two parts of the Building Regulations specifically deal with the installation of unvented hot water systems?
a) *Part B & Part G*
b) *Part G & Part L*
c) *Part J & Part L*
d) *Part L & Part K*

12. Which of the following is a typical setting for the operation of the expansion valve in an unvented hot water system?
a) *0.5 bar*
b) *1.5 bar*
c) *3 bar*
d) *6 bar*

13. Which of the following is a typical temperature at which an energy cut-out device would activate in an unvented hot water storage system?
a) *35–45°C*
b) *60–65°C*
c) *80–85°C*
d) *90–95°C*

14. The Building Regulations require that water temperatures in unvented hot water systems should never exceed which of the following temperatures?
a) *50°C*
b) *60°C*
c) *80°C*
d) *100°C*

15. The test pressure for copper pipework in an unvented hot water storage system is:
   a) *Equal to the working pressure*
   b) *1.5 times the working pressure*
   c) *Twice the working pressure*
   d) *Three times the working pressure*

16. The minimum distance from the outlet of a tundish to the first elbow in a D2 discharge pipe is:
   a) *100mm*
   b) *150mm*
   c) *300mm*
   d) *600mm*

17. Which of the following documents shows the position of an unvented hot water storage system in a new-build dwelling?
   a) *Building Regulations approved document*
   b) *Installation drawings*
   c) *Manufacturer instructions*
   d) *Bill of quantities*

18. Which one of the following components has an integral test device?
   a) *Pressure-reducing valve*
   b) *Check valve*
   c) *Line strainer*
   d) *Temperature-relief valve*

19. Which of the following should be carried out when draining an unvented hot water storage cylinder?
   a) *Open a hot water tap*
   b) *Open a cold water tap*
   c) *Remove the line strainer*
   d) *Remove the pressure-reducing valve*

20. Nuisance discharge at an expansion valve could be caused by which of the following?
   a) *Faulty temperature-relief valve*
   b) *Faulty motorised valve*
   c) *Burst diaphragm on the expansion vessel*
   d) *Blocked line strainer*

This chapter builds on the revision completed at Level 2, Chapter 9: Above-ground discharge systems; you should therefore read through that chapter and familiarise yourself with its content prior to progressing through this Level 3 chapter.

By the end of this chapter you should be able to demonstrate understanding of the following above-ground discharge systems topics which will assist you in completing knowledge assessment in the Above-Ground Discharge Systems Unit of the Level 3 Certificate in Domestic Plumbing Studies:

- Sources of information:
  - Technical standards
- Types of above-ground sanitary pipework system:
  - Primary ventilated stack system
  - The HEPvO system as an alternative to traps
  - The stub-stack system
  - WC connected direct to drain
- Macerator WC installation – additional points
  - Macerator WC commissioning requirements
- Testing above-ground systems:
  - Soundness testing
  - Performance testing

Sources of Information

There are a number of information sources that plumbers may have to use to obtain the necessary detail to undertake their work on above-ground discharge systems.

Technical standards

The main statutory requirement for the installation of this type of system is the Building Regulations Approved Document H – Drainage and Waste Disposal. New installation, extension or major modification work on these systems (including above-ground soil and waste pipework) must be notified to the local authority prior to the work taking place, or the work must be carried out by a firm who is a member of a recognised competent persons scheme.

Approved Document H is supported by BS EN 12056 – Gravity Drainage Systems – providing the fine points of detail on the installation of above-ground sanitary pipework systems.

Did you know?

Certain types of work relating to sanitary appliance installation must be notified to the local water undertaker as well as possibly local building control; Chapter 13 – Advanced cold water systems, provides more detail.

Types of above-ground sanitary pipework system

In this section we'll build on the detail provided at Level 2 by considering the application and use of the various system types. At Level 2 we considered the following main system types:

- primary ventilated stack system – this is used in situations where appliances are closely grouped around the stack and the stack is large enough to limit pressure fluctuations without the need for a separate ventilating stack
- secondary ventilated stack system – this system can be used where there are pressure fluctuations in the stack that could affect trap seals. All appliances must be closely grouped around the main stack, eliminating the need for branch ventilating pipework
- ventilated branch discharge system – this type of system is used in circumstances where there may be large numbers of sanitary fittings in ranges or where appliances have to be dispersed at a distance from the main discharge stack.

Did you know?

The primary ventilated stack system is considered the norm for the vast majority of domestic properties, as it is particularly suited when appliances are closely grouped around the main stack and is cost-effective in the use of materials.

In practice you will probably only see these last two types of system in very large domestic properties where the scale of the system could be classed as an industrial job. There are also solutions other than branch ventilating pipework that may be considered in domestic systems to overcome long pipe runs, so we'll concentrate on the primary ventilated stack system in the main, as covered in your Level 3 qualification.

Primary ventilated stack system

Let's take a look around the stack and its key features, from the base upwards.

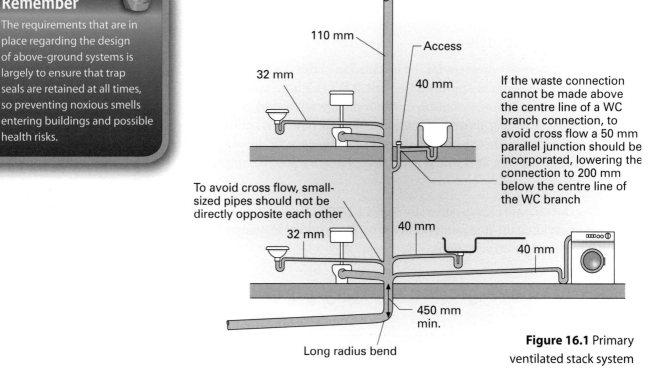

Figure 16.1 Primary ventilated stack system (single stack)

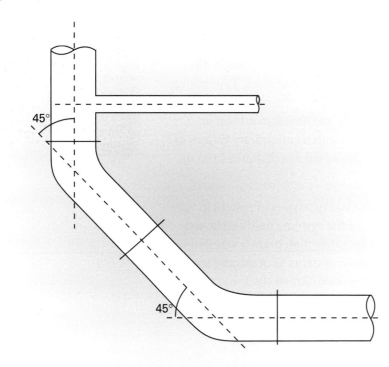

Figure 16.2 Two bends at the foot of a stack

Base of the stack

- the stack system must be connected to the foul-water drainage system; it goes without saying that under no circumstances must it be connected to the rainwater system
- the bend at the foot of the stack should minimise the possibility of back-pressure (compression) occurring, it is therefore preferable that two 45° bends are used, as shown in the following diagram, or alternatively a long radius bend may be used with a minimum centre-line radius of 200mm

- any branch discharge pipe should not discharge into the stack lower than 450mm above the invert level of the drain for buildings up to three storeys (with taller buildings that figure increases and in high-rise buildings it may be a requirement to provide a separate stack to the lower floors).

Main discharge stack

Figure 16.3 shows the minimum size of discharge stack required, related to the capacity of the stack.

Minimum diameters for discharge stacks	
Stack size (mm)	Max. capacity (litres/sec)
50*	1.2
65*	2.1
75†	3.4
90	5.3
100	7.2

Notes:
* No WCs.
† Not more than 1 WC with outlet size <80 mm.

Figure 16.3 Table – minimum discharge stack size

- as can be seen from the table, smaller stacks can be used to serve appliances with no WCs connected. If one WC is connected with an outlet of less than 80mm, the stack diameter may be 75mm. With WC outlets greater than 80mm, the minimum diameter should be not less than 100mm; whatever the case, the internal diameter of the stack should not be less than the largest trap or branch discharge pipe
- offsets in the wet portion of the stack should be avoided. If they cannot be avoided in a building of less than three storeys then there should be no branches within 750mm of the offset.

Remember

To clear blockages, rodding points should be provided in discharge stacks to give access to any lengths of pipe that cannot be reached from any other part of the system.

Did you know?

Discharge stack pipework is sized using a process called the discharge unit method, where each appliance is represented by a number of units. Pipes have a maximum number of units that they can take – so the pipe can be properly sized.

Branch discharge pipework

Figure 16.4 identifies acceptable methods of connecting branch discharge pipework into the discharge stack.

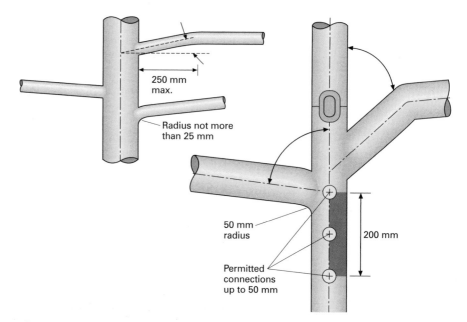

Figure 16.4 Branch discharge connection to main stack

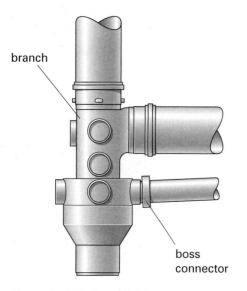

Figure 16.5 Soil manifold

- referring to the top diagram, branch connections of less than 75mm should be made at a 45° angle or with a 25mm bend radius, the bottom diagram shows a branch discharge pipe of over 75mm diameter, which must either connect to the stack at a 45° angle or with a minimum bend radius of 50mm
- a branch discharge pipe should not connect into the main discharge stack in a way in which cross flow could occur in any other branch; the bottom diagram shows the prohibited zone distance (opposite the WC connection) in which a branch discharge pipe may not be connected, a distance of 200mm
- Figure 16.5 shows a soil manifold (collar boss); this may be used to connect a number of branch discharge pipes to the main discharge stack, the large annular space in the manifold overcomes any pressure effects
- the branch discharge pipe should be at least the same diameter as the appliance trap (Chapter 9, Figure 9.12, page 165) at level 2 shows the minimum trap sizes for a range of appliances

- approved Document H of the Building Regulations places a restriction on the maximum length of branch discharge pipework if the system is not ventilated, as shown in the diagram below

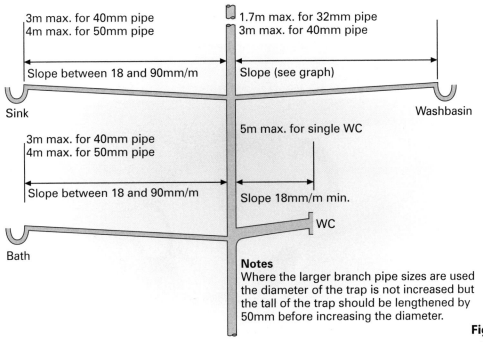

3m max. for 40mm pipe
4m max. for 50mm pipe

1.7m max. for 32mm pipe
3m max. for 40mm pipe

Slope between 18 and 90mm/m

Slope (see graph)

Sink

Washbasin

5m max. for single WC

3m max. for 40mm pipe
4m max. for 50mm pipe

Slope between 18 and 90mm/m

Slope 18mm/m min.

WC

Bath

Notes
Where the larger branch pipe sizes are used the diameter of the trap is not increased but the tall of the trap should be lengthened by 50mm before increasing the diameter.

Figure 16.6 Maximum length of unventilated branch discharge pipework

- care must also be taken to ensure that the pipe is installed within the specific tolerances shown for gradient – too shallow and the pipe will be susceptible to blockage, too steep and trap seal loss may occur
- basins are treated slightly differently in the Regulations, Figure 16.7 shows the maximum length of branch that can be used for specific pipe gradients

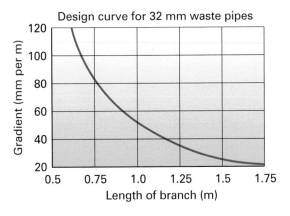

Design curve for 32 mm waste pipes

Gradient (mm per m)

120
100
80
60
40
20

0.5   0.75   1.0   1.25   1.5   1.75
Length of branch (m)

Figure 16.7 Length of basin branch discharge pipes

- rodding points must be provided to branch discharge pipework that cannot be reached by removing traps or appliances with internal traps.

Dealing with long or steep branch discharge pipework runs

There are circumstances in domestic properties in which the required pipe length may be too long or the gradient may be too steep. In such cases the only option if undesirable trap seal loss is to be avoided is to ventilate the pipework; this can be achieved in the following ways:

> **Definition**
>
> Ventilation means the introduction of air into the pipework system to equalise the pressure.

- the more likely option is the installation of an air-admittance valve sited in the pipework in the vicinity of the trap, or fitting a re-sealing trap as an alternative to a conventional trap

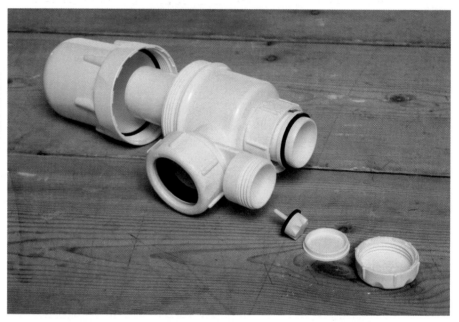

> **Remember**
>
> Air-admittance valves and resealing traps contain moving parts and will therefore require periodic maintenance to ensure that they continue to work effectively.

Figure 16.8
Resealing/anti-vac trap

- by installing a branch ventilating pipe to the branch discharge pipe near the trap and ventilating direct to outside air, i.e. the installation of a vent pipe from the waste terminating in a permissible location to outside air (at least 900mm above any opening when the outlet is sited within 3m of it); this is usually not carried out in domestic properties
- by installing branch ventilating pipework from the branch discharge pipework to a ventilating stack – see Figure 16.9.

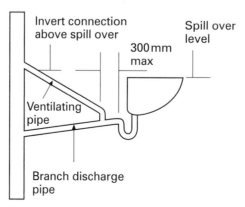

Figure 16.9
Branch ventilation pipework

This one is unlikely on a domestic job, but you may come across the need to consider it:

- the branch ventilating pipe should connect to the branch discharge pipe within 750mm of the trap
- the ventilating pipe must connect into the dry portion of the stack (ventilating pipe) above the highest spillover level of the appliance
- there must be a continuous incline from the discharge pipe to the ventilating stack
- ventilating pipes to one appliance should be a minimum of 25mm diameter, if the branch is longer than 15m or has more than five bends, it should increase to 32mm.

Common branch discharge pipework

Although not preferred, it is possible to install common branch discharge pipework to two sanitary appliances. Figure 16.10 shows the requirements for the common pipework connections.

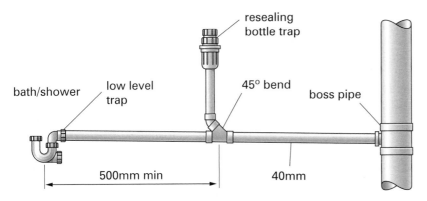

Figure 16.10 Common branch discharge pipework

- a 45° entry tee must be used to the basin waste to ensure that the basin discharge is properly swept in the direction of flow
- the minimum distance between the bath/shower and basin is 500mm and the basin must be fitted with a resealing trap
- the maximum overall length of run is 3m in total for a 40mm pipe, this can be exceeded if the main pipe run is increased to 50mm diameter pipe.

Ventilating the discharge stack

Discharge stacks must be ventilated to ensure proper operation of the system and particularly the avoidance of trap seal loss. Ventilation of the discharge stack can be achieved in two possible ways:

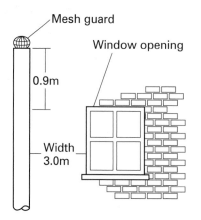

Figure 16.11
Ventilation to outside air

Ventilation to outside air

- discharge stack ventilating pipework (the dry part of the stack above the highest connection) may be reduced in size in one- and two-storey houses to not less than 75mm
- ventilating pipework should finish at least 900mm above an opening when the outlet is sited within 3m of the opening
- the ventilating pipework must be terminated with a wire cage (bird cage).

Termination with an air-admittance valve

An alternative to ventilation to outside air is the installation of an air-admittance valve.

Figure 16.12
Air-admittance valve

- this type of valve can only be used inside the building as it will not work properly if it freezes
- they should be positioned in such a location that air is freely available at their inlet and should be accessible for maintenance or repair
- they shouldn't adversely affect the performance of the below-ground system
- they are not suitable for use in dusty atmospheres

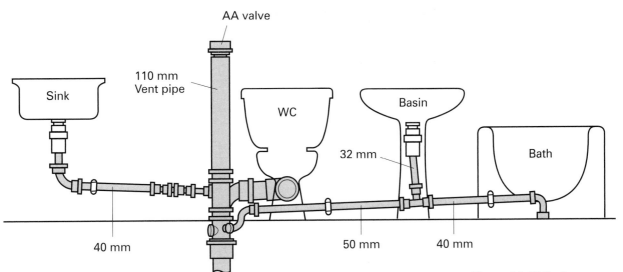

Figure 16.13 Drainage run (termination with air-admittance valves)

- the head (highest point) of any drainage system must be fully ventilated by a ventilating stack
- in a drainage run, one in five properties must be served by a ventilating stack, with the remainder terminated by an air-admittance valve.

The HEPvO system as an alternative to traps

The HEPvO valve can be used as an alternative to a trap. The valve uses a tough collapsible membrane as an alternative to a trap seal. Any back pressure causes the collapsible membrane to fully seal. The valve overcomes the effects of siphonage and back pressure that would normally be experienced by a trap.

Figure 16.14 Hepworth valve

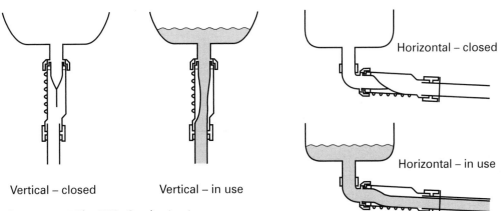

Figure 16.15 The HEPvO valve in-situ

As back pressure and siphonage are avoided, the valve can be fitted:

- on long pipe runs
- with steeper gradients.

Don't forget that a minimum pipe fall is essential to prevent blockage in the pipe – even with this system.

The stub-stack system

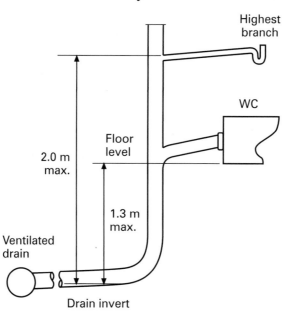
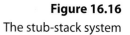

Figure 16.16

The stub-stack system

The stub stack tends to be suited to use in properties with second bathrooms, the head of the drain still requires to be properly ventilated. Essentially the stack is unventilated, there are therefore maximum distances between appliances and the invert level of the drain:

- maximum of 1.3m between drain invert and bottom of the WC
- maximum of 2m between the drain invert and the highest appliance branch.

WCs connected direct to the drain

WCs are permitted to be connected direct to the drain, provided that the bottom of the WC is within 1.3 m of the drain invert level as shown in Figure 16.17.

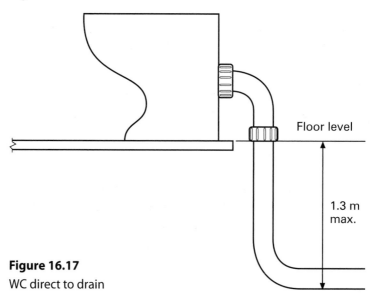

Figure 16.17

WC direct to drain

Macerator WC installation – additional points

Key installation requirements are:

- the macerator WC must only be used in a property in which there is also a conventional WC
- electrical wiring must be by an unswitched connection unit usually fused to 5A
- the discharge pipework from the unit is sized based on length of pipe run and height of lift.

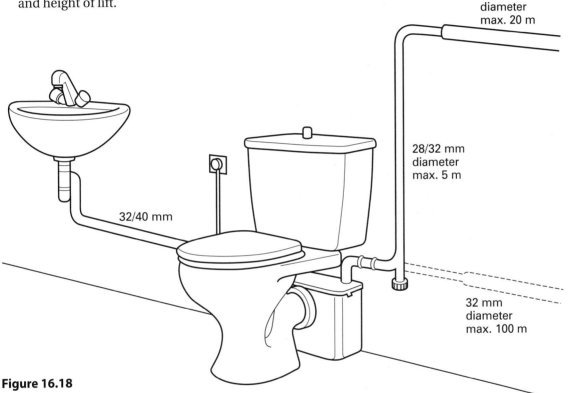

32/40 mm diameter max. 20 m

28/32 mm diameter max. 5 m

32/40 mm

32 mm diameter max. 100 m

Figure 16.18
Macerator WC

The drawing above shows a small Saniflo unit connecting WC and basin, larger units are available, capable of serving a full shower room. Key requirements of the pipe run with this manufacturer are:

- there is a maximum horizontal pumping distance of 90m
- any vertical lift must take place at the beginning of the pipe run, not the end
- on a horizontal run the 19mm pipe must increase to 32mm after approximately 12m
- 2 x 45° bends must be used at changes of direction (not elbows)
- if the horizontal pipe run is well below the unit, an air-admittance valve must be fitted to the high point of the pipework.

Remember

It's good practice when installing cold water pipework to use bends as opposed to elbows; they reduce frictional resistance in the pipework and assist in reducing noise levels.

Macerator WC commissioning requirements

- on completion of the installation the supply and discharge pipework should be tested for soundness
- the electricity supply to the unit should be fused at 5A and be protected by a 30mA RCD
- fill the cistern, check for leaks and adjust the float-operated valve
- turn on the electrical supply and flush the WC once
- the motor on the unit should run for 10 to 30 seconds (depending on length of pipe run)
- if the motor runs longer, a fault is indicated so check:
  - there is no blockage in the pipe run
  - there are no kinks in the flexible hose connections
  - the non-return valve is working correctly
- flush the WC several times to check for leaks
- check the float-operated valve and appliance taps for dripping (this can cause intermittent operation of the pump).

Testing above-ground systems

Soundness testing

All new installations or modifications to existing systems should be tested for leakage prior to their use. The diagram below shows the soundness test being carried out.

Figure 16.19 Soundness test procedure

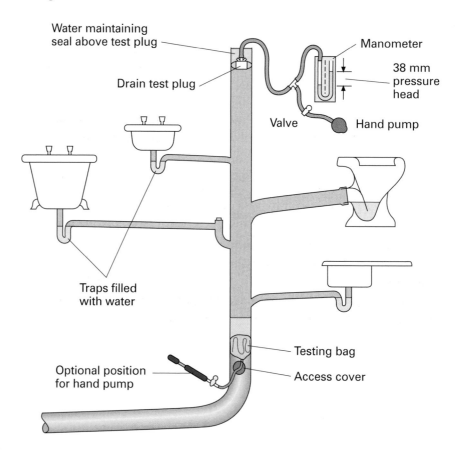

The test is carried out using air with the system pumped up to a test pressure of 38mm water gauge for a period of three minutes. During that period there should be no significant loss of pressure. If a pressure loss occurs then a leak is usually detected using soap solution.

Performance testing

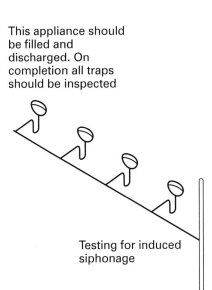

This appliance should be filled and discharged. On completion all traps should be inspected

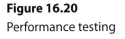

Testing for induced siphonage

Dipstick painted matt black

25 mm min.

Inspecting the depth of the trap seal after a performance test

Figure 16.20
Performance testing

Performance testing procedures for larger systems are quite complicated; BS EN 12056 part 2 details a procedure for such systems. With domestic systems the testing process is easier:

- independent branch discharge pipes to appliances are tested by filling the appliance to the overflow level and discharging water out of the appliance, the amount of water retained in the trap should be measured using a dipstick; the test must be repeated three times and the worst reading must be taken as the actual reading
- with combined branch discharge pipes, both appliances are tested simultaneously, again the test should take place three times, with the worst reading being taken as the actual reading.

Short answer questions

1. Under the Water Supply (Water Fittings) Regulations, water in a WC pan presents what category of fluid risk?
2. What is the main requirement to be considered when spacing sanitary appliances?
3. Which Approved Document in the Building Regulations details the requirements for installing above-ground sanitary pipework systems?
4. The position of sanitary appliances in a new-build dwelling would be found in which type of document?
5. Which type of above-ground sanitary pipework system is more likely to be used where appliances are installed in ranges and some appliances are sited at a distance from the main stack?
6. What two types of bend could be used at the base of a main discharge stack?
7. Where should rodding points be installed in a main discharge stack?
8. What is the maximum length of unventilated branch discharge pipework to a basin?
9. What three methods could be used to ventilate excessive lengths of branch discharge pipework?
10. Under the current Water Regulations what is the maximum flush volume for a WC cistern?

Multiple-choice test

1. Which British Standard provides guidance on above-ground sanitary pipework installation?
   a) BS EN 1289
   b) BS 6700
   c) BS 8000
   d) BS EN 12056

2. Which of the following most closely describes the primary ventilated stack system?
   a) All appliances should be at a distance from the main stack
   b) Some appliances must be at a distance from the main stack
   c) All appliances are closely grouped around the main stack
   d) A separate ventilating pipe is connected to the base of the stack

3. In a two-storey property what is the lowest level above the invert of the drain at which a branch discharge pipe may be connected?
   a) 150mm above the drain
   b) 250mm above the drain
   c) 450mm above the drain
   d) 750mm above the drain

4. What method is used to calculate the size of discharge pipework required on a job?
   a) Discharge-unit method
   b) Velocity method
   c) Flow-sharing method
   d) Pressure-loss method

5. What is the minimum size of main discharge stack that can be used to connect two WCs with 80mm diameter outlets?
   a) 50mm
   b) 65mm
   c) 75mm
   d) 100mm

6. The following diagram shows the bath waste connected below the WC connection in order to avoid cross flow. What must the minimum dimension be between the centre lines of the two pipes to avoid cross flow?
   a) 100mm
   b) 200mm
   c) 300mm
   d) 400mm

Figure 16.21

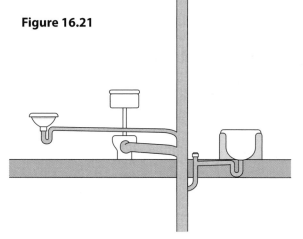

7. Referring to Figure 16.21, this minimum dimension does not apply if the waste (branch) pipework is connected using which type of device?
   a) Straight pipe boss
   b) Collar boss
   c) Drain connector
   d) Strap-on collar

8. A branch discharge pipework connection to a discharge stack should be made via a junction with a minimum radius of:
   a) 10mm
   b) 15mm
   c) 25mm
   d) 50mm

9. Which of the following may cause a blockage in branch discharge pipework?
   a) Pipework at too steep a gradient
   b) Pipework that has too shallow a gradient
   c) Pipework that is too smooth
   d) Pipework that is solvent welded

10. A branch ventilating pipe should be connected to a branch discharge pipe within what distance of the trap?
    a) 500mm
    b) 750mm
    c) 1000mm
    d) 1500mm

11. The basin connection to a combined branch discharge pipe should be made with which of the following?
    a) 45° entry tee
    b) 45° elbow
    c) 90° elbow
    d) 90° entry tee

12. Ventilating pipework outside a building must rise to what height above a nearby opening into the building?
    a) 500mm
    b) 700mm
    c) 900mm
    d) 1100mm

13. The Hepworth valve contains which of the following:
    a) Water seal
    b) Collapsible membrane
    c) Air admittance valve
    d) Non-return valve

14. The maximum height between the drain invert level and the highest sanitary appliance waste connection in a stub stack system is:
    a) 1000mm
    b) 1300mm
    c) 1500mm
    d) 2000mm

15. Nuisance operation of a WC macerator unit may be caused by:
    a) Incorrect water level in the WC cistern
    b) Dripping float-operated valve in the WC
    c) Leaking branch discharge pipework
    d) Faulty WC handle

16. The protective tape applied to sanitary appliances at the manufacturer's premises should be removed at which stage of the job?
    a) Before installing the sanitary appliances
    b) After the sanitary appliances have been installed but before commissioning begins
    c) After commissioning of the sanitary appliances has taken place
    d) By the customer on completion of the job

17. What type of documentation may be required to be filled in on completing the installation of sanitary appliances?
    a) Installation schedule
    b) Commissioning record
    c) Variation order
    d) Delivery note

18. What are the soundness test requirements for an above-ground system?
    a) 15mm water gauge for 1 minute
    b) 15mm water gauge for 5 minutes
    c) 38mm water gauge for 3 minutes
    d) 38mm water gauge for 5 minutes

19. What is the minimum depth of seal that must be retained in a trap as part of the performance test procedure?

a) 5mm

b) 10mm

c) 15mm

d) 25mm

20. How many times must a performance test be carried out to ensure retention of the trap seals in an above-ground system?

a) Once

b) Twice

c) Three times

d) Four times

17 Advanced central heating systems

This chapter builds on the revision completed at Level 2, Chapter 7: Central heating systems; you should therefore read through that chapter and familiarise yourself with its content prior to progressing through this Level 3 chapter.

By the end of this chapter you should be able to demonstrate understanding of the following central heating systems topics which will assist you in completing knowledge assessment in the Central Heating Systems Unit of the Level 3 Certificate in Domestic Plumbing Studies:

- Sources of information:
  - Technical standards
- The Requirements of Building Regulations Part L1 – gas and oil systems:
  - Boilers
  - System circulation
  - Hot water storage
  - System controls
  - Commissioning
- Vented systems approved for use under the Building Regulations – gas and oil:
  - Systems with hot water storage
  - Combination boilers
- The Requirements of Building Regulations Part L1 – solid-fuel systems:
  - The semi-gravity solid-fuel system
- Sealed central heating systems:
  - Pressure-relief valve
  - Pressure gauge
  - Expansion vessel
  - Method of filling
  - Boilers
  - Composite kits
- Other system options:
  - Microbore pipework
  - Frost thermostat with pipe thermostat
  - Pump-overrun thermostat
- Commissioning and performance testing a central heating system.

Sources of information

There are a number of information sources that plumbers may have to use to obtain the necessary detail to undertake their work.

Technical standards

- Building Regulations – these are the main regulations that must be complied with when installing central heating systems. Approved documents L1 – energy conservation – and J – heat-producing appliances – detail the main requirements for central heating systems, these can be freely downloaded from the DCLG website at www.communities.gov.uk.
- Water Regulations – these lay down the statutory requirements that must be carried out when installing, commissioning and maintaining water systems. Some aspects of central heating installation fall under the requirements of the Water Regulations. Water Regulations documentation can be freely downloaded from www.defra.gov.uk, who also produce a guidance document to the Water Regulations.
- British Standards – these support statutory documentation such as the Building Regulations, providing greater detail on installation requirements. Although British Standards are not statutory (legal) documents, they can be used in potential legal action relating to defective systems installation. The main British Standard relating to central heating systems is BS 5449 – Specification for forced-circulation hot water central heating systems for domestic premises (some aspects have been replaced by other standards).
- Manufacturer instructions – these are provided by appliance or component manufacturers to outline the installation, commissioning and maintenance requirements of their products. Manufacturer instructions usually take precedence over British Standards but should not conflict with Building or Water Regulations, which are statutory (legal) requirements.

The Requirements of Building Regulations Part L1 – gas and oil systems

Part L1 of the Regulations lays down quite stringent energy-efficiency requirements for heating systems. Here we'll look at the requirements for gas and oil systems in both new-build and existing properties.

Boilers

Gas boilers – the minimum SEDBUK efficiency must be at least 86% in new properties; in existing properties it is normally expected that the appliance efficiency will be 86%, however in exceptional circumstances, as indicated on completing the condensing boiler assessment procedure, that efficiency can go down to 78%.

Did you know?

SEDBUK stands for Seasonal Efficiency of Domestic Boilers in the UK; efficiency ratings for boilers can be determined from the manufacturer or from the website www.boilers.org.uk.

Did you know?

The condensing boiler assessment procedure is a point-scoring system that can be used with existing properties to determine in exceptional circumstances if it is permissible to install a non-condensing boiler, e.g. if a condensate pipe cannot be easily sited.

Oil boilers

- boilers installed before 1st April 2007 – in new properties the SEDBUK efficiency must be at least 85%, in existing properties the condensing boiler assessment procedure may be used
- boilers installed after 1st April 2007 – the boiler must be of the condensing type and have a SEDBUK efficiency of 86%.

System circulation

- Systems installed in new properties must be fully pumped
- In circumstances where a boiler is being replaced in an existing system, the system must be upgraded to a fully pumped system
- If a bypass is required in the system, it must be of the automatic type.

Hot water storage

New or replacement hot water storage cylinders must meet the following specification relating to insulation and area of heat-exchange coil:

- vented copper cylinders – BS 1566
- unvented cylinders – BS 7206
- thermal primary stores – the WHMA specification.

In addition all hot water storage vessels must carry proper labelling to show that they are properly approved.

System controls

- Boiler interlock – there must be a suitable wiring arrangement so that when there is no demand for either hot water or space heating the boiler and pump are turned off.
- Space-heating zones:
  - new properties with a total usable floor area of up to 150m² should be divided into two separate space-heating zones with independent temperature control; one zone must be the living room (this could be met by siting a room thermostat in the hall and placing TRVs on all other radiators)
  - new properties with a total usable floor area over 150m² should be divided into at least two separate space-heating zones, each having independent time and temperature control
  - a new system in an existing property is required to meet the above requirement, in the case of a replacement boiler in an existing system, it is acceptable for there to be just one zone.
- Water-heating zone – all dwellings must have a separate water-heating zone.
- Time control of space heating and hot water:
  - a system in a new property or a full replacement system in an existing property must have independent time control of the space-heating and hot-water circuits, e.g. by use of a programmer

> **Did you know?**
> The space-heating zone in a central heating system is the circuit feeding the radiators.

- in the case of a cylinder being replaced in an existing system, if separate time control is not provided to both circuits it is permissible to have one time clock controlling the operation of both circuits together.
- Temperature control of space heating – separate temperature control of each zone can be provided by:
  - room thermostats or programmable room thermostats in all zones, or
  - a room thermostat or programmable room thermostat in the main zone and individual TRVs on radiators in the other zones, or
  - a combination of both of the above

Figure 17.1
Thermo-mechanical hot water valve

- for existing systems in which the cylinder is being installed and there is a semi-gravity system, it is acceptable for a thermo-mechanical thermostat to be installed as a minimum.
- Temperature control of hot water – requirements are:
  - the provision of a cylinder thermostat controlling a motorised valve
  - for new properties with a total usable floor area over 150m² – two water-heating circuits with their own time and temperature control
  - for existing systems in which the cylinder is being installed and there is a semi-gravity system, it is acceptable for a thermo-mechanical thermostat to be installed as a minimum.

Commissioning

- The system should be thoroughly flushed on completion of the installation.
- A corrosion inhibitor must be added to the system.
- The system must be commissioned in line with manufacturer requirements.
- The property owner must be fully instructed in the effective operation of the system and all user operating instructions must be left on site.
- A commissioning record must be left on site.

Note: the installation of a boiler, central heating or hot water system is identified under the Building Regulations as work on a controlled service or fitting requiring either:

- notice to be given to the local authority before the work begins, or
- a compliance certificate to be issued on completion of the work by an installer who is a member of a competent persons scheme.

Vented systems approved for use under the building regulations – gas and oil

There are essentially three types of system that should be considered in new properties, and in existing properties in which a boiler is being replaced.

Systems with hot water storage

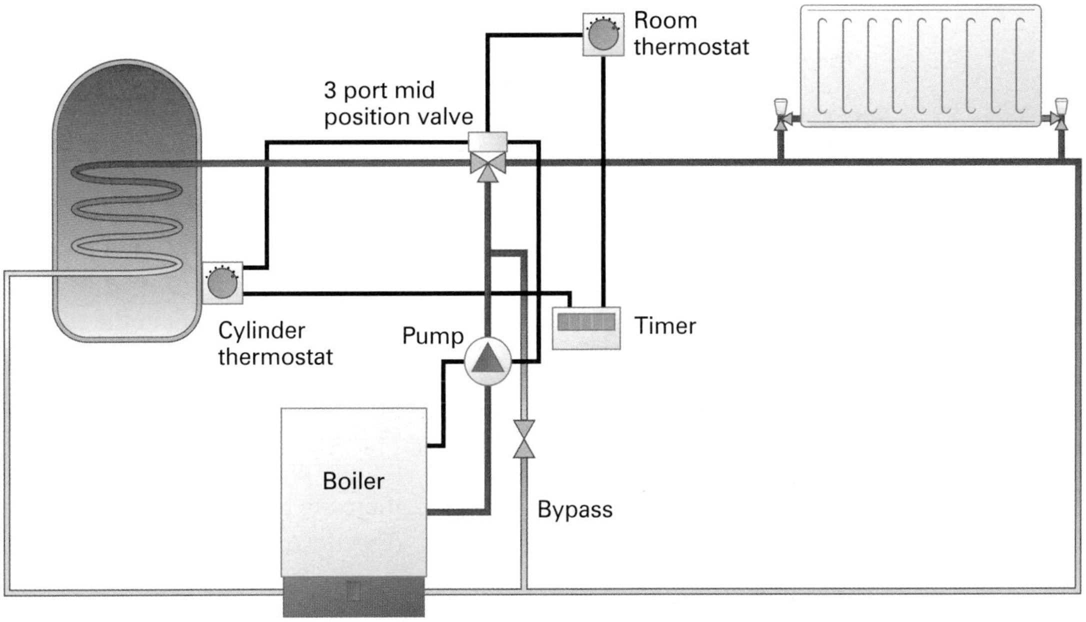

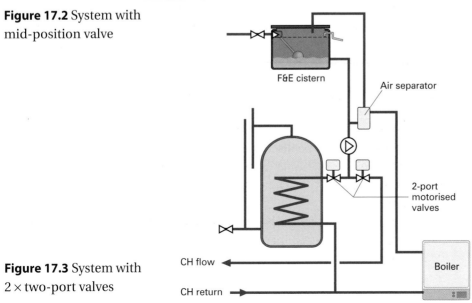

Figure 17.2 System with mid-position valve

Figure 17.3 System with 2 × two-port valves

Key features of the systems are:

- these system types are fully pumped meeting the requirements of the Building Regulations – also including full boiler interlock
- the return from the hot water cylinder must be the last connection to the return to the boiler, in order to avoid nuisance circulation in the heating circuit when it is turned off
- an air separator is shown in the 2 x two-port valve system; this can be used to close-couple the cold feed and vent pipes in the system into a desirable configuration that maintains the system under positive pressure and assists in removing air from the system
- the vent pipe must usually rise to a minimum height of 450mm above the water level in the cistern to overcome the possibility of surge effects in it
- there must be a minimum head of water over the pump in the system, this is usually the head of water generated by it divided by 3
- if TRVs are fitted, one radiator must be left without a TRV; this is usually the radiator in the room in which the room thermostat is sited

- the pipe size feeding the hot water storage cylinder will usually be 22mm
- the cold feed pipe will usually be 15mm and the open vent pipe 22mm
- remaining pipework in the system should be properly sized, there is however a rule of thumb that can be used (as shown in Figure 17.4) if pipe runs are not excessive or there are not too many changes of direction.

Copper pipe (OD)	Approx. loading
8	1.5kW
10	2.5kW
15	6kW
22	13kW
28	22kW

Figure 17.4 Rule of thumb maximum heat loads for copper pipework

Condensing boilers

Under the Building Regulations virtually all boilers, whether in new systems or being used as replacements, are required to be of the condensing type. Key features of the boiler are:

- it is capable of extracting normally wasted heat from the flue gases to the point at which water condenses in the boiler and needs to be run safely to waste
- the condensate can be discharged to:
  - soil pipe
  - waste pipe
  - gulley
  - as a last resort a purpose-made soakaway (absorption point)

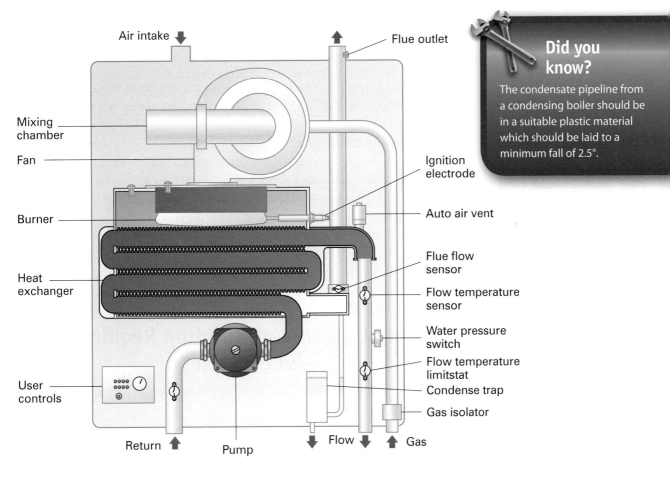

Figure 17.5 Example of a condensing boiler

- the condensate pipeline should normally be trapped (the trap is often sited in the boiler).
- care needs to be taken with siting the boiler flue as 'pluming' can occur
- the heating system from a condensing boiler can be designed to work on standard central heating water temperatures 80°C flow and 70°C return with a temperature differential of approximately 10–12°C; this will mean that the boiler does not operate in its condensing mode at all times during use. To operate fully in condensing mode the system design will have to be modified to 60°C flow and 40°C return; this is in order that the return water temperature brings the boiler down to the temperature at which all the useful heat can be drawn from the flue gases – to achieve these different temperatures the water flow rate around the system will need to be significantly reduced and the surface area of each radiator will need to be greatly increased.

Figure 17.6 Example of a combination boiler

Combination boilers

Combination boilers are now very popular as an alternative to a system of stored hot water. Key features of the system are:

- hot water is heated instantaneously (like a multi point water heater); priority is usually given to heating the hot water circuit when water is drawn off
- care must be taken when selecting the combination boiler as standard models are not suitable for feeding a large number of outlets simultaneously, although some high-flow models are available
- all the essential components are sited in the boiler, reducing the need for siting controls at different parts of the system
- condensing combination boilers are available to meet the requirements of the Building Regulations
- the boiler may be installed in a vented system (fed from an f&e cistern) or it may be installed in a sealed system – we'll look at this later.

The Requirements of Building Regulations Part L1 – solid-fuel systems

- Boilers/heating appliances must be approved by HETAS under the Regulations.
- The level of sophistication of the control system is as per identified by the manufacturer as safe to use, typically:
  - other than open fires there must be thermostatic control of the boiler
  - simple appliances such as open fireback boilers and room heaters will usually be fed from a semi-gravity system in order for them to work safely, in which case boiler interlock cannot be provided as well as temperature control of the hot water circuit. The requirements for control of the space-heating circuit are, however, as for gas and oil systems in terms of zoning requirements, time and temperature control
  - less sophisticated independent boilers such as gravity-feed boilers are as per room heaters
  - fully automatic solid-fuel boilers are available; if the manufacturer permits, it may be possible to fully pump these incorporating full boiler interlock and controls as per gas and oil systems.
- The system should be commissioned as per gas and oil.

The semi-gravity solid-fuel system

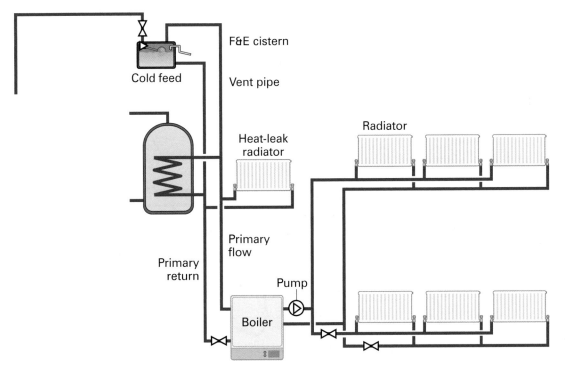

Figure 17.7 Heating circuit with heat-leak radiator

Key features of the system are:

- the gravity circulation pipework to the cylinder will be a minimum of 28mm diameter
- there should usually be a minimum of 1m circulating head between the centre line of the boiler and the centre line of the coil in the cylinder
- a special type of cylinder must be used that is suitable for gravity circulation (labelled type G)
- long horizontal pipe runs should be avoided to the cylinder; as a rule of thumb there should be 1m of vertical rise for every 3m of horizontal run
- the pipework from the boiler to the cylinder must rise continuously so that all the air is properly vented, avoiding any air locks that would prevent the circuit from operating correctly
- a heat-leak radiator (usually in the bathroom) should be connected to the hot water circuit; this radiator works on gravity circulation and may need 22mm tappings. The heat leak is required to allow heat to be dissipated from the boiler when the cylinder is up to temperature (essentially the heat leak absorbs heat from the fire on slumber when the cylinder is fully heated, so avoiding the possibility of the system reaching boiling point)
- as an additional safety measure a pipe thermostat should be connected by a permanent live (by passing the time control device) to the pump, causing the pump to operate and distribute water through the heating circuit if the boiler overheats.

Did you know?

The preferred connection method for a radiator fed by gravity circulation (such as a heat leak) is flow to the top and return at the bottom in the TBOE configuration (top, bottom and opposite end).

Sealed central heating systems

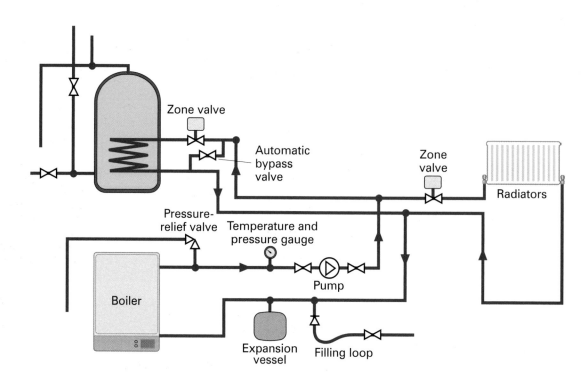

Most new central heating systems that are installed are now sealed systems, particularly combination boilers. The sealed system does not have an f&e cistern, a cold-feed pipe or an open vent pipe. The following controls are installed on the system (or may be contained in the boiler).

Pressure-relief valve

This replaces the open vent, it:

- is pre-set to discharge when the system reaches 3 bar pressure
- must be non-adjustable
- must have a manual test device
- must be connected in close proximity to the boiler
- must have a discharge pipe connected to it (preferably including a tundish) with the discharge running to a safe low-level location.

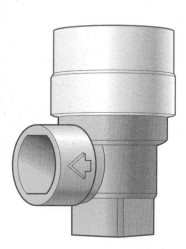

Figure 17.9
Pressure-relief valve

Figure 17.10
Pressure gauge

Pressure gauge

A pressure gauge with readings of between 0–4 bar must be sited in the location of the expansion vessel/fill point, its purpose is to assist in ensuring the correct charge pressure in the system. It is good practice to install a combined temperature and pressure gauge in order that the temperature can be monitored in the system as well.

Expansion vessel

This device replaces the f&e cistern in an open vented system. Key requirements are:

- the vessel is usually located on the suction side of the pump and preferably in a cooler part of the system
- there should be no isolating valve between the vessel and its point of connection to the system
- the vessel must be properly sized for the system; there are two factors:
    - vessel charge pressure – vessels are available for domestic properties accepting charge pressures of 0.5 bar, 1.0 bar and 1.5 bar. The appropriate vessel is selected based on the head of water in the system above the vessel, i.e. a property with 3 metres head above the vessel would require a 0.5 bar vessel as 3 metres = 0.3 bar
    - the expansion vessel needs to have sufficient volume to accept the heated water; the size of vessel is calculated using the table shown in Figure 17.12, based on the volume of water in the system and the initial charge pressure of the expansion vessel.

Before filling, the diaphragm is pushed up against the vessel by the preset initial gas charge. The gas charge supports the pressure exerted by the static head of water in the system.

On filling, the vessel contains a small amount of water.

At operating temperature the total mass of expanded water is contained in the vessel. The diaphragm is virtually static with equal pressure on either side.

Figure 17.11
Expansion vessel

Did you know?
The charge pressure in an expansion vessel will need checking at initial installation and during maintenance and may need adjusting; the simple way of doing this is to use a car-tyre pressure gauge and foot pump.

Safety valve setting (bar)	3.0		
Vessel charge and initial system pressure (bar)	0.5	1.0	1.5
Total water content of system (litres)	Vessel volume (litres)		
25	2.1	2.7	3.9
50	4.2	5.4	7.8
75	6.3	8.2	11.7
100	8.3	10.9	15.6
125	10.4	13.6	19.5
150	12.5	16.3	23.4
175	14.6	19.1	27.3
200	16.7	21.8	31.2
225	18.7	24.5	35.1
250	20.8	27.2	39.0
275	22.9	30.0	42.9
300	25.0	32.7	46.8
Multiplying factors for other system volumes	0.0833	0.109	0.156

Figure 17.12
Calculating the volume of the expansion vessel

Method of filling

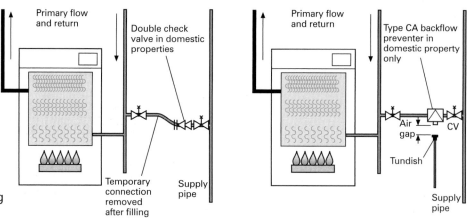

Figure 17.13 Methods of filling a sealed system

- The most popular method of filling a sealed system is using a proprietary temporary filling loop connected to the supply pipe:
    - a cold water isolation valve is included
    - a double-check valve is included in the loop to protect against backflow
    - a hose is included in the assembly; this must be fully removed when the system has been filled and charged, as it is only designed for temporary filling purposes.
- Care must be taken with the installation of the sealed system filled by this method, as if there is any form of leak, the system will run out of pressure and require constant topping up.
- An alternative to a temporary connection is to use a type CA backflow preventer, replacing the double-check valve; this permits a permanent connection to be made to the supply pipe to the system.

Boilers

A boiler used on a sealed system must be capable of withstanding the 3 bar pressure that the system may be pressurised to in a faulted condition and it must incorporate an energy cut-out device (high-limit thermostat) as well as the control thermostat.

Composite kits

Composite kits are available in which key components are sited in the one unit:

- expansion vessel
- pressure-relief valve
- pressure gauge
- filling loop.

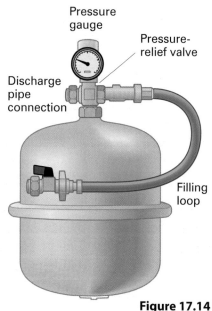

Figure 17.14
Sealed-system composite kit

Other system options

Microbore pipework

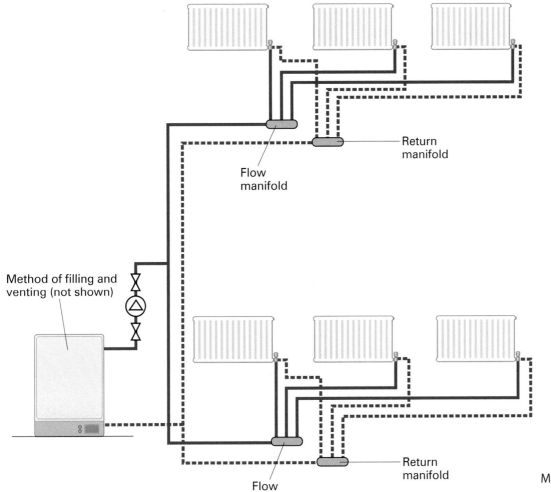

Figure 17.15
Microbore system

The radiator circuit to a central-heating system may be fed by small-diameter pipework – the microbore system using 8mm and 10mm pipework – provided that the pipework can carry the required heat load. The main features of the system are:

- manifolds must be properly sited so that pipe runs are minimised to each radiator
- the system is only suited to smaller properties
- there are two types of manifold available – Figure 17.16 shows the spider manifold.

Note: Microbore-type pipework can be used in a standard two-pipe radiator circuit fed as normal without the manifolds, provided that the pipe size is suitable to meet the heat load of the radiator.

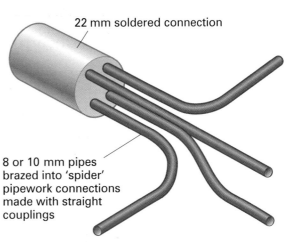

22 mm soldered connection

8 or 10 mm pipes brazed into 'spider' pipework connections made with straight couplings

Figure 17.16 Spider manifold

Frost thermostat with pipe thermostat

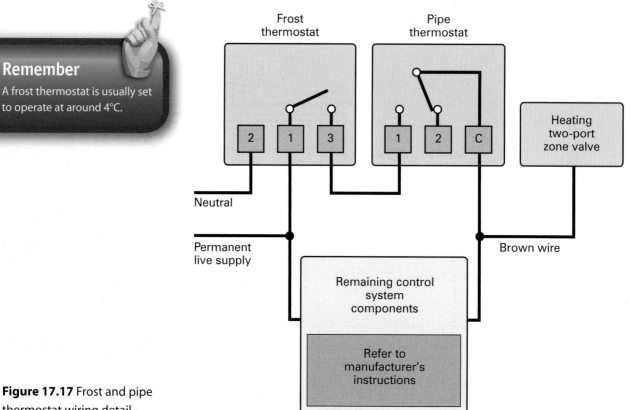

Figure 17.17 Frost and pipe thermostat wiring detail

Exposed parts of central heating systems may need to be protected by the installation of a frost thermostat. When installed, the frost thermostat overrides any time and temperature devices to make the system operate and prevent freezing. The frost thermostat installed by itself can be very wasteful in energy terms if there are prolonged periods of freezing. To minimise wastage of energy, a pipe thermostat may be wired in series with the frost thermostat, so when the frost thermostat calls for heat the boiler and the pump operate until the pre-set temperature of the pipe thermostat is reached (usually 50°C); the boiler then begins to cycle on and off but does not use as much energy.

Pump-overrun thermostat

Some boilers include a pump-overrun thermostat. This thermostat is designed to allow the pump to operate after the motorised valves have closed and the boiler turned off, in order to permit residual heat in the boiler to be dissipated in the system. In some boilers this is required to protect the heat exchanger. A bypass must be fitted and properly adjusted to operate with the pump overrun. Wiring arrangements will be different with this type of system with the pump fed from the boiler.

Commissioning and performance testing a central heating system

The following provides an outline of the commissioning/performance testing requirements:

- visual inspection – give the system a thorough check-over before filling, this includes checking to make sure that all joints are tight, pipes supported, etc.
- fill the system and check for leaks – open any valves in the system, open the fill point and bleed air from the air vents; check all joints for signs of leakage
- pressure testing – soundness test the system, usually to 1.5 times the maximum operating pressure
- cold flush – cold flush the contents of the system as a first-stage cleansing procedure
- system cleaning – re-fill, adding a proprietary cleaner to the system and operating usually for a period of two hours before draining down
- boiler commissioning – commission the boiler in accordance with manufacturer's instructions – checking the operation of key controls and setting and adjusting the pump and any bypass valve
- system balancing – balance the radiators in the system to meet the requirements of the design specification – there should usually be a temperature differential of 10–12°C between flow and return pipes in the circuit (unless different for a condensing boiler)
- the hot flush – flush the cleanser from the system whilst it is hot, then re-fill with corrosion inhibitor; check and test the operation of the system
- handover – provide an instruction to the user, hand over the operating instructions and complete the commissioning records.

Did you know?

To balance a heating system you need to know which radiator circuit is the index circuit – that's the run from the boiler to a radiator that has the greatest resistance to the flow of water, and usually the greatest load.

Did you know?

A differential digital thermometer is usually used to measure flow and return temperatures and balance a central heating system.

Short answer questions

1. What is the minimum size of primary pipework feeding the hot water cylinder in a system with a solid-fuel room heater?
2. The majority of pipework in the following system will be operating under what type of pressure?

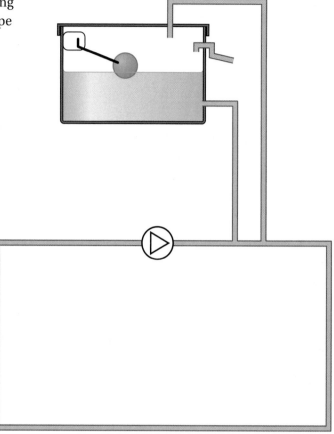

Figure 17.18

3. What is the name of the device designed to remove residual heat from a boiler after the heating and hot water circuit is turned off?
4. Under the Building Regulations, what is the requirement for controlling space-heating temperatures?
5. A pressure-relief valve in a sealed system should be designed to operate at what pressure?
6. What two types of device may be used to make branch connections in a microbore system?

7. What is the name of the point at which an expansion vessel connects to a central heating system?
8. What is the normal pressure for soundness testing a central heating system?
9. What is the most important check on an existing system when specifying a combination boiler?
10. What does SEDBUK stand for?

Multiple-choice test

1. The requirements for hearths used with solid-fuel appliances are detailed in which of the following?
   a) Water Regulations
   b) Gas Safety Regulations
   c) Construction Welfare Regulations
   d) Building Regulations

2. The recommended pipework configuration to a solid-fuel heat-leak radiator on a gravity circuit is:
   a) Top, bottom, opposite end (TBOE)
   b) Bottom, opposite end (BOE)
   c) Top, bottom, side to side (TBSS)
   d) Top, opposite end (TOE)

3. The minimum hot water storage capacity for a cylinder fed from a solid-fuel boiler is:
   a) 50 litres
   b) 100 litres
   c) 150 litres
   d) 200 litres

4. A boiler flue passing through a cupboard must be what minimum distance from any combustible material?
   a) 15mm
   b) 25mm
   c) 40mm
   d) 50mm

5. Boiler interlock can be described as:
   a) A security setting on the boiler to prevent tampering
   b) A wiring arrangement to remove residual heat from the boiler
   c) A method of providing frost protection
   d) A wiring arrangement preventing the boiler from firing when each circuit has shut off

6. A domestic central heating circuit should be protected by what size of fuse?
   a) 1 amp
   b) 3 amp
   c) 13 amp
   d) 16 amp

7. During commissioning the return water temperature at a conventional boiler should be:
   a) 50°C
   b) 60°C
   c) 70°C
   d) 80°C

8. The commissioning procedures for a solid-fuel boiler will be found in:
   a) Manufacturer instructions
   b) Building Regulations
   c) Water Regulations
   d) BS 6700

9. What type of backflow device may be used to make a permanent connection to a sealed central heating system?
   a) Type CA
   b) Type DC
   c) Type EA
   d) Type ED

10. Under the Building Regulations, when replacing a hot water storage cylinder to a gas fired semi-gravity system, what is the minimum level of control that must be provided to control the water temperature in the cylinder?
    a) Cylinder thermostat and mid-position valve
    b) Cylinder thermostat and motorised valve
    c) Thermo-mechanical valve
    d) Temperature-relief valve

11. The vent pipe in a close-coupled feed and vent arrangement must rise to what minimum height above the water level in an f&e cistern?
    a) 250mm
    b) 450mm
    c) 600mm
    d) 900mm

12. The minimum size of discharge pipe to a pressure-relief valve in a domestic sealed system is:
    a) 10mm
    b) 15mm
    c) 22mm
    d) 28mm

13. The condensate pipework from a condensing boiler should be laid at a minimum fall of:
    a) 2.5°
    b) 5°
    c) 10°
    d) 15°

14. Excess water flow in a low water content boiler is regulated by which of the following?
    a) Mid-position valve
    b) Diverter valve
    c) Automatic bypass valve
    d) Pressure-relief valve

15. The minimum size of earthing cable used to bond the main services in a domestic property is:
    a) 1mm
    b) 2.5mm
    c) 6mm
    d) 10mm

16. The pressure gauge in a sealed system should be capable of reading which of the following range of pressures?
    a) 0 to 3 bar
    b) 0 to 4 bar
    c) 1 to 4 bar
    d) 1 to 6 bar

17. What type of device can be used to increase the air pressure in an expansion vessel in a sealed system?
    a) Bicycle pump
    b) Manometer
    c) Draught gauge
    d) Digital thermometer

18. 'Kettling' in a low water content boiler can be caused by:
    a) Excessive water-flow rate
    b) Insufficient water-flow rate
    c) Low gas pressure
    d) Blocked gas pipe

19. The process of adjusting the flow rate through radiators during commissioning is called:
    a) Distributing
    b) Flow sharing
    c) Balancing
    d) Restricting

20. The additive that must be used in a new heating system before applying corrosion inhibitor is called:
    a) System leak sealer
    b) System cleanser
    c) Sulphuric acid
    d) Calcium carbonate

18 Gas supply systems

By the end of this chapter you should be able to demonstrate understanding of the following gas supply systems topics which will assist you in completing knowledge assessment in the Gas Supply Systems Unit of the Level 3 Certificate in Domestic Plumbing Studies:

- Sources of information:
  - Technical standards
- Installation of gas pipework:
  - Pipework materials
  - Pipework installation
  - Exterior pipework
  - Pipework installation – electrical safety
  - Sizing gas pipework
- Tightness testing domestic systems:
  - Tightness testing procedure – low-pressure installation
  - Tightness testing procedure – medium-pressure installation
  - Making connections to existing systems
  - Tracing gas leaks
- Purging gas supplies:
  - Meters and dials
- Checking pressures and gas rates:
  - Checking meter regulators
  - Checking/setting appliance pressures
  - Checking gas rates
- Combustion:
  - Burners
  - Incomplete combustion
- Ventilation:
  - Flueless appliances
  - Open-flued appliances
  - Appliances in compartments
  - Air vents

- Open-flue systems:
  - Classification of appliances
  - Parts of the open flue
  - Open-flue terminal locations
  - Flue construction
  - Effects of condensation on open-flue systems
- Room-sealed flue systems:
  - Classification of appliances
  - Room-sealed flue termination
  - Balanced compartments
  - Shared flues – room sealed
  - Vertex flue system
- Flue inspection and testing:
  - Open-flue system
  - Room-sealed appliances
- Unsafe situations:
  - Immediately dangerous
  - At risk
  - Not to current standards
  - RIDDOR
  - Warning labels and warning notices
- Gas controls and devices:
  - Flame-protection devices
  - Thermostats
  - Multifunctional control valves
  - Zero-rated governor
  - Ignition devices
- Gas appliances:
  - Domestic gas boilers
  - Domestic gas fires and wall heaters
  - Domestic gas cookers
  - Domestic gas water heaters.

Sources of information

There are a number of information sources that plumbers may have to use to obtain the necessary detail to undertake their work.

Technical standards

- Gas Safety Regulations – these lay down the statutory requirements that must be carried out when installing, commissioning and maintaining gas systems. Responsibility for monitoring compliance with the Gas Safety Regulations rests with the Council of Registered Gas Installers (CORGI) of which by law a gas-installation business should be a member. Breaches of the Gas Safety Regulations are dealt with by the Health and Safety Executive (HSE). A copy of the current set of the Regulations can be accessed at http://www.opsi.gov.uk/si/si1998/19982451.htm.
- British Standards – these support statutory documentation such as the Gas Safety Regulations, providing greater detail on installation requirements. Although British Standards are not statutory (legal) documents, they can be used in potential legal action relating to defective systems installation. There are a number of British Standards applicable to domestic gas work:
  - BS 5440 – Specification for installation of flues and ventilation for gas appliances of rated input not exceeding 70kW
  - BS 6891 – Specification for installation of low-pressure gas pipework up to 28mm in domestic premises
  - BS 5482 – Code of practice for domestic butane and propane gas-burning installations
  - BS 5546 – Specification for installation of hot water supplies for domestic purposes using gas appliances of rated input not exceeding 70kW
  - BS 5871 – Specification for installation of gas fires, convector heaters, fire back boilers and decorative fuel-effect gas appliances
  - BS 6172 – Specification for installation of domestic gas cooking appliances
  - BS 6798 – Specification for installation of gas-fired hot water boilers of rated input not exceeding 70kW.

Installation of gas pipework

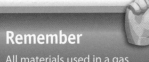

Pipework materials

The following shows the range of pipework materials suitable for use on domestic gas supply systems.

Steel

- steel pipe and fittings are required to conform to BS 1387 (medium or heavy grade), BS 3601 and BS 3604
- rigid stainless steel must conform to BS 3605 and BS 4127.

Corrugated stainless steel

- pipe and fittings are required to conform to BS 7838 – this is the Tracpipe type of piping system that uses proprietary split-ring fittings as part of the jointing process.

Malleable iron

- fittings are required to conform to BS 143 and BS 1256.

Copper

- copper tube should be manufactured to BS EN 1057
- capillary and compression joints to comply with BS 864 Part 2.

Note: Plastics, although suitable for external gas mains pipework, are not suitable for use indoors.

Key points – pipework jointing

The following outlines the general points that must be complied with when jointing gas pipework:

- any flux must remain active during the heating process only, as it cannot be flushed out of the system
- no flux should come into contact with stainless steel
- compression fittings can only be used where they are readily accessible, not under floors, in ducts etc.
- push-fit and quick-release fittings are not used for gas installations
- union joints for steel pipe must be sited in accessible locations
- hemp should not be used on threaded joints
- jointing pastes should not be used with PTFE tape.

Pipework installation

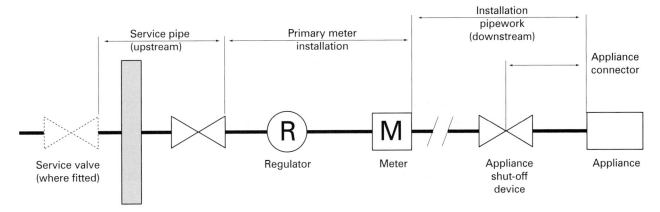

Figure 18.1 Pipework installation

The installation pipework in a gas system is the pipework downstream of the gas meter, the meter and pipework upstream of it is the responsibility of the gas supplier.

Emergency control valve

Although responsibility for this rests with the gas supplier, you will be expected to identify problems with the emergency control valve and whether it has been tampered with. The following outlines where an emergency control valve may be fitted:

- to the inlet of the primary meter; or
- to the installation pipe where it enters the building, where the meter is sited 6 metres or further away from the building; or
- inside individual flats served by a large single meter or a multiple-meter installation located in a remote or communal area.

The emergency control valve itself must:

- always be fitted and labelled to show the open and closed position
- be fitted in an accessible position and be easy to operate with a suitably fixed handle that falls safely downwards to an 'off' position.

Did you know?

A pipe should only be notched into a joist to 1/8th of its depth, otherwise an alternative pipe route should be found.

Pipes laid in wooden floors

When siting gas pipework in suspended timber floors the following applies:

- the pipework must be fully supported and notches or holes should be provided in accordance with Figure 18.2
- the floor covering should be marked to indicate there is a gas pipe below.

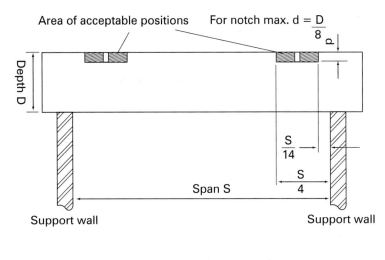

Figure 18.2
Acceptable notch and hole locations through joists

Pipes laid in solid floors

BS 6891 lays down the requirements for the installation of pipework in solid floors – Figure 18.3 shows examples of acceptable arrangements.

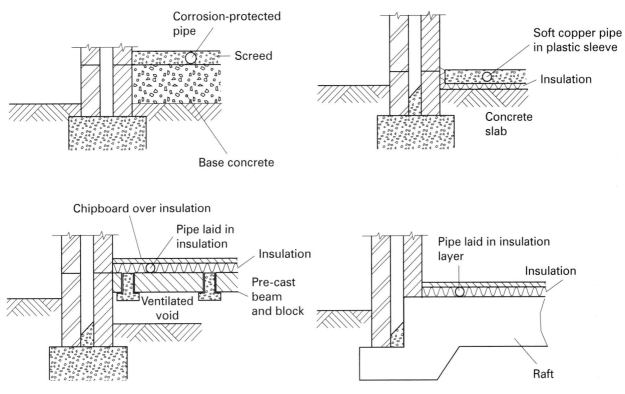

Figure 18.3 Pipework in solid floors

The following requirements must be met when laying pipes in solid floors:

- joints must be minimised wherever possible
- compression fittings must not be used
- acceptable methods of protecting the pipework in the floor are:
  - pipe laid in pre-formed ducts with accessible covers (if the pipework is laid on potentially corrosive materials then it needs to be wrapped)
  - pipes laid in the screed where the pipework materials are protected with a factory applied sheath or by wrapping
  - pipe covered with soft covering material to a minimum depth of 5mm which is resistant to the ingress of corrosive materials
  - factory-coated or wrapped copper tube passing through a large-diameter plastic sleeve, no joints are permitted in the sleeve.

Pipes in walls

The following requirements must be met when siting pipework within wall surfaces:

- keep pipes to be covered in plaster vertical
- provide ducts/access wherever possible
- pipes are not allowed to run in the cavity
- pipes passing across a cavity must be via the shortest route and must be sleeved
- pipes behind dry lining should be encased by building material
- the number of joints must be kept to a minimum
- pipes in timber studding must be secure
- all pipes are to be protected from mechanical damage and corrosion (by using factory-coated copper or by wrapping with protective tape where they may come into contact with potentially corrosive materials – in masonry walls).

Sleeving through walls

Key requirements for sleeves to gas pipework are:

- they must be made of a material capable of containing or distributing gas, e.g. copper or PVC
- copper pipework should not be sleeved with iron or steel, because of the possibility of electrolytic corrosion
- the space between the sleeve and the pipe must be capable of being sealed with an appropriate fire-resistant non-setting material; the seal should be made at one end only
- they should span the full width of the wall and be continuous without any splits or cracks
- the sleeve should vent to outside air, i.e. the seal should occur on the inside wall (other than in the case of a pipe entry to a gas meter box, which must include a seal inside the box itself)
- there must be no joints inside the sleeve
- it must be sealed on its outside at each end of the structure with a building material, e.g. mortar.

Protection against corrosion

The following requirements apply to pipework likely to come into contact with corrosive substances:

- factory-finished protection is preferred, e.g. plastic coated where pipework is to be routed through corrosive environments
- wrapping with protective tape is acceptable
- soot is very corrosive: protect pipes in fireplace openings
- test pipework before wrapping
- use stand-off clips to avoid contact with wall surfaces.

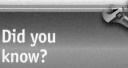

Did you know?

When using factory-sheathed copper pipe, the joints must be wrapped with protective tape to protect them as well, this wrapping must only take place after the pipework has been tested for tightness.

Did you know?

A sleeve is required when a gas pipe passes through a solid wall, to protect it from movement and the corrosive effects of the masonry materials.

Pipework in ducts and protected shafts

Cross-sectional area of duct m^2	Minimum free area of each opening m^2
Not exceeding 0.01	Nil
0.01 but not exceeding 0.05	Cross-sectional area of duct
0.05 but not exceeding 7.5	0.05
Exceeding 7.5	1/150 of the cross-sectional area of the duct

Ducts carrying gas pipework must be ventilated to prevent gas building up due to leakage, the minimum openings are as shown in Figure 18.4. Pipework must be properly fire-stopped at all points within the duct to comply with Building Regulation requirements.

The alternative to a duct is the installation of pipework in a protected shaft, which could be a stairway. The protected shaft will require ventilation. There are a number of ways in which this can be achieved. Additionally, pipework located in protected shafts, stairwells or fire escapes should be of screwed or welded steel: copper is not allowed.

Figure 18.4
Free area of duct ventilation

> **Definition**
>
> A protected shaft is a shaft that enables persons, air or objects to pass from one compartment to another, enclosed within a fire-resistant construction.

Pipe supports

Figure 18.5 shows the requirements for pipe supports to the various pipe materials.

Material	Nominal size	Interval for vertical support	Interval for horizontal support
Mild steel	Up to DN 15 DN 20 DN 25	2.5m 3.0m 3.0m	2.0m 25m 2.5m
Copper tube	Up to 15mm 22mm 28mm	2.0m 2.5m 2.5m	1.5m 2.0m 2.0m
Corrugated stainless steel	DN 10 DN 12 DN 15 DN 22 DN 28	0.6m	0.5m

Figure 18.5 Pipe support requirements

Micropoints

Micropoint fittings may be used on gas pipework. They are a special fitting to the termination of a gas pipe to which a rubber hose connection is made. Small-diameter rigid copper pipes are used to provide the gas supply to the micropoint.

Pipework installation – general requirements

The following additional points need to be considered when installing gas pipework:

- the pipework should be sited so that mechanical damage is avoided
- during pipework installation the pipe ends should be kept away from any dirt that may enter them
- pipe ends must be capped if connected to a live supply when you leave the job (even for a tea break)
- when an installation pipe is not required, it must be disconnected as close to the supply point as possible and capped off
- installation pipes must be sited at least 150mm away from electricity meters and 25mm away from electricity cables or metallic services.

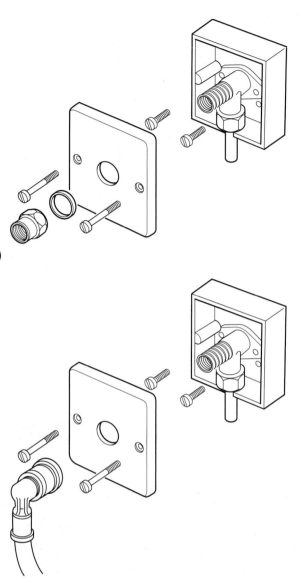

Figure 18.6 Micropoint

Exterior pipework

The following details the main requirements for externally sited installation pipework:

- the use of fittings should be kept to a minimum
- an external control valve needs to be fitted where the gas supply leaves the dwelling if connecting to an external appliance
- buried pipework in soil or vehicular driveways must have at least 375mm of cover
- buried pipework under concrete paths for pedestrians need have only 40mm of cover
- compression fittings are not allowed below ground
- where pipework is run externally above ground level it is preferable for it to be protected against corrosion with factory-applied sheathing. However, if stand-off clips are used, it is permissible to install bare copper pipes.

Did you know?

It's preferable wherever possible not to run gas installation pipework outside properties, as it is more susceptible to damage.

Pipework installation – electrical safety

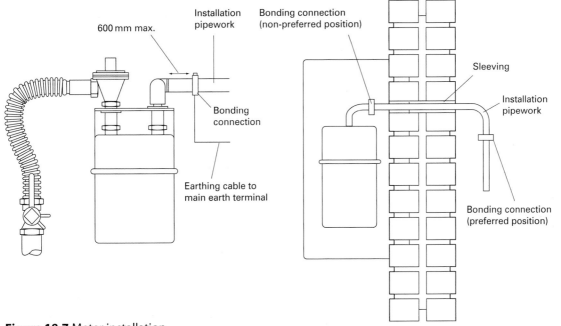

Figure 18.7 Meter installation

- All domestic gas installations must be equipotentially bonded (cross bonded) to the main earth terminal of the electricity supply. The bonding clamp must be sited at a maximum distance of 600mm from the outlet of the gas meter.
- The bonding clamp must be mechanically sound and labelled correctly: ('Safety Electrical Connection, DO NOT remove').
- If work is being carried out on an existing installation, a temporary continuity bond must be applied to maintain the electrical earth across any pipework sections that are removed – this is a key safety requirement.

Sizing gas pipework

The factors that affect the size of gas pipework required for a system are:

- gas rate of the appliance
- length of pipe run
- permissible pressure drop
- frictional resistance created by fittings.

When sizing pipework there should only be a maximum pressure drop of 1 mbar between the meter outlet and the appliance connection point; this is why it is important to size pipework properly, as this pressure drop can only be checked in situ after the pipework has been installed and not before: size it and you'll know it is correct.

Definition

Equipotential bonding is the positioning of an electrical earth conductor at a point close to the outlet of the meter connecting it to the earth terminal of the electrical supply.

Did you know?

When sizing gas pipework, fittings are treat as an equivalent straight length of pipe to make the calculations easier.

In order to pipe size you'll need the tables shown in Figures 18.8 and 18.9.

	Length of pipe (add 0.5m for each elbow or tee and 0.3m for each bend)							
Size of tube mm	3m	6m	9m	12m	15m	20m	25m	30m
	Discharge in cubic metres per hour (m³/h)							
10	0.86	0.57	0.50	0.37	0.30	0.22	0.18	0.15
12	1.5	1.0	0.85	0.82	0.69	0.52	0.41	0.34
15	2.9	1.9	1.5	1.3	1.1	0.95	0.92	0.88
22	8.7	5.8	4.6	3.9	3.4	2.9	2.5	2.3
28	18.0	12.0	9.4	8.0	7.0	5.9	5.2	4.7

Figure 18.8
Table – discharge of gas with 1 mbar pressure drop

General appliance types	Typical gas rate m³/hour
Warm-air heater	1.0
Multipoint water heater	2.5
Cooker	1.0
Gas fire	0.5
Central heating boiler	1.5
Combination bolier	2.5

Figure 18.9 Table – gas rates of appliances

Let's take a look at an example of a simple pipework calculation.

A central heating boiler operating at 1.5m³/hr of gas rate is fed by a gas pipe that is 11m long and includes four elbows. What is the required size of gas pipework?

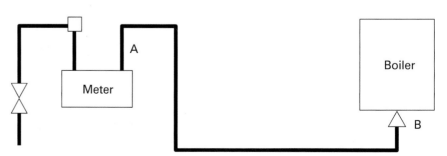

Figure 18.10 Gas pipe sizing example

Section A–B
Total length in metres with 4 elbows

Total equivalent length of section A–B (including fittings) is:

11.0m + 4 elbows @ 0.5m each = 11m + 2m = 13m total

From the table of gas rates for differing pipe sizes, if your actual length of pipe is not included you should take the next pipe size up.

So for a 15mm pipe of 15m length the available gas rate will be: 1.1m³/hr – this is below that required and therefore is not suitable.

For a 22mm pipe of 15m length the available gas rate will be 3.4m³/hr – this is above that required and therefore is suitable: 22mm is the required pipe size.

Tightness testing domestic systems

A test for gas tightness needs to be carried out:

- whenever a smell of gas is suspected or reported
- on newly installed pipework
- whenever work is carried out on a gas fitting that might affect its gas tightness (including pipework, appliances, meters and connections)
- before restoring the gas supply, after work on an installation
- prior to the fitting of a gas meter on new or existing pipework installations
- on the original installation prior to connecting any extension.

Tightness testing is carried out using either a:

- water gauge – 300mm length for natural gas, up to 1m with LPG, or an
- electronic gauge – this needs to be regularly calibrated to ensure it maintains its accuracy.

> **Did you know?**
> Tightness testing is the newer term used for soundness testing or pressure testing.

Existing gas pipework and new installations connected to the meter are usually tested with gas; new installations may be tested with air before the meter is fitted, requiring a test tee and a suitable pump as shown in Figure 18.11.

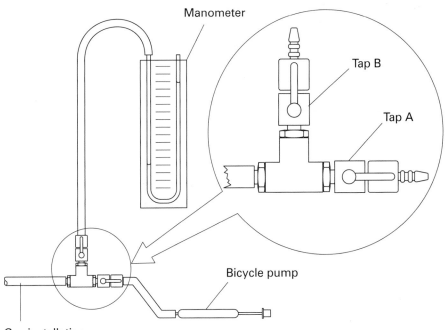

Figure 18.11 Testing with air

Tightness testing procedure – low-pressure installation

The tightness testing procedure on new and existing systems is a four-stage process:

- the visual inspection
- 'let-by' test
- pipework only test
- complete installation.

Visual inspection

- Check the completed installation and ensure that all sections to be tested are connected.
- Make a visual inspection of all pipework and joints to ensure they have been correctly made. Ensure all open ends have been properly capped off.
- Make sure that any appliances fitted are isolated, i.e. turned off at the isolation valve.
- It is important that pipework only is tested, as there is no allowable drop. This is whether the pipework is new or existing.
- Connect a correctly zeroed pressure gauge to the system at the test point on the meter.
- Check the section of pipework between the emergency control valve and governor with leak detection fluid.

'Let-by' test

This test is carried out to ensure that the emergency control valve is not passing gas ('letting by'):

- slowly raise the pressure to 10 mbar and isolate the supply
- if the pressure rises more than 0.5 mbar over a one-minute period then the meter control is passing gas in the closed position
- if passing gas then the gas emergency service provider must be contacted and the installation not put into use.

Pipework only test

All appliances must be isolated, cookers removed from bayonets etc.:

- slowly raise the pressure to 20 mbar and turn off the supply (do not raise any higher as it may cause meter lock-up resulting in incorrect readings)
- allow one minute for temperature stabilisation
- record any pressure loss in the next two minutes
- if there is no perceptible pressure loss (i.e. below 0.5 mbar for a water gauge and 0.3 mbar for a digital gauge) and there is no smell of gas, then the installation has passed the test
- if the test has failed then the leak must be found or the installation sealed and made safe.

Figure 18.12
Manometer at 20 mbar

Complete installation

Once it has been established that the pipework is sound and not leaking then the appliance isolation valves must be turned on and the full system tested. Remember some cookers have fold down lids that turn off the supply to the control valves so with this type of cooker the test should be carried out with the lid in the open position:

- slowly raise the pressure to 20 mbar and turn off the supply
- again, do not raise to pressures higher than 20 mbar as this may cause the meter regulator to lock up
- allow one minute for temperature stabilisation
- record any pressure loss in the next two minutes.

With new installations there is no allowable pressure drop for new appliances.

For existing installations a permissible pressure drop is allowed at the appliances, provided there is no smell of gas and the drop is not on the pipework:

- installation with a U6/G4 meter – loss of up to 4 mbar acceptable, provided there is no smell of gas
- installation with an E6 meter – loss of up to 8 mbar acceptable, provided there is no smell of gas
- where no meter is fitted in the dwelling, such as a flat supplied by a communal meter, then up to 8 mbar loss is allowed.

If the test is failed then the leak must be found or the installation sealed and made safe.

Tightness testing procedure – medium pressure installation

This procedure differs from testing low-pressure gas pipework.

Stage 1 – Test ECV

- Turn off gas at the ECV and connect gauge.
- Carry out let-by test on ECV.
- Release pressure from installation and hold open release mechanism lever on side of regulator.
- No more than 0.5 mbar rise should take place over the next minute; if more than 0.5 mbar then ECV is letting by, contact emergency service provider.

Figure 18.13
Medium-pressure regulator/ release mechanism

Stage 2 – Test regulator

- Allow release mechanism lever on regulator to return to off position.
- Open ECV.
- No more than 0.5 mbar rise should take place over the next minute; if more than 0.5 mbar then the regulator is letting by: contact the emergency service provider.

Stage 3 – Tightness test

- Following a successful let-by test on both the ECV and the regulator, release all pressure from installation and switch off
- Slowly raise pressure to 19 mbar (no higher to prevent regulator lock-up)
- Allow one minute for stabilisation
- Check pressure loss over next two minutes
- The following applies:
  - pipework only: no drop allowed
  - new appliances: no drop allowed
  - existing appliances fitted:
    a) U6/G4 meter: 4 mbar drop with no smell of gas
    b) E6 meter: 8 mbar drop with no smell of gas.

Making connections to existing systems

- Before the final connection is made to the system, the existing system must be tested for soundness, if the pressure drop is within acceptable limits and provided there is no smell of gas, it should be recorded; otherwise, the customer must be advised and the leakage resolved before making the connection.
- On making the final connection the system needs to be re-tested: the pressure loss should be no greater than the original test reading.

Tracing gas leaks

On suspecting leakage from a gas pipe or an appliance, the first stage is to carry out a tightness test on the installation; this should reveal that there is some form of leakage. If an unacceptable pressure drop is established or a smell of gas exists, the leak needs to be traced. Either of the following can be used:

- portable electronic gas detector – used around control valves and pipe joints to trace the source of the leakage
- testing short sections of pipe with leak-detection fluid around key weep points.

Remember

There should be no pressure loss on the gas pipework in either a new or existing system.

Purging gas supplies

Once the gas pipework has been successfully installed and proved gas tight, before it can be put into operation it needs to be purged. Great care needs to be taken when purging the supply: gas must not be allowed to build up in any confined space, as an ignition source could cause an explosion. Good ventilation should be provided as part of the purge procedure by opening doors and windows, and there should be no smoking or naked lights in the building during the purge procedure.

Purging is carried out by opening a gas line, e.g. turning on a gas tap and letting gas through until it fills the pipe. There is a minimum volume of gas that must be put through the meter as detailed in BS 6891 – not less than five times the badge capacity per meter revolution of the meter mechanism.

Meters and dials

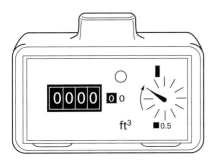 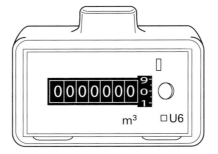

Figure 18.14
Meters and dials

The data badge on the meter shows the meter capacity. For an imperial U6 meter this is usually 0.071ft^3.

The purge volume is therefore $5 \times 0.07 = 0.35\text{ft}^3$.

E6 electronic meters require a purge volume of 0.010m^3 of gas.

Purging is carried out by drawing gas through the appliance furthest from the meter, then drawing a small amount from the remaining appliance branches. Gas must be properly ventilated from the building before appliances or naked lights are used.

Checking pressures and gas rates

Checking meter regulators

For gas appliances to work successfully it is essential that the gas pressure is kept constant. To achieve this a meter regulator (governor) is installed. Systems must however be checked to make sure that the regulator is properly adjusted and supplying gas at the correct pressure. The following tests show the procedures for checking this:

Working pressure

Figure 18.15 Checking working pressure

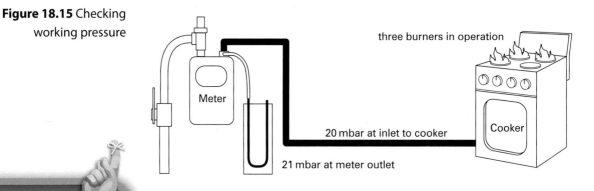

Figure 18.15 Checking working pressure

three burners in operation

Meter

20 mbar at inlet to cooker

Cooker

21 mbar at meter outlet

> **Remember**
> Working pressure is determined with one appliance operating on full.

Working pressure is checked by attaching a pressure gauge to the meter test point and operating just one appliance on full – if the cooker is used, three burner rings must be alight. The working pressure recorded on the gauge should be 21 mbar+/- 1mbar, i.e. 20–22 mbar. If the pressure is outside those limits the gas supplier should be contacted. Remember – only the gas supplier is allowed to break the seal on the regulator and adjust it.

Standing pressure

> **Remember**
> Standing pressure is checked at the meter with no appliances working.

Following the check for working pressure and as an additional check, it is worth confirming the standing pressure. This is the reading with all the appliances off, which should be between 21 and 25 mbar. If the reading is outside these figures, it's an indication that the regulator is not properly adjusted.

Checking/setting appliance pressures

Following the check to ensure that the meter regulator is working correctly, the pressures at appliances need to be checked and adjusted (if necessary). The correct burner pressure will be detailed either:

- on the appliance dataplate, or
- in the manufacturer instructions.

The first test is to attach a gauge to the test point at the inlet to the appliance regulator, the pressure reading should be no more than 1 mbar less than the working pressure reading at the meter. If it's less than this, there is a problem with the pipework system, such as blockage or under-sized pipework.

> **Remember**
> A test point should be checked for leakage with soap solution after use.

If the inlet test proves satisfactory then the gauge should be attached to the test point on the outlet side of the appliance regulator and the appliance left to operate for a period of approximately 10 minutes. The reading on the gauge should be checked against the required reading of the burner pressure on the dataplate; if it's a fixed-rated appliance then the pressure reading is non-adjustable and should be as requirements. Appliances such as boilers are often range-rated appliances where the burner pressure can be adjusted, based on the output requirement of the appliance. If it's a range-rated appliance the main pressure adjuster should be set to the correct appliance reading.

Checking gas rates

Following checks on the appliance burner pressure, one more check should be carried out: the appliance gas rate. This is a check to ensure that the gas rate consumed by the appliance is correct, as a check of working pressures alone would fail to reveal:

* partially blocked injectors
* oversized injectors.

Both of these could result in incorrect combustion in the appliance and potential safety issues.

There are two calculation procedures based on whether the meter is an imperial meter or a metric meter.

Imperial U6 meter

We need to know the calorific value (CV) of the gas. Usually:

* natural gas average CV is 38.76 MJ/m³ Gross or 1040 btu/ft³
* propane average CV is 93.1 MJ/m³ Gross or 2496 btu/ft³
* butane average CV is 121.8 MJ/m³ Gross or 3265 btu/ft³.

The formula for checking gas rate is:

$$\frac{\text{Seconds in one hour (3600)} \times \text{the CV of the gas (1040 btu/ft3)}}{\text{Number of seconds for one revolution of the dial}}$$

Example:

The time taken for one revolution of the test dial is 84 seconds

$$\frac{3600 \times 1040}{84 \text{ seconds}} = 44{,}571 \text{ btu/hr}$$

Convert btus to kW by dividing by a constant of 3412:

$$\frac{44{,}571}{3412} = 13.06\text{kW}$$

(this should be the approximate appliance dataplate reading)

Metric G4/E6 Meter

There is no test dial with this meter so the gas rate is determined by identifying the amount of gas burned across a fixed period.

$$\frac{3600 \times \text{m}^3 \times \text{CV of gas in Mj/m}^3/3.6}{\text{time in seconds}}$$

This calculation can be simplified further as the CV of gas is usually fixed at:

38.76 / 3.6 = 10.76

Example:

Over a 90-second period:

- the first meter reading was 41276.040m³
- the second meter reading was 41276.075m³.

The amount of gas used was 0.035m³.

Gas rate is:

$$\frac{3600 \times 0.035 \times 10.76}{90} = 15.06\text{kW}$$

Again, this can be checked against the dataplate on the appliance.

As an additional point, this calculation produces the gross rating of the appliance. Some appliances quote net figures. So with the calculation shown above, you would divide the gross figure by one of the constants shown below (dependent on the fuel type):

- natural gas – 1.1
- propane – 1.09
- butane – 1.08.

So in our previous calculation the net value would be 15.06/1.1 = 13.69kW.

Combustion

When gas is burnt, it is essential that a correct mixture of gas and air is established, to permit complete combustion. If the combustion process is not correct then the deadly gas carbon monoxide can be produced. When natural gas is burnt, the ratio of gas to air should be 10:1, to ensure a proper chemical reaction takes place – this is called the stoichiometric mixture.

Figure 18.16 shows some of the key properties of gas in relation to the combustion process.

Characteristic	Natural gas*	Propane	Butane	Notes
Specific gravity (SG of air=1.0)	0.6	1.5	20	Methane will rise but propane and butane will fall to low level
Calorific value	39MJ/m³	93MJ/m³	122MJ/m³	Appliances are designed to burn a particular gas
Stoichiometric air requirements	10:1	24:1	30:1	Methane requires 10 volumes of air to 1 volume of gas. LPG requires more
Supply pressure	21 mbar	37 mbar	28 mbar	Appliances must be matched to the gas used
Flammability limits	5 to 15% in air	2 to 10% in air	2 to 9% in air	Ranges within which gas/air mixtures will burn
Flame speed	0.36 m/sec	0.46 m/sec	0.45 m/sec	This is the speed at which a flame will burn along a gas mixture
Ignition temperature	704°C	530°C	408°C	Approximate temperatures
Flame temperatures	1930°C	1980°C	1996°C	Approximate temperatures

* Methane

Figure 18.16
Key properties of gases

Burners

Gas is burnt at the burner. A wide variety of different types is available; most work on the principle of the pre-aerated flame as shown above. Burners can also be:

- atmospheric – natural draught or air supply
- forced draught – a forced air supply is provided, usually driven by a fan.

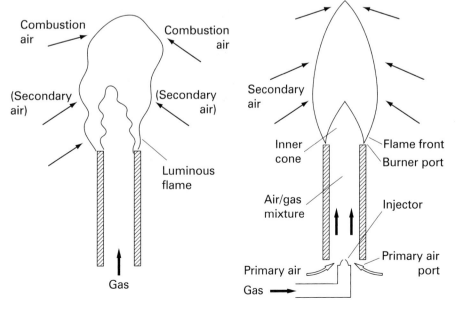

Figure 18.17
Post- and pre-aerated flames

Post-aerated flame

Pre-aerated flame

There are two issues that may occur when an incorrect gas supply is provided at a burner:

- lighting back – this occurs when the speed of the air/gas mixture is too low and the flame burns its way back down the burner tube
- flame lift – this occurs when the flame speed is too high and the flame is pushed away from the burner ports.

Incomplete combustion

If combustion is not correct then incomplete combustion can occur – this can be very dangerous. Carbon monoxide is a possible product of incomplete combustion, with a concentration of only 0.04% in the air being fatal – poisoning happens because carbon monoxide is taken into the bloodstream more easily than oxygen so the body is starved of oxygen. Figure 18.18 shows the effects of carbon monoxide on adults, with the saturation of haemoglobin in the body shown as a percentage.

% CO	Symptom
0 to 10%	No obvious symptoms
10 to 20%	Tightness across the forehead, yawning
20 to 30%	Flushed skin, headache, breathlessness and palpitation on exertion, slight dizziness
30 to 40%	Severe headache, dizziness, nausea, weakness of the knees, irritability, impaired judgement, possible collapse
40 to 50%	Symptoms as above with increased respiration and pulse rates, collapse on exertion
50 to 60%	Loss of consciousness, coma
60 to 70%	Coma, weakened heart and respiration
70% or more	Respiratory failure and death

Figure 18.18 Carbon monoxide effects on adults

Typical causes of incomplete combustion

- Lack of oxygen – air may be restricted to the burner or there may be a partial blockage of the flue outlet.
- Overgassing – incorrect burner pressure and/or wrong injector size giving more gas than the appliance was designed for.
- Chilling – this occurs when a flame touches a cold surface or is exposed to a cold draught; the flame pattern is disturbed and sooting may occur, causing even more problems.
- Flame impingement – when flames touch each other or touch a cold surface they 'impinge' and this may cause poor combustion; this may happen if a burner is not positioned correctly in the appliance.
- Vitiation – reduced oxygen levels in a room will cause the air to become 'vitiated' (made impure) and will affect combustion.

Visible signs of incomplete combustion

- yellow flames at the burner
- sooting – usually on the radiants or the appliance heat exchanger
- staining – usually around the flue or draught diverter.

If these issues are encountered they must be dealt with by a CORGI-registered business; if required the appliance must be safely isolated according to the procedures laid down in the industry unsafe situations procedure.

Ventilation

Ventilation may be required for the following:

- flueless appliances
- open-flued appliances
- appliances in compartments.

Flueless appliances

Figure 18.19 identifies the ventilation requirements (openings) required for flueless appliances.

Remember

It's essential that any signs of incomplete combustion are acted on straight away, as they indicate a potentially life-threatening problem.

Type of appliance	Max. appliance rated input (net)	Room volume (m³)	Permanent vent size cm³	Openable window or see note b
Domestic oven, hotplate, grill or any combination thereof	None	<5 5 to 10 >10	100 50 (a) see below Nil	Yes
Instantaneous water heater	11kW	<5 5 to 10 10 to 20 >20	Installation not allowed 100 50 Nil	Yes
Space heater in a room	45W/m² of heated space		100 plus 55 for every kW (net) by which the appliance rated input exceeds 2.7kW (net)	Yes
Space heater in an internal space	90W/m² of heated space		100 plus 27.5 for every kW (net) by which the appliance rated input exceeds 5.4kW (net)	Yes
Space heaters conforming to BS EN 449:1997 in a room	45W/m² of heated space		50 plus 27.5 for every kW (net) by which the appliance rated input exceeds 1.8kW (net)	Yes
Space heaters conforming to BS EN 449:1997 in an internal space	90W/m² of heated space		50 plus 13.7 for every kW (net) by which the appliance rated input exceeds 3.6kW (net)	Yes
Refrigerator	None		Nil	No
Boiling ring	None		Nil	No

Notes:
(a) If the room has a door direct to outside then no permanent vent is required
(b) Alternatives include adjustable louvres, hinged panel etc. that open directly to outside

Figure 18.19
Ventilation requirements – flueless appliances

Open-flued appliances

Open-flued appliances over 7kW heat input must be provided with ventilation at a rate of 5cm² (free area) for every kW appliance input in excess of 7kW.

Calculations are now based on net kW ratings, so there may be a need to convert the figure if the kW rating is given in gross. This can be done by dividing the gross rating by 1.1 for natural gas, as in:

8.0kW gross / 1.1 = 7.3kW net.

Example:

What is the ventilation required for a natural gas boiler rated at 12kW gross heat input?

Convert gross to net – 12 / 1.1 = 10.9kW

10.9kW – 7kW = 3.9kW

3.9 x 5cm² = 19.5cm² free area.

Multiple appliances

The following outlines the procedures for identifying ventilation requirements for multiple open-flued appliances in rooms.

1. One or more appliances totalling in excess of 7kW net. In a single room such as a through lounge – 5cm² per kW (net) of total rated heat input above 7kW.
2. Two or more gas fires – up to a total rated heat input of 7kW (net or gross) each 14kW. In a through room ventilation not normally required. For a higher kW rating allow an additional 5cm²/kW above 14kW.
3. Two or more appliances. Single room or internal space – calculate the total ventilation requirements of all appliances based on the greatest of the following:
   - total rated heat input of flueless space heating appliances
   - total rated heat input of open-flue space heating appliances
   - maximum rated heat input of any other type of appliance.

Example:

A gas boiler of 17kW (net) is installed in the same room as a gas fire rated at 4kW (net).

The ventilation requirement is:

17kW + 4kW = 21kW

21kW – 7kW = 14kW (adventitious ventilation deducted for only one appliance)

14kW x 5cm² = 70cm² free area.

Appliances in compartments

Definition

A compartment is a housing specially designed or adapted to house a gas appliance.

Typically a compartment will be a small room in which a gas appliance is sited. Because of its size, the room will need air circulation through it at both high and low level, to ensure that heat does not build up in the compartment.

Open-flued appliances require the following ventilation at high and low level, in addition to any air required for proper combustion of the appliance.

Vent position	Appliance compartment ventilated	
	To room or internal space (see note (a))	Direct to outside air
	cm^2 per kw (net) of appliance Maximum rated input	cm^2 per kw (net) of appliance Maximum rated input
High-level	10	5
Low-level	20	10
(a) a room containing an appliance compartment for an open-flued appliance will also require ventilation		

Figure 18.20
Compartment ventilation for open-flued appliances

Before reviewing the need for compartment ventilation with room-sealed appliances, the manufacturer instructions should be checked, as some room-sealed appliances do not necessarily need it. If compartment ventilation is required then Figure 18.21 should be used.

Vent position	Appliance compartment ventilated	
	To room or internal space	Direct to outside air
	cm^2 per kw (net) of appliance Maximum rated input	cm^2 per kw (net) of appliance Maximum rated input
High level	10	5
Low level	10	5

Figure 18.21
Compartment ventilation for room-sealed appliances

Example:

An 18kW (gross) room-sealed boiler is sited in a compartment with ventilation to outside air. What is the free area of ventilation required?

Convert gross to net: 18 / 1.1 = 16.4kW

High level – 5cm² × 16.4 = 82cm²

Low level – 5cm² × 16.4 = 82cm².

Air vents

Requirements for air vents for ventilation purposes are:

- they should be non-closable
- no flyscreen with dimensions less than 5 mm² should be fitted
- they should be corrosion-resistant and stable
- the actual free area of the air vent is the size of slots or holes used (this applies to both sides of the ventilation arrangement, i.e. air vent and outside air brick)
- they shouldn't be positioned where they are likely to be easily blocked, e.g. by leaves or snow
- the inner and outer grilles must be connected by means of a liner to prevent blockage of the air passage
- they should be positioned so that there is a minimum separation distance from any flue terminal.

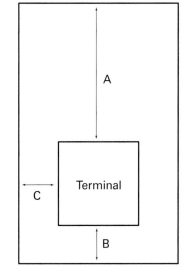

Figure 18.23
Proximity of air vents

Air vent position	Appliance input (kW)	Room sealed		Open flue	
		Natural draught	Fanned draught	Natural draught	Fanned draught
		Separation distance (mm)			
A Above a terminal	0 to 7	300	300	300	300
	> 7 to 14	600	300	600	300
	> 14 to 32	1500	300	1500	300
	> 32	2000	300	2000	300
B Below a terminal	0 to 7	300	300	300	300
	> 7 to 14	300	300	300	300
	> 14 to 32	300	300	300	300
	> 32	600	300	600	300
C	0 to 7	300	300	300	300
	> 7 to 14	400	300	400	300
	> 14 to 32	600	300	600	300
	> 32	600	300	600	300

Figure 18.22 Minimum air vent distance from flue terminal

Air vent free area

The free area of air vent is established by measuring the actual width and length of the slots.

Using the example shown above, if the length of the slots are 65mm (Band C) and the depth is 8mm, the free area is calculated as follows:

65mm x 8mm × 10 = 5200mm².

There are 100mm² in a cm², so free area = 52cm².

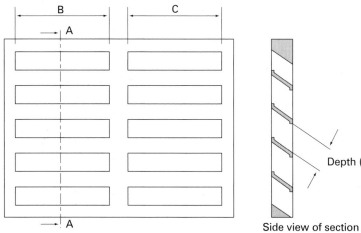
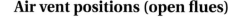

Depth (D)

Side view of section A–A

Figure 18.24 Free area of air vents

- The British Standard details procedures for determining the size of ventilator required when the air for combustion has to be transferred through more than one room.
- Care must be taken when siting air vents in rooms containing extractor fans, as they can adversely affect the performance of the appliance; it is possible that additional ventilation may be required to overcome the air being extracted by the fan.

Air vent positions (open flues)

Figure 18.25 shows possible positions of air vents provided for the ventilation of open-flued appliances.

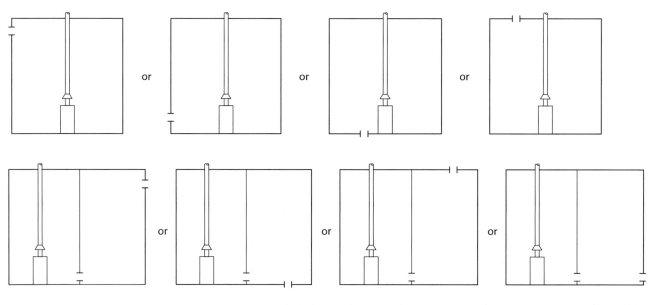

Figure 18.25 Ventilator positions – open-flued appliances

Air vents in compartments

Open-flued appliances

Figures 18.26 and 18.27 show the possible location of air vents to serve the compartment.

Figure 18.26 Air vents to compartments (open-flued)

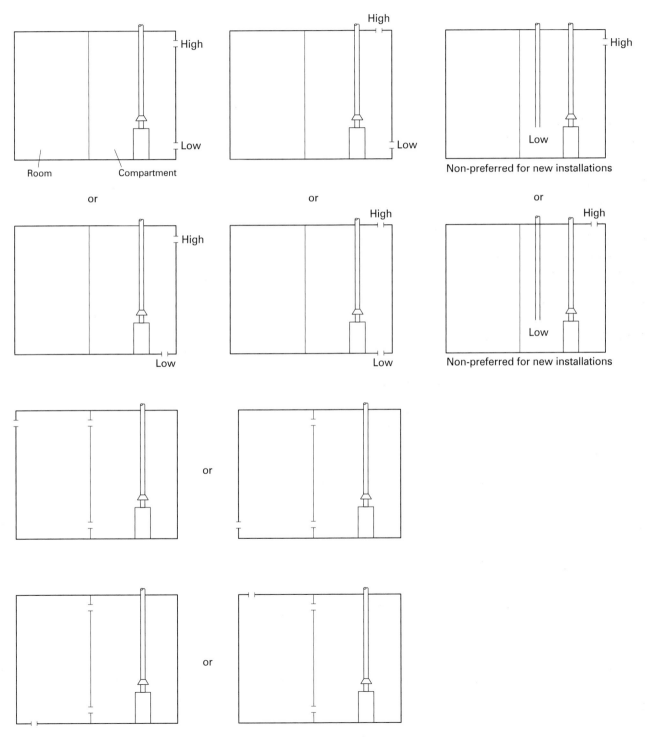

Non-preferred for new installations

Non-preferred for new installations

Figure 18.27 Air vents to compartments (open-flued) (continued).

Room-sealed appliances

Figures 18.28 and 18.29 show the possible location of air vents to serve the compartment.

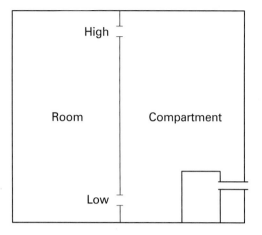
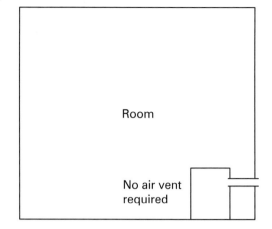

Figure 18.28 Air vents to compartments (room sealed)

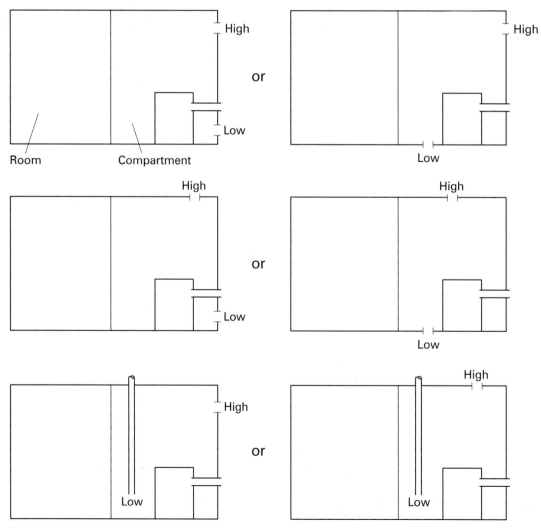

Figure 18.29 Air vents to compartments (room sealed) (continued)

Open-flue systems

Classification of appliances

Figure 18.30 shows the classification of the different types of open-flued appliance.

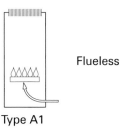

Flueless

Type A1

Open-flued types

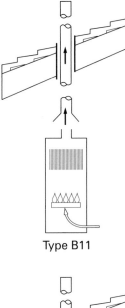

Type B11

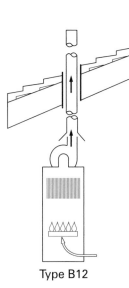

Type B12

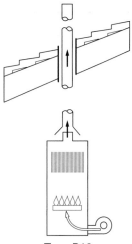

Type B13

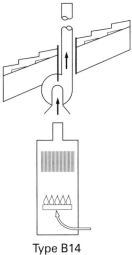

Type B14

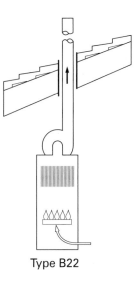

Type B22

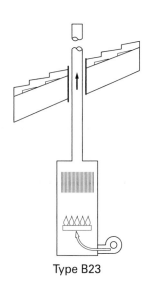

Type B23

Figure 18.30 Classification of flueless and open-flue appliances (type A and B)

Parts of the open flue

Open (conventional) flues are spilt into four parts:

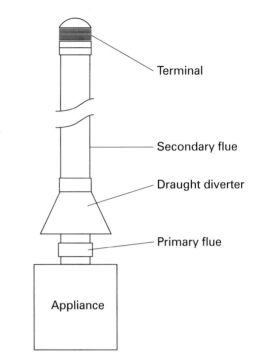

Figure 18.31 Parts of an open-flue system

- the primary flue is part of the appliance and creates the flue pull to clear the combustion products from the combustion chamber
- the draught diverter:
  - diverts any downdraught from the burner
  - allows dilution of flue products
  - breaks any excessive pull on the flue
- the secondary flue directs all the products of combustion to the terminal, its direction routing and materials are important in ensuring it works properly:
  - avoid/horizontal/shallow runs
  - keep bends to a maximum of 45°
  - keep flues internal (wherever possible)
  - a 600mm rise from the appliance to the first bend should be provided
  - the flue size should usually be a minimum of the appliance outlet size
- the terminal is sited at the outlet to the secondary flue; it is designed to:
  - stop birds, rain etc. entering the flue system
  - minimise downdraught
  - help the flue gasses discharge from the flue.

Terminals

Open-flue terminals come in many shapes and sizes, they must however be approved for use with gas appliances and have limited openings of between 6 and 25mm. Some examples are shown in Figures 18.32 and 18.33.

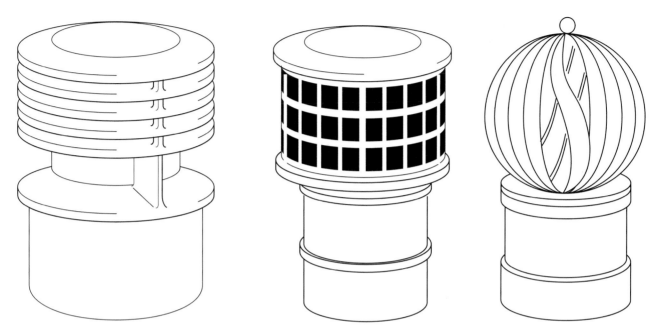

Figure 18.32 Types of open-flue terminal

Ridge terminals tend to be used on new properties:

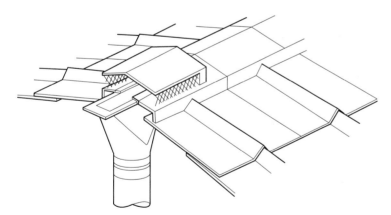

Figure 18.33 Ridge terminal

Open-flue terminal locations

The position at which open flues terminate is important in ensuring that the flue works effectively and removes the possibility of problems such as downdraught occurring. This is a dangerous condition that causes the products of combustion to be spilled back into the room in which the appliance is sited. Figures 18.34 and 18.35 show examples of acceptable flue termination arrangements with pitched and flat roofs.

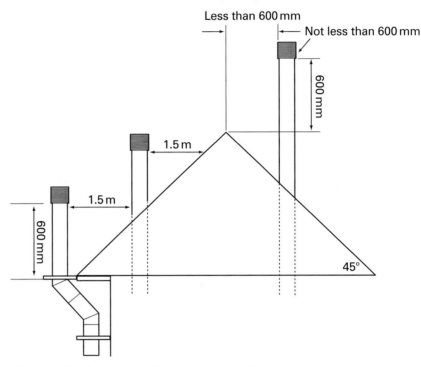

Figure 18.34 Flue termination – pitched roofs

Flue construction

The following lists the key requirements of the various types of flue material that can be used with open-flue systems:

- twin-wall metal – there are two types of twin-wall flue available:
  - air gap only – this is suitable for internal lengths only, or if sited externally, for lengths up to 3m
  - fully insulated – may be sited internally or externally
  - where a pipe passes through a floor/ceiling, appropriate fire-stopping must be provided incorporating a sleeve separating the flue from the combustible material with an annular space of 25mm between the sleeve and pipe wall which is packed with non-combustible material
- vitreous enamel – this is a single-skin flue pipe that is only suitable for internal use; it is normally used to make the initial (short) connection between the appliance and the flue system

Remember

It's essential that the flue construction meets the minimum standard requirements in order for it to work properly and not prove a danger to life.

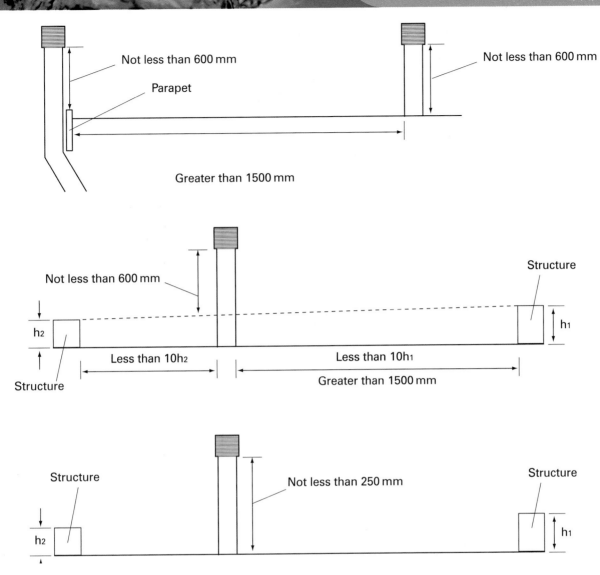

Figure 18.35 Flue termination – flat roofs

- flexible stainless-steel flue liner – these are used to line existing chimneys that do not have a suitable clay lining as part of the building structure. For the liner to work correctly it must be:
  - sealed at the top and bottom
  - one continuous length
  - without tight radius bends
- pre-cast concrete blocks – these are built into the walls of new domestic properties:
  - flue block must conform to BS 1289 and must be fitted to manufacturer instructions
  - any excess cement must be removed from the inside of the flue block during construction
  - no air gaps should be left in the joints during the jointing process
  - the connection from the flue blocks to the ridge terminal must be made with twin-wall insulated pipe, using the correct fittings.

Effects of condensation on open-flue systems

An open flue must be able to keep the flue gases at their maximum temperature to avoid the problems associated with excessive condensation forming in it and preventing the flue working correctly. Figure 18.36 shows the maximum length of open flues that can be used with gas fires in order to minimise condensation.

Flue exposure	Condensate-free length		
	225 mm² brick chimney: or pre-cast concrete block flue of 1300 mm²	125 mm flue pipe	
		Single wall	Double wall
Internal	12 metres	20 metres	33 metres
External	10 metres	Not allowed	28 metres

Figure 18.36 Maximum length of gas fire open flues

When chimneys exceed certain lengths they are required to be lined, dependent on the type of appliance fitted.

Appliance type	Flue length
Gas fire	> 10 m (external wall)
	> 12 m (internal wall)
Gas fire with back boiler	Any length
Gas fire with circulator	> 10 m (external wall)
	> 12 m (internal wall)
Circulator	> 6 m (external wall)
	> 1.5 m (external length and total length > 9m)
Other appliance	Flue lengths greater than in Table 6.13

Figure 18.37 Flue lining requirements

Room-sealed flue systems

Classification of appliances

The following shows the classification of the different types of room-sealed appliance.

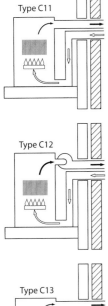

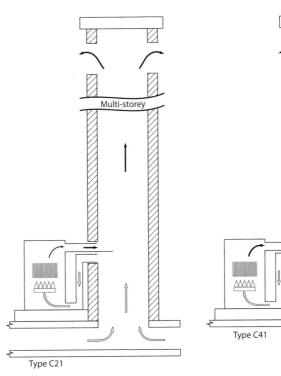

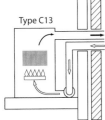

Figure 18.38 Classification of room-sealed appliances (type C)

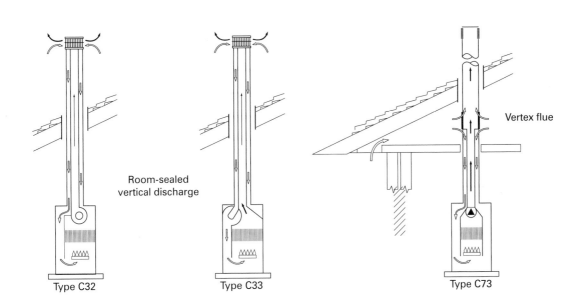

Room-sealed flue termination

Terminals to room-sealed appliances must be sited so that:

- combustion products are prevented from entering the building through any nearby opening
- free air movement is permitted
- any nearby obstacles do not cause air imbalance around the terminal.

Figure 18.39 is used to determine acceptable positions for room-sealed flue terminals.

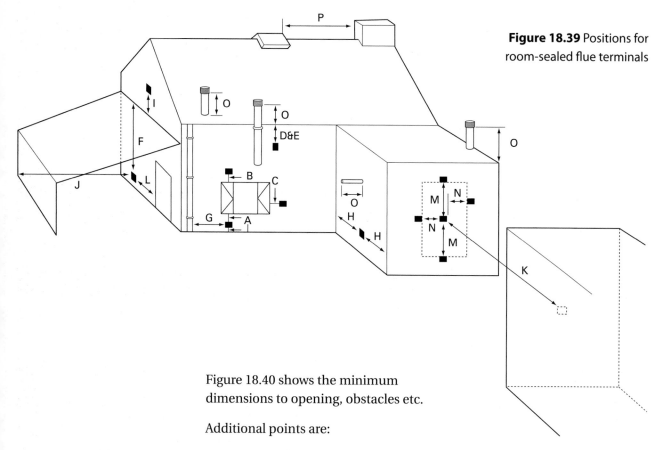

Figure 18.39 Positions for room-sealed flue terminals

Figure 18.40 shows the minimum dimensions to opening, obstacles etc.

Additional points are:

- a flue guard must be provided to a terminal that is sited 2m or less below ground level or if persons have access to touch it, e.g. on a balcony
- a terminal must not be sited more than 1m below the top level of a basement area, light well or retaining wall.

Dimension	Terminal position	Heat input (kW net)	Natural draught	Fanned draught
A – see note 1	Directly below an opening, air brick, opening window, door etc.	0–7 kW >7–14 kW >14–32 kW >32–70 kW	300 mm 600 mm 1500 mm 2000 mm	300 mm 300 mm 300 mm 300 mm
B – see note 1	Above an opening, air brick, opening window, door etc.	0–7 kW >7–14 kW >14–32 kW >32–70 kW	300 mm 300 mm 300 mm 600 mm	300 mm 300 mm 300 mm 300 mm
C – see note 1	Horizontally to an opening, air brick, opening window, door etc.	0–7 kW >7–14 kW >14–32 kW >32–70 kW	300 mm 400 mm 600 mm 600 mm	300 mm 300 mm 300 mm 300 mm
D	Below gutters, drain pipes or soil pipes	0–70 kW	300 mm	75 mm
E	Below eaves	0–70 kW	300 mm	200 mm
F	Below balconies or car-port roofs	0–70 kW	600 mm	200 mm
G	From a vertical drain pipe or soil pipe	0–70 kW		1500 mm – see note 4
H – see note 2	From an internal or external corner	0–70 kW	600 mm	300 mm
I	Above ground, roof or balcony	0–70 kW	300 mm	300 mm
J	From a surface facing a terminal – see note 3	0–70 kW	600 mm	600 mm
K	From a terminal facing a terminal	0–70 kW	600 mm	1200 mm
L	From an opening in the car-port into the dwelling	0–70 kW	1200 mm	1200 mm
M	Vertically from a terminal on the same wall	0–70 kW	1500 mm	1500 mm

Figure 18.40 Positioning of room-sealed flue terminals *(continues overleaf)*

Dimension	Terminal position	Heat input (kW net)	Natural draught	Fanned draught
N	Horizontally from a terminal on the same wall	0–70 kW	300 mm	300 mm
O	Above intersection with the roof	0–70 kW	N/A	Manufacturer's instructions
P	Between a chimney and a ridge terminal		1500 mm (300 mm between similar ridge terminals)	

Note 1 In addition the terminal should not be closer than 150 mm (fanned) or 300 mm (natural) from an opening in the building fabric for the purpose of accommodating a built-in element such as a window frame.

Note 2 This does not apply to building protrusions less than 450 mm, e.g. a chimney or an external wall, for the following appliance types – fanned draught, natural draught up to 7 kW, or if detailed in the manufacturer's instructions.

Note 3 Fanned-flue terminal should be at least 2m from any opening in a building that is directly opposite and should not discharge POCs across an adjoining boundary.

Note 4 This dimension may be reduced to 75 mm for appliances up to 5 kW (net) input.

Figure 18.40 Positioning of room-sealed flue terminals *(continued)*

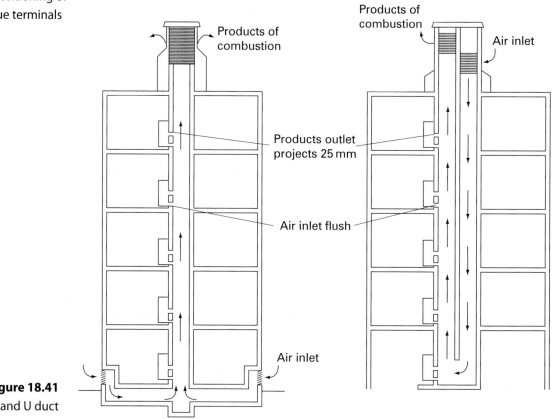

Figure 18.41 SE and U duct

Balanced compartments

Larger installations can make use of a balanced compartment. This is where an open-flued appliance is sited in a sealed, fire-resistant enclosure. Particular attention needs to be taken to ensure that there are no holes in the building structure and the entry door must be self-closing.

Shared flues – room-sealed

There are two flue systems of this type that are used in high-rise buildings – the SE Duct and the U Duct, shown in Figure 18.41.

The gas appliances used with these types of flue system are specially adapted versions of room-sealed appliances and should only be replaced by these special versions. The landlord is responsible for the maintenance of the shared flue system, which must be checked annually.

Vertex flue system

The air supply in this appliance is taken from a draught break sited in the secondary flue in the roof space. The draught break must be sited at least 300mm above the level of any roof insulation and the flue above the break must have a vertical height of at least 600mm before any bend.

Flue inspection and testing

Open-flue system

Visual inspection

The following outlines the requirements for undertaking a visual inspection on a flue system:

- flue materials – are fit for purpose and are as required under BS 5440
- installation – the flue system is correctly installed with appropriate bracketing, etc.
- corrosion – there are no visible signs of corrosion on metallic pipes
- bends – are at the permissible angles, 90° bends are not permissible
- firestop spacing – flue pipes through combustible materials are properly firestopped with a minimum distance of 25mm between the flue pipe and combustible materials
- termination – is of the correct type and in an acceptable position
- signs of spillage – if it's an existing appliance, are there any signs of spillage at the draught diverter or above gas fires?

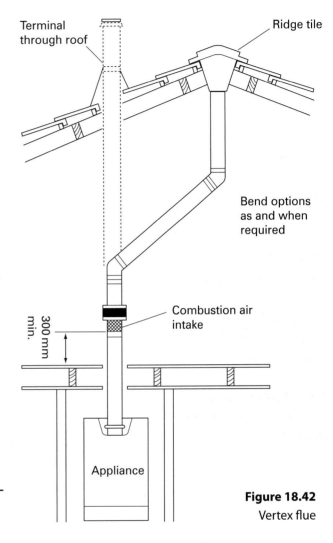

Figure 18.42
Vertex flue

Remember

Flue testing is a very important part of the commissioning process, as it ensures that the flue is working correctly and does not present any dangers.

Flue-flow testing

A flue flow test is undertaken on completion of the visual inspection.

Figure 18.43 Flue flow testing no pull and pulling

The following outlines the flue flow test procedure:

- check there is an adequate air supply
- close all doors and windows in the room/adjoining room
- check with a match or taper for some pull; the flue may need warming before lighting the smoke pellet; it is pointless lighting a pellet unless there is some draught available, as the room would fill with smoke
- position pellet at base of flue, and light. Note: the pellet should produce at least 5m³ of smoke in a 30-second burn time
- check entire length of flue to ensure that there is no leakage of smoke into the property, including the loft space
- check that smoke is seen to come out from only one terminal and that the termination is correct
- any faults must be rectified and the flue re-tested before the appliance is fitted/refitted and put into operation.

Spillage testing

A spillage test is carried out on completion of the flue flow test.

The following outlines the spillage test procedure:

- close all doors and windows in the room
- switch any fans in the room to maximum; don't forget fans exist in appliances such as tumble driers
- turn on the appliance to full setting and leave on for five minutes

Figure 18.44
Spillage test in progress

- light a smoke match and check for spillage at the draught diverter or canopy; manufacturer's instructions will give exact details of positioning
- all smoke, apart from the odd wisp, must be drawn into the flue
- if the test fails it is permissible to leave the appliance running for a further ten minutes and then re-test; a satisfactory test is essential
- if fans are present in adjoining rooms, then the interconnecting doors are opened, fans switched to maximum and the previously satisfactory spillage test must now be repeated
- any appliance found to be spilling products of combustion is 'immediately dangerous' and must be disconnected.

Room-sealed appliances

Key checks with this type of appliance are:

- correct location of the flue terminal
- correct fitting of the flue assembly including its jointing in line with manufacturer instructions
- correct sealing of the appliance case.

This last point is particularly important with fanned flued appliances with the fan on the inlet to the boiler creating positive pressure inside the appliance casing. If there is a leak on the casing seal then products of combustion may be forced into the room. Additional checks for this type of appliance are:

- carry out a visual inspection of the case seal to check for any gaps or defects
- light the appliance and check round the entire case with leak-detection fluid
- if a leak is detected and it cannot be rectified then the appliance should not be used.

Unsafe situations

The gas industry has developed an unsafe situations procedure to deal with a range of gas dangers. The unsafe situations are categorised according to the severity of risk created by the danger.

Immediately dangerous (ID)

This is an installation that is an immediate danger to life or property if is operated or left connected to the gas supply. Key actions are:

1. Where possible, with the user's permission, try to rectify the fault.
2. Failing rectification of the fault, explain the danger to the user.
3. Disconnect the appliance and cap off, with the owner's permission.
4. Attach a 'DO NOT USE' label.
5. Complete a warning notice.
6. Ask a responsible person to sign the paperwork.

At risk (AR)

This is an installation that could create a risk to life or property.
Key actions are:

1. Where possible, with the user's permission, try to rectify the fault.
2. Failing rectification of the fault, turn off the appliance and explain that continued use is at the user's own risk.
3. Attach a 'DO NOT USE' label.
4. Complete a warning notice.
5. Ask a responsible person to sign.

Not to current standards (NCS)

Other situations that can be identified as faults but are not immediately dangerous or at risk are classed as 'not to current standards'. NCS faults should be reported to the customer and it is recommended that this is carried out in writing.

RIDDOR

Certain unsafe situations are deemed to be so unsafe that under the Reporting of Diseases and Dangerous Occurrences Regulations (RIDDOR) they must be reported to the Health and Safety Executive. A special form known as F2508G is produced by the installer for the purposes of reporting dangerous gas occurrences.

The current edition of the CORGI Unsafe Situations Procedure Booklet outlines the various unsafe situations and the classification of each situation as ID, AR or NCS.

The flowchart in Figure 18.45 is a useful aid to identifying the actions to take in unsafe situations.

Warning labels and warning notices

Warning labels are used to advise of various actions. The common labels include:

- the 'DO NOT USE' label is applied to an installation/appliance that has been categorised as ID/AR
- compartment ventilation warning label – advising against affecting the ventilation to the compartment
- compartment ventilation and storage warning label – advises regarding not affecting the ventilation and indicating that the compartment is not suitable for storage
- balanced compartment warning label – advises about interfering with the seals to the compartment, about not leaving doors open, etc.

Warning notices are standard forms (usually in triplicate) giving the user details of the fault and the action that has been taken; they are normally used in conjunction with the 'DO NOT USE' label.

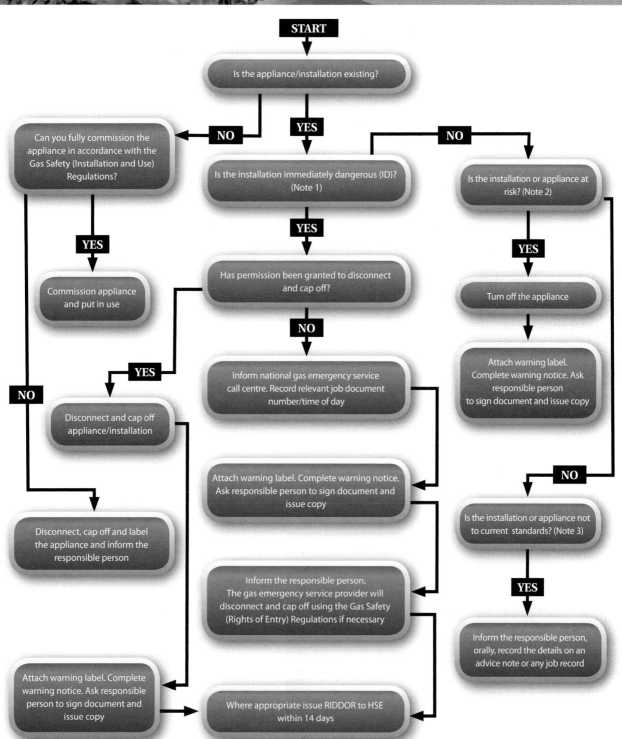

START

Is the appliance/installation existing?

NO → Can you fully commission the appliance in accordance with the Gas Safety (Installation and Use) Regulations?

YES ↓ Commission appliance and put in use

NO ↓ Disconnect, cap off and label the appliance and inform the responsible person

YES → Is the installation immediately dangerous (ID)? (Note 1)

YES ↓ Has permission been granted to disconnect and cap off?

YES → Disconnect and cap off appliance/installation

NO ↓ Inform national gas emergency service call centre. Record relevant job document number/time of day

Attach warning label. Complete warning notice. Ask responsible person to sign document and issue copy

Inform the responsible person. The gas emergency service provider will disconnect and cap off using the Gas Safety (Rights of Entry) Regulations if necessary

Attach warning label. Complete warning notice. Ask responsible person to sign document and issue copy

Where appropriate issue RIDDOR to HSE within 14 days

NO → Is the installation or appliance at risk? (Note 2)

YES ↓ Turn off the appliance

Attach warning label. Complete warning notice. Ask responsible person to sign document and issue copy

NO ↓ Is the installation or appliance not to current standards? (Note 3)

YES ↓ Inform the responsible person, orally, record the details on an advice note or any job record

Notes
1. One which if operated or left connected to a gas supply will be an immediate danger to life or property
2. One which if operated may lead to a situation that could create a risk to life or property
3. One which is not in accordance with current Regulations, Codes of Practice or Standards and Specifications but does not constitute either an ID or AR risk

Figure 18.45 Unsafe situations flow chart

Gas controls and devices

Flame protection devices

These devices are designed to prevent unlit gas from entering the appliance if:

- the pilot or main burner fails to light
- the pilot or main burner is extinguished.

These devices are now commonly called flame-supervision devices (FSDs).

There are a number of different types of devices that may be used in gas appliances.

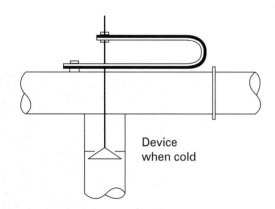 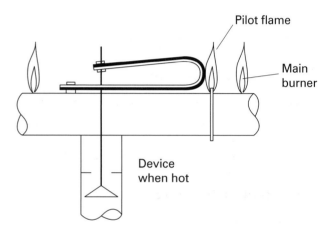

Figure 18.46 Bi-metallic strip

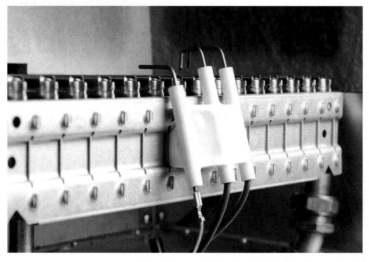

Figure 18.47 Flame rectification

Bi-metallic strip

This device works on the principle of two different metals that expand at different rates. When heat is applied the strip bends, owing to the dissimilar metals causing opening and closing of the gas valve. The bi-metallic strip does not provide very close control and is not now widely used.

Flame conduction and rectification

These work on the principle of the chemical reaction in a flame producing electrically charged ions, the ions flowing through an electrode rectifying the AC output to a DC output. This operates a relay connected to a gas valve.

If the flame fails the flow of ions is terminated and the flame cuts out almost instantaneously. This type of flame supervision device is commonly used on boilers.

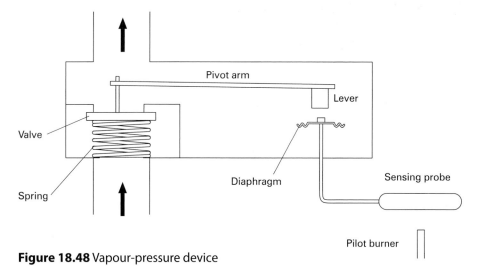

Figure 18.48 Vapour-pressure device

Vapour-pressure device

This device has a sensing probe that contains a liquid which turns to vapour when heated; this vapour has a much greater volume than in its liquid state and can be used to operate a valve. Vapour-pressure devices are more likely to be found in non-electric gas cookers.

Thermo-electric device

This device works on the basis of heat applied to a thermocouple which in turn operates a solenoid valve causing gas to flow. If the thermocouple goes cold, either because the pilot light is not lit or the pilot flame has moved away from the thermocouple, it will go cold, causing the electrical flow in the thermocouple to cease and the solenoid valve to close.

> **Definition**
>
> A thermocouple is a device made from two dissimilar metals that are joined at one end; the other end is connected to a solenoid valve. When heat is applied to the joined ends a small electric circuit is established, sufficient to operate the solenoid valve and cause gas to flow.

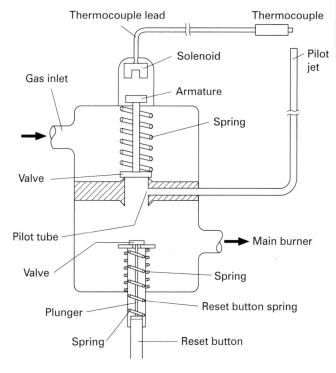

Figure 18.49 Thermo-electric valve – closed position

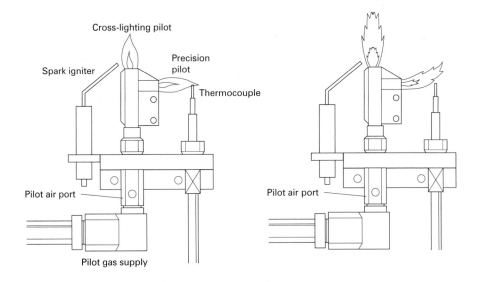

Figure 18.50
Atmospheric sensing device – lack of oxygen resulting in gas valve closure

Atmospheric sensing device

This device works on the principle that if the combustion air becomes contaminated resulting in a reduction in the supply of oxygen, the specially designed pilot lifts away from the thermocouple, causing closure of the gas valve. Atmospheric sensing devices are commonly fitted to flueless or open-flued appliances to provide added protection against incorrect combustion in the appliance.

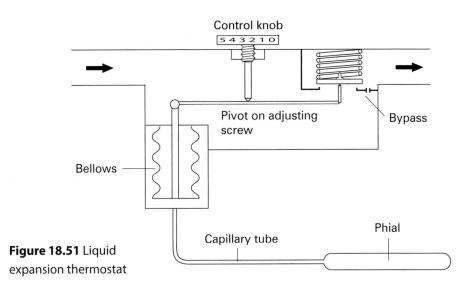

Figure 18.51 Liquid expansion thermostat

Thermostats

Liquid expansion thermostat

This device works on the principle of heat being sensed by a remote phial containing a liquid that expands when heated. On heating the bellows move, causing a reduction in gas flow to the burner. A small bypass port is provided to ensure that a small amount of gas is available at the burner, even when the gas valve is fully closed; this is to ensure that the main oven burner remains alight. When the oven cools, the liquid contracts, moving the bellows and causing an increase in gas flow. Liquid expansion thermostats are usually used on cookers.

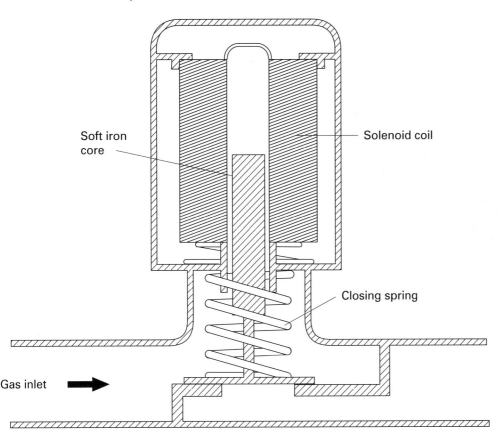

Soft iron core

Solenoid coil

Closing spring

Gas inlet

Figure 18.52 Solenoid valve

Electric thermostat and solenoid valve

Typically an electrical thermostat will be built into an appliance such as a boiler, working on a similar principle to the oven thermostat, but in this case the bellows will expand and operate an electric switch. The switch in turn is connected to a solenoid valve, causing gas to flow into the appliance. This control combination will typically control the main appliance gas flow to the appliance burner.

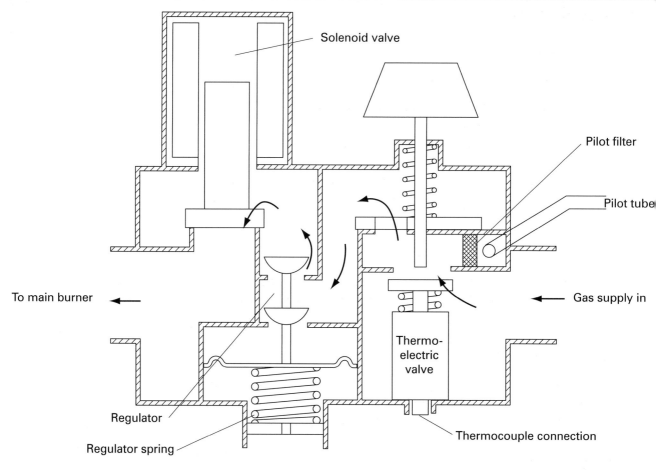

Figure 18.53 Multifunctional control valve

Multifunctional control valve

This device contains several of the control devices mentioned earlier, all sited in the one unit. This provides for space saving and ease of operation. Multifunctional control valves are usually fitted to boilers providing the following control operations:

- main control cock
- constant pressure regulator (adjustable)
- solenoid valve
- flame supervision device (thermocouple)
- igniter.

Figure 18.54
Zero-rated governor

Zero-rated governor

These are now commonly fitted to forced-draught boiler burners. The device works on the principle of suction pressure being created by a fan which activates the governor to allow gas to the main burner. If the fan fails to operate, the governor will not open and gas will not be supplied to the appliance.

Ignition devices

Spark igniters

Spark ignition comes in two forms:

- piezo-electric – a push-button activates crystals to produce approximately 6000 volts at the igniter, creating a spark. This lighter tends to be used for lighting pilots on boilers/water heaters, or lighting a burner on a gas cooker
- mains transformers – a step-up transformer connected to an electrode creates a spark of up to 15,000 volts; these devices are now very common on boilers and cooker ovens.

Permanent pilots

A pilot light is lit either by a taper or using a piezo igniter. Permanent pilots are now gradually being phased out on gas appliances, as they are wasteful in energy.

Filament igniters

These are not used on new appliances but you may still find them on some old ones. They contain a filament that glows when energised from a battery. The heat from the filament lights the pilot light on the appliance.

Gas appliances

Domestic gas boilers

Types of gas boiler

Boilers tend to fall into the following categories:

- regular (traditional) boilers – these have been available for many years and are available as:
  - floor standing
  - wall mounted
  - fire back.

Floor standing and wall mounted models are available with open or room-sealed flueing arrangements. Room-sealed models may also include a fan as part of the flue system. The installation of regular boilers under the Building Regulations is now largely not permitted, as they do not meet the minimum efficiency requirements laid down.

- System boilers – these boilers contain a range of control components within the boiler casing, such as sealed system equipment and pump. System boilers are usually of the wall-mounted room-sealed type and may be regular boilers or condensing.

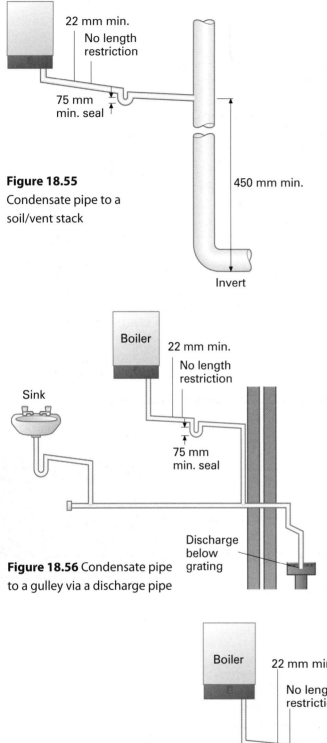

Figure 18.55
Condensate pipe to a
soil/vent stack

22 mm min.
No length
restriction

75 mm
min. seal

450 mm min.

Invert

Boiler

22 mm min.
No length
restriction

Sink

75 mm
min. seal

Discharge
below
grating

Figure 18.56 Condensate pipe
to a gulley via a discharge pipe

- Combination boilers – these appliances supply central heating and hot water from the one unit without the need for a separate storage cylinder. The hot water is usually supplied on an instantaneous basis, with hot water taking priority over the central heating when it is drawn off. They come in wall-mounted and floor-standing options and may be regular boilers or condensing.

- Condensing boilers – these boilers are capable of extracting additional heat from the flue gases (over and above that normally extracted by a regular boiler) to the extent that water vapour collects in the combustion chamber in the form of a weak acid that must be safely discharged to waste.

Condensate pipework

Condensate pipework from boilers must be in a suitable plastic material to avoid corrosion, with the pipework preferably run internally as much as possible to avoid freezing during the winter months. Pipework should be laid to a fall of 2.5 degrees or 50mm per metre run of pipe. Figures 18.55–18.59 show acceptable methods of disposing of the condensate safely to waste.

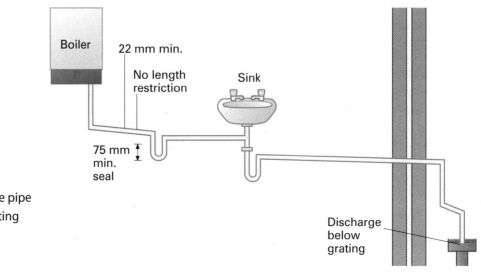

Boiler

22 mm min.
No length
restriction

Sink

75 mm
min.
seal

Discharge
below
grating

Figure 18.57 Condensate pipe
to a gulley via a waste fitting

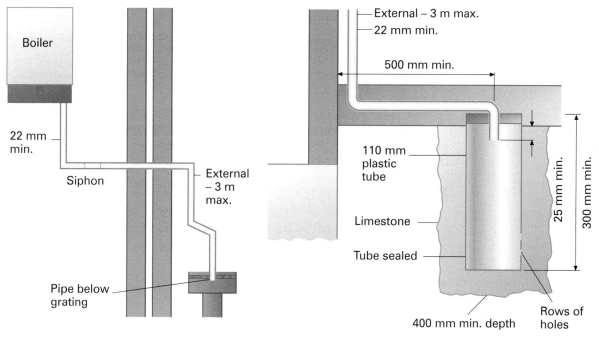

Figure 18.58 Condensate pipe to a gulley via a condensate siphon

Figure 18.59 Condensate pipe to an absorption point

Key boiler installation requirements

General

- new boilers must carry the CE mark showing that they are approved and tested for use in the UK
- the appliance dataplate must be checked to confirm that it is suitable for use with the gas supplied to it
- flue outlets must be correctly positioned and any condensate pipe correctly run.

Installation and location

- a boiler fuelled by LPG should not be installed in a cellar or basement
- room-sealed boilers can be installed in any room, however there are stringent requirements relating to their installation in bathrooms/ shower rooms and it is not particularly recommended that they are installed in bedrooms, bedsits or cloakrooms
- boilers fitted in garages or loft spaces should have frost protection
- boilers must be provided with adequate air supply for combustion and ventilation as shown in BS 5440
- there must be sufficient clearance between the boiler and any combustible materials, the distance will either be prescribed by the manufacturer or be a minimum of 75mm if no guidance is provided by the manufacturer.

Did you know?

The main British Standard dealing with the installation of boilers is BS 6798.

Boiler compartments

- the compartment must be a fixed, rigid structure
- the compartment must have ventilation for cooling (unless indicated otherwise by the appliance manufacturer)
- the air vents to an open-flued boiler in a compartment must not communicate via a bathroom/shower room
- open-flued boilers that have air vents communicating with a bedroom cannot be sized greater than 14kW heat input
- a notice must be fixed warning against using the compartment as a storage cupboard.

Understairs cupboard installations

- for premises of two storeys or less, the cupboard must meet the same requirements as for compartments shown above
- with premises over two storeys, the internal surfaces of the cupboard must be suitably lined to provide a minimum of 30 minutes' fire resistance
- air vents for combustion and ventilation must be directly to outside air.

Bathroom/shower room installations

- these should be avoided wherever possible
- the electrical controls must not be in reach of bath/shower users
- particular attention needs to be made to the correct earthing (bonding) of the boiler and associated pipework.

Bedrooms and bed-sitting rooms

- these should be avoided wherever possible
- a maximum open-flued appliance size of 14kW gross heat input is permitted
- open-flued appliances must be fitted with atmospheric sensing devices.

Roof space installations

- flooring must be provided to give adequate access to the boiler
- fixed lighting must be available
- a loft ladder or purpose made access must be provided
- a guard to prevent contact with stored materials must be fitted.

Domestic gas fires and wall heaters

Gas fires

1. Radiant or convector gas fire to BS 5871 part 1:
- a minimum 125mm diameter flue is normally required
- this type of fire normally requires the installation of a closure plate which is sealed to the fireplace opening
- purpose-provided ventilation is not normally required for appliances up to 7kW heat input.

2. Inset live fuel effect (ILFE) gas fire to BS 5871 part 2:
- a minimum 125mm diameter flue is normally required
- the fire is located either fully or partially inset into a builder's opening
- purpose-provided ventilation is not normally required for appliances up to 7kW heat input.

3. Decorative fuel effect (DFE) gas fire to BS 5871 part 3:
- a minimum 175mm diameter flue is normally required (similar to solid fuel appliances) including:
  - existing masonry chimney
  - existing masonry chimney lined for a solid fuel appliance
  - single or double walled metal flue pipe (dependent on length and location)
  - lined masonry chimney
  - precast flue block system for solid fuel.
- the fire is located in a builder's opening or fireplace recess and may also be fitted under a purpose-made canopy
- purpose-provided ventilation of at least 100cm² is normally required for appliances up to 20kW heat input
- terminals must not restrict the exit of the flue products. Any chimney pot must not be less than 175mm across its axis.

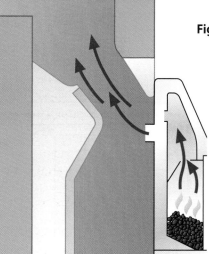
Figure 18.60 Radiant/convector gas fire

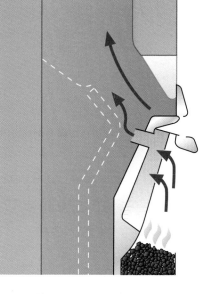
Figure 18.61 Inset live effect gas fire

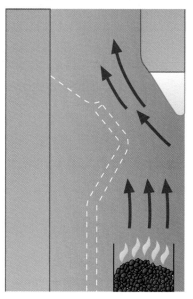
Figure 18.62 Decorative fuel effect gas fire

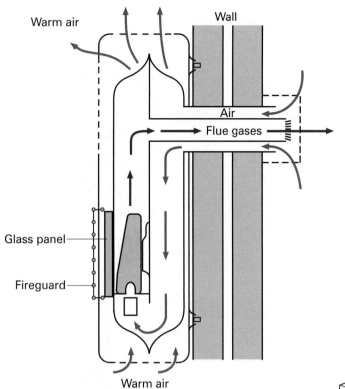

Warm air

Wall

Air

Flue gases

Glass panel

Fireguard

Warm air

Figure 18.63
Room-sealed wall heater

Room-sealed wall heaters

As these are room-sealed appliances they are a safer alternative to the open-flued gas fire. They work on the principle of air in the room being circulated by convection across the hot appliance heat exchanger, which in turn heats the room.

Stoves

Essentially these types of appliance vary little from gas fires; refer to manufacturer instructions for key information on ventilation requirements, etc.

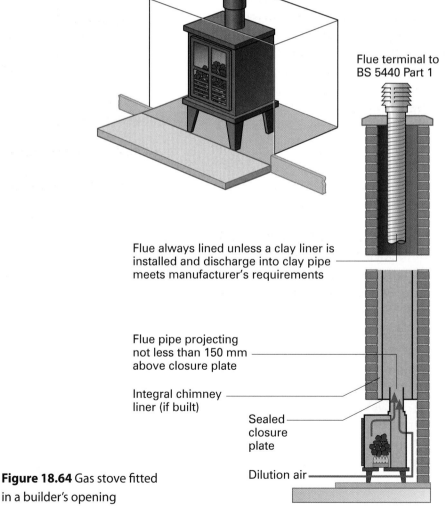

Flue terminal to
BS 5440 Part 1

Flue always lined unless a clay liner is installed and discharge into clay pipe meets manufacturer's requirements

Flue pipe projecting not less than 150 mm above closure plate

Integral chimney liner (if built)

Sealed closure plate

Dilution air

Figure 18.64 Gas stove fitted in a builder's opening

Condensing gas fires

This appliance uses a fan to entrain combustion air from the room, through the heat exchanger and through a 28mm plastic flue pipe. The flue pipe must fall continuously from the appliance to the discharge point in order that condensate is effectively removed, and a safety device such as an air-pressure switch must be fitted to shut down the gas supply in the event of fan failure.

General installation requirements

- Open-flued or indeed flueless appliances must not be sited in bathrooms or shower rooms.
- Open-flued appliances over 12.7kW net input must not be fitted in a room used for sleeping. Open-flued appliances below this figure are permissible provided they are fitted with an atmospheric sensing device.
- The flue to which the appliance is fitted must be suitably constructed.
- There must be a gas tap (service valve) fitted to the appliance for the purposes of service and maintenance.

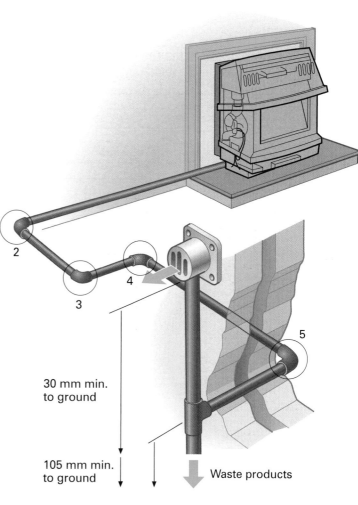

30 mm min. to ground

105 mm min. to ground

Waste products

Figure 18.65 Condensing gas fire

Pre-installation checks

The following outlines the pre-installation checks that should be made prior to the installation of a gas fire:

- visually inspect the flue and check for suitability
- carry out a flue-flow test
- check that the ventilation is suitable
- test any existing installation for tightness.

Closure plate

Some gas appliances require the installation of a closure plate which is sealed to the fireplace opening with heat-proof tape capable of resisting temperatures of up to 100°C. The plate usually includes an air-relief opening which must be maintained to ensure effective operation of the appliance/ flue system.

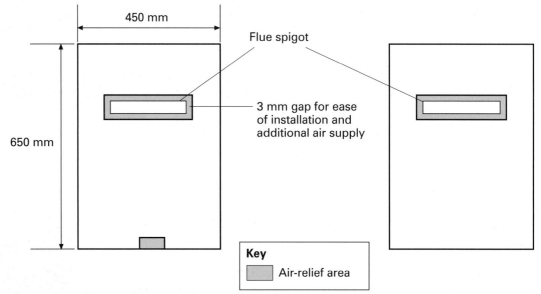

Figure 18.66 Closure plate example

Existing flues/chimneys

Before fitting a closure plate the following requirements need to be checked for existing flues:

- the flue system must not be blocked
- the chimney must be swept if it was previously serving a solid-fuel appliance
- dampers or restrictors must be removed or at least permanently fixed in the open position
- the catchment or void space must be adequate, as shown in Figure 18.67
- all openings in the fireplace opening for pipework, etc. must be properly sealed
- the flue must normally only serve one appliance and one room.

Debris catchment	Masonry chimneys			Block chimneys/flue systems to BS715	
Min. void volume in dm³	Unlined	Lined clay, cement or metal		New/unused	Previously used
		New/unused	Previously used		
2		✓		✓	
12	✓		✓		✓
Min depth in mm				✓	
75		✓			✓
100	✓		✓		

Figure 18.67 Minimum void volume and depth below gas fire spigots

Surrounds and hearths

If the appliance is installed in a builder's opening, fireplace recess or flue box, the hearth must:

- extend throughout the whole base of the opening
- project at least 300mm in front of the naked flame or incandescent part of the fire-bed
- project at least 150mm beyond each side of the naked flame or incandescent part of the fire bed.

If the appliance is free-standing then the hearth must extend completely beneath the naked flame or incandescent part of the fire bed projecting at least 300mm from all sides of the naked flame.

The hearth should not be less than 12mm in thickness and be of a non-combustible material such that its underside cannot reach a temperature higher than 80°C. Greater hearth thickness may be specified by some appliance manufacturers.

Gas supply

A restrictor elbow connected by a chrome tube to the gas fire may be used as an appliance isolation point, in all cases an isolation valve must be provided. Any gas pipework sited in the fireplace recess must be suitably protected against corrosion.

Definition

Incandescent means glowing parts of the appliance.

Domestic gas cookers

Gas cookers may be:

- free standing
- slide in
- built in.

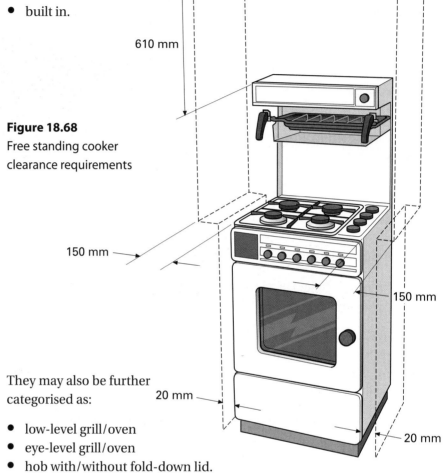

610 mm

Figure 18.68
Free standing cooker
clearance requirements

150 mm

150 mm

20 mm

20 mm

They may also be further
categorised as:

- low-level grill/oven
- eye-level grill/oven
- hob with/without fold-down lid.

Cooker installation requirements

- The cooker must bear a CE mark to show that it is approved for installation in the UK.
- The appliance dataplate must be checked to ensure that it is suitable for the gas supplied to it.
- Specific clearance from combustible materials must be provided as shown in Figures 18.68–18.70.
- Cookers must not be sited in bathrooms or shower rooms.
- Unless it is a single burner, a cooker must not be sited in a bedsitting room of less than 20m³.
- LPG cookers must not be sited in basements or below ground level.
- Draughts should be avoided when siting the appliance.
- Care should be taken when siting in the proximity of curtains.
- A stable base must be provided for a floor-standing cooker.
- Ventilation requirements must comply with BS 5440 shown on page 352 of this guide.

Figure 18.69 Grill clearance requirements

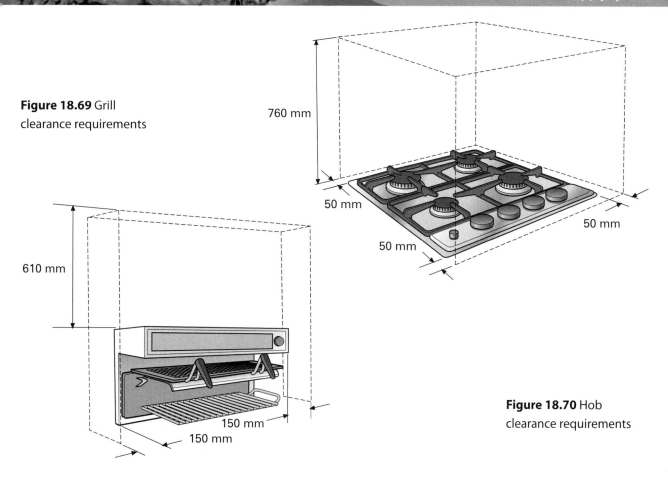

760 mm

50 mm

50 mm

50 mm

610 mm

150 mm

150 mm

Figure 18.70 Hob clearance requirements

Gas connection

Fixed appliances such as a hob sited in a worktop will normally be connected by rigid pipework, which must include an isolation valve. Slide-in appliances will normally be connected by a flexible appliance connector for use with a self-sealing plug-isolation device. Key requirements of this type of installation are:

- the flexible connection should not suffer undue strain and should be kept away from heat sources
- the bayonet fitting should be securely fixed to the wall using a proprietary fitting
- the hose should hang downwards
- different hoses are used for LPG from their natural gas counterparts.

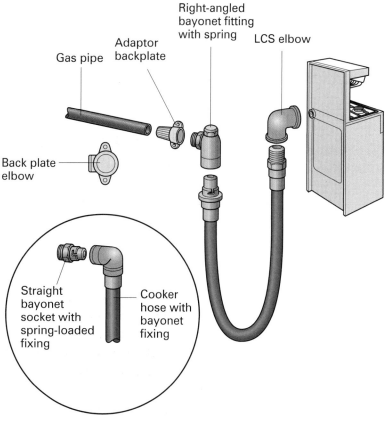

Gas pipe

Adaptor backplate

Right-angled bayonet fitting with spring

LCS elbow

Back plate elbow

Straight bayonet socket with spring-loaded fixing

Cooker hose with bayonet fixing

Figure 18.71 Flexible-appliance gas connections

Stability bracket

A free-standing cooker with a flexible connection must be fitted with a stability device firmly secured to the wall or floor to prevent over-turning of the appliance.

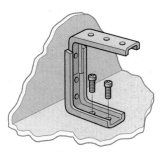

Floor fixing

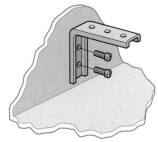

Wall fixing

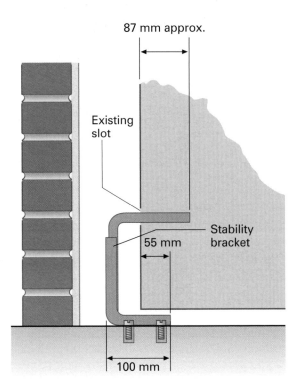

Figure 18.72 Stability bracket

Domestic gas water heaters

There are two main types of instantaneous water heater:

- single point – this type of appliance, as its name suggests, supplies only one outlet point and is usually of the flueless type
- multipoint – these are larger heaters that can supply a number of outlets; the appliance is usually flued by a room-sealed flue.

Gas water heater controls

Fan-assisted water heaters are available, their controls are similar to those shown for a gas boiler and will not be detailed further here. The following range of components can form part of a typical natural draught water heater (please note that some parts are not used in single-point heaters).

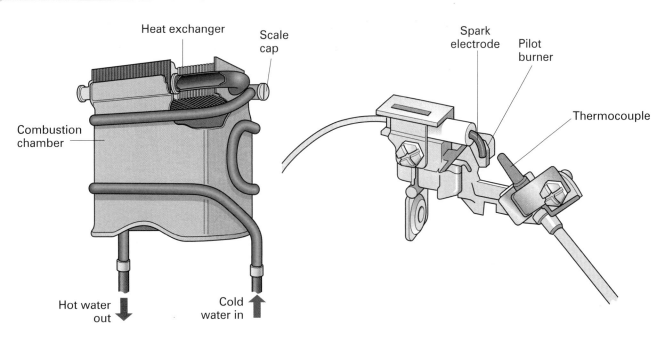

Figure 18.73 Heat exchanger

Figure 18.74 Flame-supervision device

Heat exchanger

Heat from the burner is transferred to the heat exchanger containing a large finned surface area. As the water is heated instantaneously, the slower the water passes through the exchanger, the hotter it becomes.

Flame-supervision device (FSD)

The water heater usually includes a thermocouple type flame-supervision device that energises a thermo-electric valve with heat from a pilot light. If the pilot light fails, the thermo-electric valve closes and gas will not pass into the appliance.

On flueless appliances a thermal switch and/or atmospheric sensing device will be included to prevent the appliance from overheating and working if combustion air becomes depleted of oxygen.

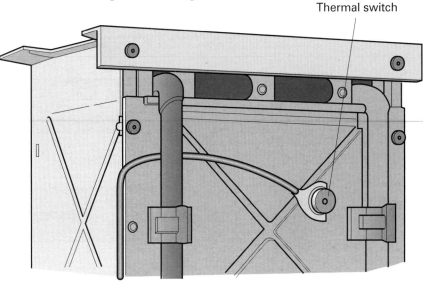

Figure 18.75
ASD/thermal switch

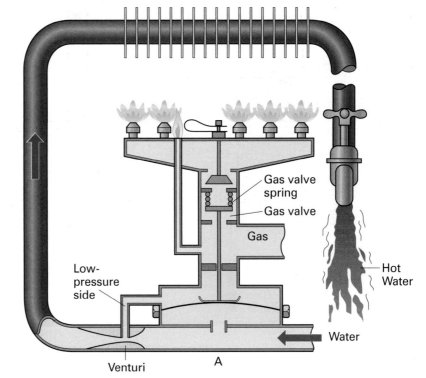

Figure 18.76 Automatic valve in open position

Gas valve spring

Gas valve

Gas

Low-pressure side

Hot Water

Water

Venturi

A

Automatic valve

The heater contains an automatic valve which turns the gas supply on to the main burner when a tap is opened. The amount of gas entering the appliance is determined by the water flow rate through the appliance.

Temperature selector

More sophisticated models contain electric thermostatic control components. Simple heaters can contain a temperature selector; this device simply increases or reduces the amount of water flowing through the venturi and hence the rate of gas flowing to the burner.

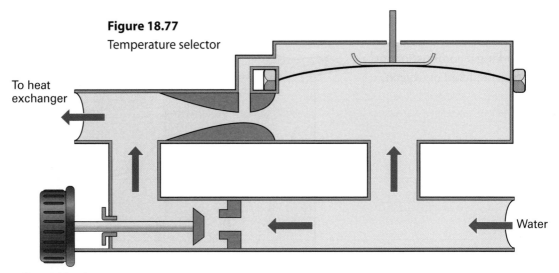

Figure 18.77
Temperature selector

To heat exchanger

Water

Control knob

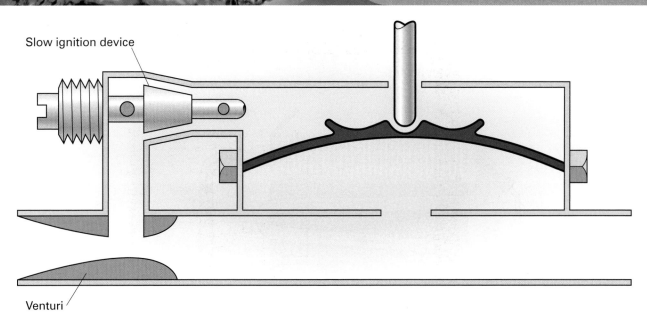

Slow ignition device

Venturi

Figure 18.78 Slow ignition device

Slow ignition device

A slow ignition device is included in larger water heaters such as multipoints, to allow the burner to ignite safely and quietly, owing to the large quantity of gas it consumes and so prevent noisy ignition. The simplest form of slow ignition device is the loose ball shown in Figure 18.78.

Multipoint water heater

Figure 18.79 shows the components in situ in a large multipoint water heater.

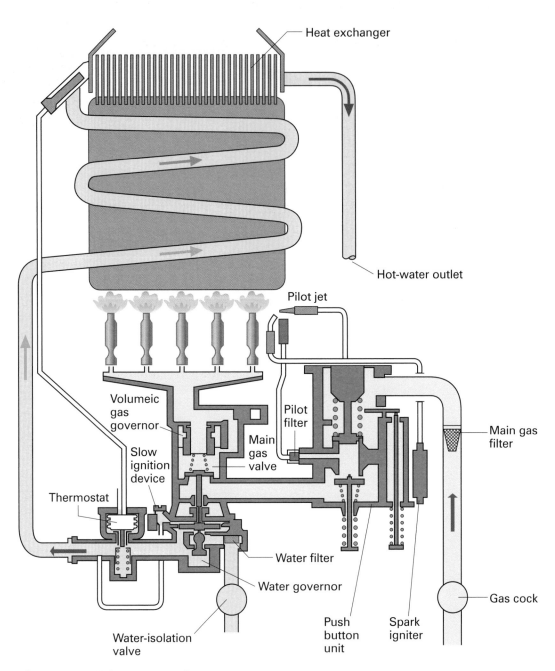

Figure 18.79 Multipoint water heater

Key water heater installation requirements

The following points must be considered in installing a water heater:

- the appliance must carry a CE mark to confirm that it is approved for use in the UK
- the appliance dataplate must indicate that it is suitable for the gas supplied
- a flueless heater must only be used to provide water in the room in which it is sited
- all new instantaneous water heaters must be room-sealed or if single-point flueless they must have an atmospheric sensing device
- only room-sealed appliances can be fitted in bathrooms and shower rooms
- if they are to be installed in rooms used for sleeping:
  - all appliances over 14kW heat input must be room-sealed
  - appliances less than 14kW can be room-sealed or flueless, provided the ASD is fitted
  - rooms with a volume less than 20m³ can only be fitted with room-sealed appliances
- flueless appliances must not be fitted in compartments or cupboards.

Did you know?
BS 5546 lays down the requirements for installing water heaters.

Short answer questions

1. Which two items of statutory legislation lay down the requirements for installing gas appliances?
2. Is it acceptable to use hemp on threaded joints to gas pipework?
3. State two methods of protecting copper gas pipework sited in an existing fireplace opening.
4. What are the four stages of tightness testing a low-pressure installation?
5. What is the gas rate of an appliance fed by a U6 meter if the time taken for one revolution of the test dial is 62 seconds and the CV of the gas is 1040 btu/ft³?
6. What is the dangerous gas that may be produced as a result of incomplete combustion?
7. What is the free area of ventilation required for correct combustion of a 23kW gross open-flued boiler?
8. What is the free area required for compartment ventilation of a 23kW net open-flued boiler in which the air will be provided from a room in the building?
9. Under the gas industry unsafe situations procedure, what will an open-flued appliance spilling its products of combustion into a room be categorised as?
10. What is the name of the device fitted to a gas water heater that prevents noisy ignition?

Multiple-choice test

Part 1 – Questions 1 to 10 require access to the Gas Safety (Installation and Use) Regulations. These may be accessed at: http://www.opsi.gov.uk/si/si1998/19982451.htm.

1. Which one of the following installations is covered under the Gas Safety Regulations?
   a) Gas boiler fitted in an ACS centre
   b) Gas cooker fitted in a training centre
   c) Bunsen burner in a college
   d) Gas boiler in a rented property

2. Which of the following is directly responsible for ensuring that a gas operative is competent to undertake gas work?
   a) Employer
   c) Health & Safety Commission
   b) Employee
   d) CORGI

3. Under the gas regulations, when breaking into existing gas pipework, resulting in exposed gasways that either contain or have contained gas, the operative must:
   a) Not smoke or use any ignition source
   b) Only use push-fit fittings
   c) Only use compression fittings
   d) Remove all the gas from the pipework with a vacuum pump

4. All gas appliances must be fitted with which of the following:
   a) Permanently fixed flue
   b) Means of isolation
   c) Terminal
   d) CO detector

5. Under the Regulations, when a gas supplier has been informed of a gas leak, they must attend to the escape within what time period?
   a) 30 minutes   c) 12 hours
   b) 1 hour   d) 24 hours

6. Which of the following materials is prohibited from use in a new gas pipework system?
   a) Corrugated stainless steel
   b) Low-carbon steel
   c) Copper
   d) Lead

7. If a gas operative needs to leave site, under the Regulations any incomplete or disconnected section of gas pipework must be:
   a) Turned off at the emergency control valve
   b) Sealed with an appropriate gas fitting
   c) Reported to the customer
   d) Plugged with cloth to prevent dirt ingress

8. Under the Regulations, the handle of an emergency control valve must be:
   a) Parallel to the axis of the pipe when in the open position

b) *Parallel to the axis of the pipe when in the closed position*

c) *Removed on commissioning a new installation*

d) *Fully locked in its open position*

9. When installing a flued domestic gas appliance, an installer must ensure that:
   a) *The flue is metallic*
   b) *The flue is completely accessible throughout its length*
   c) *Gas is supplied through permanently fixed rigid pipework*
   d) *Capillary fittings are not used in the pipework system*

10. Under the Regulations, an installer of a second-hand gas appliance must:
    a) *Verify it as in a safe condition to use*
    b) *Not use second-hand appliances*
    c) *Label the appliance as second-hand*
    d) *Service the appliance before installation*

Part 2

11. A gas pipe through a cavity wall is sleeved in order to prevent:
    a) *The removal of the pipe*
    b) *Gas escaping into the cavity*
    c) *A decrease in pressure in the pipe*
    d) *An increase in pressure in the pipe*

12. Copper tube for use in gas pipework systems must conform to the requirements of:
    a) *BS EN 875*   c) *BS 5440*
    b) *BS EN 1057*   d) *BS 6700*

13. How much cover must be provided above buried exterior pipework with pedestrian traffic?
    a) *25mm*   c) *150mm*
    b) *40mm*   d) *375mm*

14. What is the maximum distance from a meter outlet to the main continuity bond to a gas pipework system?
    a) *100mm*   c) *600mm*
    b) *250mm*   d) *1000mm*

15. What is the recommended minimum distance between gas supply pipework and electrical cables?
    a) *10mm*   c) *100mm*
    b) *25mm*   d) *150mm*

16. A 'let-by' test on a low-pressure installation should be carried out across which of the following time periods?
    a) *30 seconds*   c) *2 minutes*
    b) *1 minute*   d) *3 minutes*

17. During tightness testing, what is the maximum pressure drop on gas pipework fitted with a U6 meter?
    a) *No pressure drop is allowed*
    b) *2 mbar*
    c) *4 mbar*
    d) *8 mbar*

18. A gas escape can be traced using which of the following?
    a) *A lighted taper*
    b) *Multi-meter*
    c) *Soap solution*
    d) *Flue gas analyser*

19. What is the gas purge volume for an installation containing an E6 meter?
    a) $0.010m^3$ c) $0.050m^3$
    b) $0.035m^3$ d) $0.10m^3$

20. What is the maximum allowable pressure drop between a gas meter and an appliance inlet when sizing gas pipework?
    a) *0.5 mbar*   c) *1.5 mbar*
    b) *1.0 mbar*   d) *2.0 mbar*

21. An appliance that has a flame whose speed is too high and being pushed away from the burner ports is said to be suffering from:
    a) *Lighting back*   c) *Flame lift*
    b) *Oxygen depletion*   d) *Undergassing*

22. What is the ventilation required for a boiler of 15.7kW net heat input?
    a) $30.2 cm^2$ c) $87 cm^2$
    b) $43.5 cm^2$ d) $102.2 cm^2$

23. An air vent to a gas appliance in which air is provided through a cavity wall must be:
a) Open to the cavity
b) Fitted with a flyscreen
c) Fitted with a shutter
d) Continually sleeved

24. What is the minimum distance between an open-flued appliance outlet and the first bend in the flue pipe?
a) 250mm   c) 600mm
b) 500mm   d) 1000mm

25. The minimum space between an open flue pipe and any combustible material is:
a) 10mm   c) 50mm
b) 25mm   d) 75mm

26. Vitreous enamel flue pipe is not recommended for:
a) Connecting to a gas boiler in a kitchen
b) Connecting to a stove in a lounge
c) Connecting to a range in a kitchen
d) Connecting to a terminal outside the building

27. The minimum distance between a room-sealed fanned draught boiler terminal and a gutter should be:
a) 50mm   c) 250mm
b) 75mm   d) 300mm

28. Under what height above ground level should a room-sealed flue terminal be fitted with a flue guard?
a) 150mm   c) 2000mm
b) 600mm   d) 2500mm

29. The draught break to a vertex flue system should be sited a minimum of what height above any loft insulation?
a) 150mm   c) 600mm
b) 300mm   d) 900mm

30. What type of test is carried out to determine the suitability of an existing chimney for use with a gas appliance?
a) Flue leakage test   c) Infiltration test
b) Air leakage test   d) Flue flow test

31. A new gas fire to be installed in a bedsitting room must be fitted with which of the following?
a) Electronic ignition
b) Fanned flue
c) Atmosphere sensing device
d) Condensate discharge pipe

32. What type of device minimises noisy ignition in a gas water heater?
a) Automatic valve   c) Slow ignition
b) Temperature selector   d) Venturi

33. What type of device is used to prevent a free-standing cooker from overturning?
a) Bayonet and hose   c) Siting bracket
b) Stability bracket   d) Screw fixings

34. An LPG gas boiler must not be sited in which of the following locations?
a) Roof space   c) Under-stairs cupboard
b) Compartment   d) Basement

35. Which of the following documents must be left with the customer on commissioning a gas appliance?
a) A plan of the completed installation
b) Bill of quantities
c) Appliance user instructions
d) Boiler installation template

19   Employment rights and responsibilities

By the end of this chapter you should be able to demonstrate understanding of the following employment-rights topics which will assist you in completing knowledge assessment in the Additional Unit of the Level 2/3 Certificate in Domestic Plumbing Studies:

- Discrimination:
  - Discrimination on the grounds of race
  - Sex discrimination
  - Discrimination on the grounds of religion or belief
  - Discrimination on the grounds of sexual orientation
  - Discrimination against disabled people
- Basic employment rights:
  - Statement of employment
  - Entitlement to paid leave
  - Termination of employment
  - Wages and statutory sick pay
  - Maternity/paternity leave
  - Time off work
  - Minimum wage
  - Working hours
- The plumbing industry:
  - Plumbing industry bodies
  - Career development.

Discrimination

Discrimination on the grounds of race

It's unlawful to discriminate against someone, either directly or indirectly, on the grounds of race, colour, nationality – including citizenship – or ethnic origin, under the Race Relations Act 1976. Racial harassment is defined as a form of discrimination.

Did you know?

Discrimination on the grounds of a person's accent does not count under the Race Relations Act.

As with other forms of discrimination, it can be either direct or indirect on the grounds of race.

- Direct discrimination may include treating somebody less favourably on the grounds of their race, colour, ethnicity or national origin.
- Indirect discrimination can occur when an employer applies an apparently general rule that in practice disadvantages people of a particular race, colour, ethnicity or national origin, and which cannot be justified.

This form of discrimination applies to the way employers recruit, train and promote their staff, to how they select people for dismissal on the grounds of redundancy, and to employers who refuse to provide a reference for an employee after they have left.

Sex discrimination

As with other types of discrimination, sex discrimination can be direct – treating somebody less favourably on the grounds of their sex – or indirect – applying an apparently general rule which in practice disadvantages one sex and which cannot be justified. It includes the way employers recruit, train, promote and dismiss people. Former employees have the right to bring an action after they have left against an employer who discriminates against them.

The penalties for sex discrimination can be high, both for organisations and individuals, since there is no limit on compensation.

There are no length-of-service or age requirements in bringing a claim, and claimants who are employees do not need to have left employment.

The law is explicit that less favourable treatment of women on the grounds of pregnancy or maternity leave counts as unlawful sex discrimination.

The law makes sexual harassment – and harassment on the grounds of sex – explicitly unlawful in employment or vocational training. Sexual harassment can include insensitive jokes, displays of sexually explicit material, sexual innuendos or lewd comments or gestures.

Pay and conditions

Women and men are entitled to equal pay and conditions for work of equal value. Work may be different from that of a colleague of the opposite sex, but it can be considered of equal value if it is similar or the same in terms of the demands of the job.

Discrimination on the grounds of religion or belief

Discrimination against an employee or job candidate on the grounds of their religion or belief became unlawful from December 2003 under the Employment Equality (Religion or Belief) Regulations.

The regulations apply to discrimination on the grounds of religion or religious belief. They cover discrimination on the grounds of perceived as well as actual religion or belief and the religion or belief of colleagues and/or customers.

As with other forms of discrimination, the legislation recognises both direct and indirect discrimination on the grounds of religion or belief.

- Direct discrimination may occur in areas such as recruitment, selection, training, promotion, selection for redundancy or dismissal, when one person is treated less favourably than another because of their actual or perceived religion or beliefs.
- Indirect discrimination occurs when an employer applies a provision or practice that disadvantages people of a particular religion or of particular religious beliefs and which cannot be justified.

The regulations also outlaw:

- harassment – unwanted conduct that violates people's dignity or creates an intimidating or offensive atmosphere
- victimisation – treating people less favourably because of something they have done under or in connection with the regulations, such as making a formal complaint of discrimination or giving evidence in a tribunal case.

There are no length-of-service or age requirements in bringing a claim, and where the claimant is an employee, they do not need to have left employment.

Discrimination on the grounds of sexual orientation

Discrimination against an employee or job candidate on the grounds of their sexual orientation became unlawful from December 2003.

The Employment Equality (Sexual Orientation) Regulations apply to discrimination on grounds of orientation towards persons of the same sex (lesbians or gays), the opposite sex (heterosexuals) and the same and opposite sex (bisexuals). They cover discrimination on the grounds of perceived as well as actual sexual orientation and the sexual orientation of someone with whom the person associates or works.

As with other forms of discrimination, the legislation recognises both direct and indirect discrimination on the grounds of sexual orientation.

- Direct discrimination may occur in areas such as recruitment, selection, training, promotion, selection for redundancy or dismissal or in awarding employment-related benefits, when one person is treated less favourably than another because they are – or are thought to be – lesbian, gay, bisexual or heterosexual.

- Indirect discrimination occurs when an employer applies a provision, criterion or practice that disadvantages people of a particular sexual orientation and which cannot be justified.

From 5 December 2005, indirect discrimination could also occur where a civil partner is treated less favourably than a married employee on a range of employment rights and employee benefits, including the right to:

- make a request for flexible working
- statutory paternity leave and pay for a newborn child or newly adopted child
- vocational training
- access to a benefit that is given to a married employee – such as a pension or private health care.

Discrimination against disabled people

It is unlawful for any employer, regardless of size, with the exception of the armed forces, to directly discriminate against a disabled person because they are disabled. Also they must not discriminate against a disabled person for a reason related to their disability, unless this can be justified.

What counts as a disability?

The Disability Discrimination Act 1995 defines a disability as a physical or mental impairment that has a substantial and long-term adverse effect on the ability to carry out normal day-to-day activities. This doesn't include drug or alcohol abuse or a tendency to start fires, steal or physically abuse others, amongst other exclusions.

What employers must not do

An employer mustn't treat a disabled person less favourably than other members of staff. For instance, they cannot refuse to interview, employ, train or promote a disabled person, simply because of their disability. Since 1 October 2004, harassment on the grounds of disability has also been explicitly outlawed.

What employers must do

Employers have a duty to make reasonable adjustments to enable a disabled person to work or continue working.

Penalties for discrimination

Where an employment tribunal finds that disability discrimination has occurred, penalties can be high, since there is no limit on compensation.

There are no length-of-service or age requirements in bringing a claim and where the claimant is an employee, he or she does not need to have left employment.

Basic employment rights

Under employment legialstion you are entilted to the following employment rights:

Statement of employment

Employment law requires that you receive a statement of employment (previously known as contracts and conditions of employment) within two months of starting work. The statement should usually cover the following:

- the name of your employer and your name
- the date your employment started
- your job title and a summary of your duties
- the period of employment, stating whether it is a permanent position
- the place of work
- how much you will be paid, how often, and the method of payment; it should also include information such as travel allowances and any deductions from pay
- hours of work
- holiday entitlement
- procedures for dealing with absence from work through illness, or for other reasons, and how to notify the employer if absent
- details of pension scheme if applicable
- details of how to terminate employment (for example, length of notice required by both you and your employer)
- disciplinary rules and procedures (these are usually contained in a separate document such as a staff handbook)
- grievance procedures (which again could be contained in a staff handbook).

> **Did you know?**
>
> An employer must enter into negotiation with you before making amendment to your statement of employment.

Entitlement to paid leave

On starting a job you qualify immediately for holiday leave and pay. You have a statutory entitlement to four weeks of paid leave a year, the four weeks may include payment for bank holidays.

Termination of employment

In order to dismiss you your employer must provide good grounds for the dismissal, if you have been in employment for 12 months or more, a claim of unfair dismissal can be made to an employment tribunal if the grounds are deemed to be unfair. The notice period in terms of a dismissal should be as follows:

- a minimum of one week if employed between one month and two years
- an additional week's notice for every continuous year of employment between two and twelve years
- a minimum of 12 weeks' notice if in continuous employment for 12 years or more.

> **Did you know?**
>
> Your employer is not obliged to allow you to carry over paid leave from one year to another.

Wages and statutory sick pay

An employer is required to provide a payslip showing:

- your gross wages earned (before deductions)
- the amounts of and reasons for any deductions, e.g. national insurance
- your net or take-home pay.

If you are off sick for four consecutive days or more (assuming a doctor's certificate is provided) you are entitled to Statutory Sick Pay (SSP). SSP is paid by the employer in the same way that wages are paid; records must therefore be kept of payments made and absences lasting over four days. The employer is responsible for payment of SSP for up to 28 weeks.

Maternity/paternity leave

Maternity leave

All pregnant employees – regardless of length of service or the hours they work – are entitled to:

- paid time off for antenatal care
- normal sick-pay rights for pregnancy-related sickness
- at least 26 weeks' paid maternity leave – Ordinary Maternity Leave.

All pregnant employees and those on Ordinary Maternity Leave are entitled to:

- their normal contractual benefits, e.g. holiday rights
- the right to return to the same job.

Some mothers qualify for Additional Maternity Leave as well as Ordinary Maternity Leave.

To qualify they must have at least 26 weeks' service (full or part-time) by the end of the fifteenthth week (the qualifying week) before the Expected Week of Childbirth.

Women with this service can take up to another 26 weeks' leave, starting at the end of Ordinary Maternity Leave. Additional Maternity Leave is unpaid.

A woman who has taken additional maternity leave has the right to return to the same job, or if that is not reasonably practical, to a similar job.

Paternity leave

Employees with at least one year of service are entitled to 13 weeks' unpaid parental leave for each child, which can be taken before their child is five, and if agreed can be added to normal maternity, paternity or adoption leave. Leave must be taken in blocks or multiples of one week.

Time off work

Employers are required to give time off work for a number of reasons such as jury service, to attend trade union training sessions, etc. In addition, employees aged 16 and 17 who did not reach a certain standard of education at school, have the right to reasonable time off with pay while working to study for a qualification that will help them reach that standard.

Minimum wage

The National Minimum Wage Act lays down the minimum wage that must be paid to workers in the following categories:

- main adult rate – aged 22 and over
- development rate – 18- to 21-year-olds
- 16- to 17-year-old workers.

Note: Apprentices under the age of 19 are not entitled to the NMW; nor are apprentices aged 19 to 25 who are in the first 12 months of their apprenticeship.

Working hours

Requirements for working hours are laid down in the Working Time Regulations. Workers aged 18 or over cannot be forced to work for more than 48 hours a week on average. However, most workers can agree in writing to work longer than the 48-hour limit. The agreement must be signed by the worker. Workers can cancel the opt-out agreement whenever they want to, although they must give their employer at least seven days' notice. For young workers (under 18) the maximum working week is 40 hours.

Did you know?

The standard working week for plumbing operatives as laid down by the JIB is 37.5 hours.

The plumbing industry

The plumbing industry is part of:

- The Mechanical Engineering Services (MES) sector, also including the following industries:
  - heating and ventilating
  - refrigeration and air conditioning
  - gas fitting.

- The Mechanical Engineering Services Industry forms part of the wider Building Services Engineering Industry, containing:
  - plumbing
  - heating and ventilating
  - refrigeration and air conditioning
  - electrical installation.

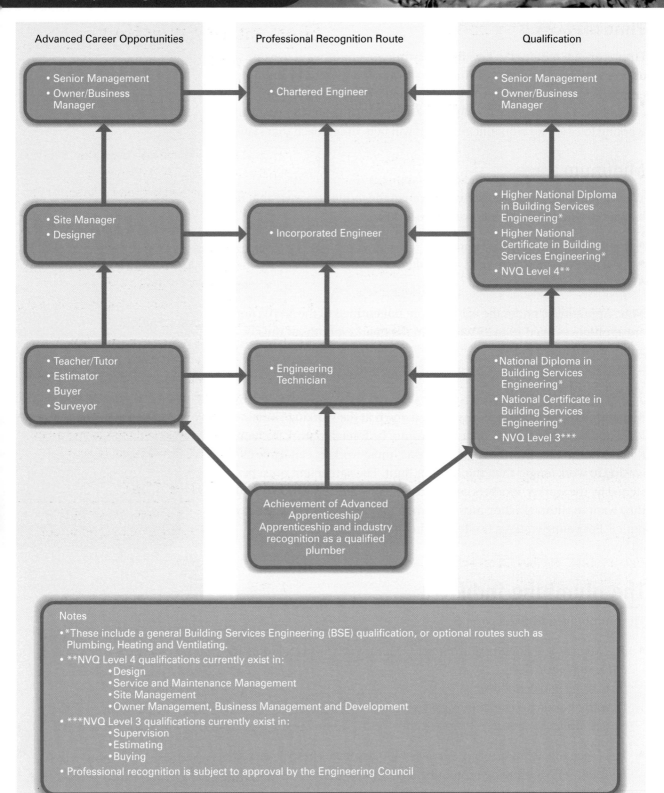

Figure 19.1 Career development paths

Plumbing industry bodies

The following outlines the key plumbing industry bodies:

- Association of Plumbing and Heating Contractors (APHC) – the principal plumbing employers' trade association in England and Wales, providing a range of services to its employer members.
- AMICUS – the principal trade union representing the interests of plumbing employees and providing a range of services to its members.
- Joint Industry Board for Plumbing and Mechanical Engineering Services (JIB for PMES) – an interface between employers and the union in setting national terms of pay and conditions for operatives in the industry.
- Institute of Plumbing and Heating Engineering (IPHE) – the professional institute representing individual members in issues such as technical development and standards development.
- SummitSkills – the sector skills council reponsible for the education and training needs of the industry, e.g. qualifications and labour needs.
- JTL – the national training provider for the industry, providing apprenticeship opportunities for plumbers and electricians.

Career development

Figure 19.1 shows the career-development paths that can be progressed in the industry.

Short answer questions

1. Which Act defines discrimination on the grounds of race?
2. Which employers are exempt from the requirements of the Disability Discrimination Act?
3. An employee's employment conditions will be detailed in which type of document?
4. Which Act is designed to protect the safety of people at work?
5. How long does a worker have to be in employment with a company before a claim for unfair dismissal can be made for non-payment of the national minimum wage?
6. What are the two types of discrimination on the grounds of sexual orientation?
7. What is a father's right to paternity leave?
8. What type of document will be required in order for an employer to pay Statutory Sick Pay?
9. Which organisation is the plumbing employers' trade association in England and Wales?
10. Which external assessment tests form part of the Plumbing NVQ Level 3 qualification?

Multiple-choice test

1. In what year was the Employment Equality (Religion or Belief) Regulations introduced?
   a) 1995
   b) 2000
   c) 2003
   d) 2005

2. Who is exempt from the requirements of the National Minimum Wage Act?
   a) All employees
   b) All employees aged 16 to 18
   c) All employees over 21
   d) Apprentices under 19 years of age

3. What type of procedure will an employee use when in dispute with their employer over their terms and conditions of employment?
   a) Grievance procedure
   b) Conflict procedure
   c) Arbitration procedure
   d) Conciliation procedure

4. Companies must give employees access to a stakeholder pension if they employ more than how many members of staff?
a) 2
b) 5
c) 7
d) 10

5. Which organisation in the plumbing industry sets the pay and conditons of plumbing operatives?
a) AMICUS
b) APHC
c) SummitSkills
d) JIB for PMES

6. How long after commencing work does an employee become entitled to receive holiday pay?
a) Immediately
b) 1 month
c) 6 months
d) 12 months

7. An employee must receive a statement of employment within what period after commencing employment?
a) 1 week
b) 2 weeks
c) 1 month
d) 2 months

8. What period of notice must be given to an employee who has been with a company for 6 months?
a) 1 day
b) 1 week
c) 2 weeks
d) 1 month

9. The minimum paid holiday entitlement for employees is:
a) 1 week
b) 2 weeks
c) 4 weeks
d) 8 weeks

10. A claim for unfair dismissal would be heard by:
a) A Magistrate's Court
b) A Crown Court
c) The European Court
d) The Employment Tribunal

Chapter 1 – Health and safety

Short answer questions

1. When employing five or more operatives (more than four)
2. Before the work commences
3. A permit-to-work system
4. Injuries resulting in three days off work
5. Mechanical lifting device
6. The work must cease in the immediate location and the matter must be reported to the employer/site agent
7. Local exhaust ventilation is preferred or full breathing apparatus
8. High-impact resistant with clear lenses
9. The helmet must be replaced immediately
10. Low-voltage cordless power tools

Multiple-choice test

1. c) an employer is responsible for providing personal protective equipment
2. a) HASAWA applies to all operatives on construction sites
3. d) the Health and Safety Executive is responsible for the enforcement of health and safety legislation
4. a) blue asbestos must only be removed by licensed contractors
5. c) canteen facilities, the other items fall under different legislation requirements
6. c) safety glasses must be worn at all times when lead welding
7. b) rubber gloves will provide the most effective protection
8. c) Weil's disease (Leptospirosis)
9. d) a dust mask will provide adequate protection for this, provided it is replaced when the filter is clogged
10. d) 110V transformers are yellow

11. b) three months is the recommended interval for PAT testing on construction sites
12. a) each time a power tool is used a visual inspection should take place to check that it is in a safe condition to use
13. b) Class 1 for heavy industrial use
14. c) 75° or a ratio of 4 up to 1 out
15. c) the ladder should project approximately 1m above a working platform
16. a) guard rails and toeboards must be fitted above 2m in height
17. d) COSHH stands for Control of Substances Hazardous to Health
18. c) propane is extremely flammable
19. a) freeze burns are possible from cylinders drawing gas at too high a rate
20. b) a mandatory sign is shown, using a white symbol on a blue background
21. b) danger electric shock
22. a) Class A involving solid materials
23. d) a foam extinguisher has a cream panel
24. a) location of the incident so that assistance may be despatched as soon as possible
25. a) the first action in the event of a fire should be to raise the alarm
26. d) headache tablets are not items of first aid and should not be stored in a first-aid kit
27. a) burns should be treated by bathing with cold, clean water
28. b) removal by an insulator (non-conductor) such as dry timber; wet timber can conduct electricity
29. b) mushroom-headed chisels are a danger to eyesight, in particular through flying splinters
30. c) under PUWER, operatives must be properly trained and instructed in the use of work equipment

Chapter 2 – Effective working relationships

Short answer questions

1. Building Regulations Part L
2. Building plans
3. Public Limited Company
4. Deals with the costs on a project, negotiates payments from clients and arranges payments to suppliers and sub-contractors
5. Supervises a number of specific trade operatives, e.g. plumbers
6. He/she is involved in the design of structures from a safety perspective, making sure that they function correctly and are not subject to collapse
7. To check that work meets the minimum requirements laid down in the Water Regulations by reviewing notifications of work before it takes place and checking work after it has been carried out
8. Formal communication means in writing with a record of the communication, it is therefore by e-mail
9. NVQ Level 3 in Plumbing
10. The matter should be reported to a company official such as a manager in order that the problem can be addressed

Multiple-choice test

1. c) Water Regulations deal with cold water systems installation issues
2. d) approximately 80% of businesses employ between one and four operatives
3. a) a description of a limited company is provided
4. c) the architect creates building designs
5. b) a clerk of works (project manager) carries out this role
6. d) construction is not part of the BSE sector
7. c) day-to-day responsibility for an apprentice is dealt with by the plumbing supervisor
8. d) this type of communication is usually by verbal instruction
9. c) the response to this question essentially relates to the job responsibilities of the plumbing operative, typically a major work item such as this should be handed to the supervisor for resolution given the cost implications
10. c) politeness will assist with positive communication

Chapter 3 – Key plumbing principles

Short answer questions

1. $7.7 \times 1000 = 7700$kg
2. kg/m³
3. $6 \times (30 - 5) \times 0.00018 = 0.027$m or 27mm
4. Clip-on thermometer or differential digital thermometer
5. 100°C
6. Temporary hardness
7. Patina
8. 1 metre head = approx. 0.1 bar, so 10 metres = 1 bar
9. Radiation
10. Formula V=I×R, $240 = 2 \times R$, R = 120 ohms

Multiple-choice test

1. c) water is at its maximum density at 4°C
2. b) the pascal can also be expressed as N/m²
3. c) plastics tend to have a higher expansion rate than their metal counterparts
4. b) $15 \times (60 - 20) \times 4.2 = 2520$ kJ
5. a) copper is the best conductor of heat
6. c) 1 metre = 0.1 bar, so 0.8 bar = 8 metres
7. b) the rate of electrolytic corrosion is primarily affected by the relative positions of the two metals in the electromotive series
8. c) relative density is the density of a substance in comparison with the density of water
9. b) $5 \times 9.81 = 49.05$ kPa/m²
10. c) siphonage will only occur if the receiving container is below the container from which the water is drawn
11. b) a double-trap WC functions on siphonic action
12. c) gravity circulation takes place by convection
13. d) nitrates
14. d) when flashing to steam it can expand by up to 1600 times its original volume

15. b) on changing state from a liquid to a gas the molecules move further apart
16. b) elbows will create the greatest frictional resistance
17. d) lead is not a ferrous metal
18. b) amperes are the SI unit for electrical current
19. a) watts = volts × amps, 700 = 240 × A = 2.92A, approx. 3A
20. c) the mcb for an immersion heater is sized at 16A

Chapter 4 – Common plumbing processes

Short answer questions

1. This type of information would be contained in a job specification
2. By covering them with dust sheets, taking care at all times to avoid tripping hazards
3. A quotation is used for fixed prices
4. X dimension = 12 mm, for the 2 fittings 2 × 12 = 24 mm, length of pipe is 850 – 24 = 826 mm
5. Maximum diameter of a hole is 0.25 of the depth of the joist
6. Teeth pointing forward
7. Copper tube wheel cutter
8. It is more important to ensure the availability of the WC than other equipment by the end of the working day
9. Mirror screws
10. Ensure that the escape is reported to the gas emergency service provider as soon as possible

Multiple-choice test

1. b) a work programme details when work the different types of work should be carried out to construct the property
2. c) a delivery note should be provided when materials are brought to site
3. b) the BSI Kitemark is a recognised marking for tested and approved products
4. a) when removing cylinders the most important action is to plug the tappings in order to avoid any spillage; significant spillage can seep through dust sheets
5. b) fetching some sheets should be the most logical answer to the problem
6. c) the matter must be reported to the customer either directly or indirectly by the plumbing company; the work must only be carried out by competent staff working in CORGI registered businesses
7. b) distance taken by bend is 5 × 15 × 2 × 3.14/4 = 118mm; overall length of pipe is (550 + 400) – 118 = 832mm
8. d) maximum distance from the joist bearing is span/4, 5000/4 = 1250mm
9. d) the joint is an example of a push-fit fitting
10. c) a capillary end-feed fitting requires solder wire
11. b) a manipulative compression (type B) fitting
12. c) Grade Y is used for underground supply pipework
13. c) LCS tube is bent with a hydraulic bender
14. c) medium-grade LCS is colour-coded blue
15. a) using adhesive tape across the hole will provide grip and avoid slippage damage to the tile
16. b) spring toggle type of fixing
17. c) maximum vertical clipping distance of 2.4m
18. d) a subcontractor is under contract to the main contractor
19. a) a building control officer checks and approves work as conforming to the Building Regulations
20. b) on completing a job the customer must be provided with any user instructions for the equipment installed

Chapter 5 – Cold water systems

Short answer questions

1. 15mm
2. 10 litres/60 seconds = 0.6 litres/second
3. Isolation valve such as a supply stop valve
4. Cisterns up to a capacity of 1000 litres
5. Isolate the pump from the supply, preferably at the consumer unit, remove and retain the fuse or lock the mcb and check for safe isolation using an approved voltage-indicating device
6. To place a warning notice adjacent to the isolation point advising that the supply should not be turned on

7. When carrying out work in larger properties such as an industrial/commercial premise

8. Quarter turn pillar or mixer tap

9. BS 1212 part 1 Portsmouth type valve

10. The washer is loose or split

Multiple-choice test

1. b) since 1999, Water Regulations have been in place, outlining the statutory requirements for the installation of cold water systems

2. c) manufacturer installation instructions will provide detailed guidance

3. c) the maximum depth for external supply pipework is 1350mm

4. a) The vertical length of the pipe must be insulated down to a depth of 750mm

5. a) cold water service pipework is colour-coded blue

6. a) a means of draining off the system should be provided after the supply stop valve

7. b) an indirect system of cold water supply should be used in domestic properties with low supply pressures

8. b) 100 litre is the minimum recommended storage capacity

9. b) a service valve is fitted to a cold water to a cold water storage cistern for isolation/ maintenance purposes

10. a) Water Regulations recommend connections in the base of the cistern to minimise the build-up of sludge

11. d) a warning pipe includes a filter to prevent the ingress of insects

12. b) checking the number and type of connections from the cold water storage cistern should identify whether the system is direct or indirect

13. a) a cold water cistern fitted without a lid will prevent the greatest risk

14. b) 25mm is the minimum distance

15. a) low-carbon steel must not be used on hot and cold water systems

16. a) 1.2m is the maximum recommended clip distance for a horizontal 15 mm pipe

17. d) Water Regulations identify that the test pressure should be 1.5 times the maximum working pressure

18. d) a soundness test must be maintained over 60 minutes

19. c) Water Regulations identify that no dead-legs must be left on supply pipework so removal of the complete tee is required

20. b) open ends must be properly sealed in case the supply is inadvertently turned on

21. a) by re-washering the valve

22. c) a circlip is associated with a tap that has a non-rising spindle

23. a) given the need to maintain toilet facilities in this type of property the best and indeed most cost-effective solution is to do the work outside normal working hours

24. b) some cisterns require a plastic support plate at the float valve, the omission of this can lead to a high pitched vibration as the float valve closes

25. d) no action is necessary, a supply stop valve may be fitted as a service valve

26. a) the question describes a classic case of a small air lock in the pipework

27. c) a defect in the seat in a pillar tap can usually be overcome by the use of a reseating tool

28. c) the pipework joints to a cold water storage cistern are made with plastic washers and PTFE tape (where required)

29. a) Pinholing is more likely to be caused by acidic water

30. c) A temporary continuity bond must be used to ensure that the pipework system continues to be connected to earth

Chapter 6 – Hot water systems

Short answer questions

1. Water Supply (Water Fittings) Regulations; Building Regulations

2. Drain valve

3. Gate valve

4. For safety purposes, should the supply to the cold water storage cistern fail, hot supplies to appliances will run out before cold

5. Single impellor pump (one pipe feed only after the mixer valve)

6. Modern systems usually employ polybutylene plastics

7. Sink pillar or mixer tap with non-rising spindle
8. To avoid parasitic one-pipe circulation and undue energy consumption
9. Sufficient allowance has not been provided for thermal movement, the pipes are running tight against timber materials such as the joist
10. Apply a temporary continuity bond

Multiple-choice test

1. d) the building plan will provide this information
2. a) materials provided on site by a merchant will be outlined in a delivery note which will normally require a signature from a representative of the plumbing company
3. a) a single-feed indirect cylinder uses an air bubble to separate the waters
4. c) 28mm pipework is the minimum recommended circulator size
5. b) 22mm minimum open-vent pipe size
6. c) the minimum head recommended is usually 1000mm; however, manufacturer instructions must be consulted at all times
7. a) the open-vent pipe to the primary circuit must discharge over the feed and expansion cistern
8. d) no valve must be fitted, to ensure that in an overheat situation the system is safe
9. c) a multipoint appliance provides a number of outlets
10. b) trace heating applied to pipework dead-legs reduces water wastage and energy consumption
11. b) the f&e cistern must be sized to contain the expanded system water without overflowing
12. d) there should be a clear path between the cylinder and the open-ended vent pipe over the cold water storage cistern, which for safety purposes should not contain any type of valve
13. a) a secondary circulation pump will be controlled by a time clock with water flow through the secondary circuit only occurring while the building is occupied
14. b) a magnesium sacrificial anode is used
15. b) 110 litres is regarded as a minimum storage capacity for a small domestic property

16. b) limescale build-up is caused by temporarily hard water
17. c) an immersion heater is usually set at 60–65°C
18. a) owing to the effects of stratification, the water temperature will be greater at the top of the cylinder than the bottom
19. b) a secondary circulation system is shown
20. a) only capillary fittings jointed with lead-free solders must be used
21. c) open ends of systems connected to the live supply even though they have been isolated at a stop valve must be properly blanked to prevent the supply being turned on
22. b) 30 minutes' standing time for water temperature stabilisation purposes
23. c) a plumber is most likely to encounter this type of record when working in an industrial property in which the work activity may be strictly regulated
24. c) thermostatic mixer valves may contain integral check valves
25. b) a leaking packing gland if water appears only when the tap is opened
26. d) overheating could be caused by thermostat failure
27. b) the cold feed pipe to the cylinder should be isolated to minimise the need for draining the system and drawing off hot water
28. c) this is a symptom of the hot water pipework being run too close to the cold and heating of the cold water pipework taking place when water is not being drawn off
29. b) a low-pressure manual mixer valve should be fed from a balanced (equal) low pressure supply such as from storage; connections must not be made from the supply pipework
30. b) the cold feed pipe must fall continuously to the hot water cylinder; falling into the cistern will mean that it is rising as it comes out of the cistern, so creating an airlock

Chapter 7 – Central heating systems

Short answer questions

1. Building Regulations Approved Document L1
2. Fully pumped system with 2 × two-port valves
3. In order to avoid unwanted circulation when the central heating circuit is turned off
4. 10 litre nominal capacity
5. To improve the circulation in the gravity primary circuit to the hot water storage cylinder by using some influence from the central heating pump
6. Site approximately 1.5 m from floor level
   Avoid draughty areas
   Position in a location where it can freely sense the room air temperature
7. Automatic bypass valve
8. It must discharge over the feed and expansion cistern
9. Check to ensure that the pressure pins to the TRV body on each are operating freely and are not subject to sticking in the closed position
10. Use the safe isolation procedure:
    - remove and retain the fuse
    - use an approved voltage-indicating device to check for isolation
    - test the operation of the voltage-indicating device before use (test on a known supply)
    - test the operation of the device after the test to make sure it is working
    - only work on the component if all points of the procedure have been met.

Multiple-choice test

1. c) manufacturer instructions provide this type of information
2. b) the one-pipe circuit is a continuous loop, so the last radiator will be cooler than the first
3. c) the minimum recommended size is 28 mm
4. b) 22mm is the minimum recommended open-vent pipe size
5. a) 15mm is the minimum recommended cold-feed pipe size
6. d) an air separator is used to closely group the cold-feed and open-vent connections
7. b) 'pumping over' of the vent pipe is likely as the open vent pipe is connected at a point of high pump pressure
8. c) it is normal practice to raise it to a height of not less than 450mm
9. c) 25mm is the absolute minimum distance
10. a) a mid-position valve can provide heat to both circuits together
11. b) a remote sensor is used with a thermostatic radiator valve
12. b) a pipe thermostat is wired in series with the frost thermostat to minimise the amount of energy used to keep the components free of frost
13. b) a room heater has a water thermostat which regulates by means of a flap the quantity of air permitted to enter the fire-box and hence the rate of burning
14. c) the description outlines a condensing boiler
15. d) a common port is usually marked Port AB showing that it carries supplies to both space and hot water circuits in the system
16. b) automatic air vents are sited at the highest points in a system (where necessary) to vent them of air
17. a) panel radiators require air flow for convection purposes to make them provide the desired heat output
18. b) usually recommended as 1.5 times the maximum working pressure
19. b) a neutralising compound is used prior to treatment with a corrosion inhibitor
20. c) is the most important action; although d) is possible, it would normally be considered impractical in a domestic property
21. c) creating a temporary vacuum is the most economical, provided air cannot enter the system; whilst d) may be considered more economical it is very risky and could create significant water damage, so would not normally be considered
22. b) this fault identifies a circulation problem in the system likely to be attributable to pump failure
23. c) a TRV must be sited in an area of free air circulation in the room, the fitting of a remote sensor head to the TRV sited away

from the bookcase should overcome the problem

24. b) the question describes a leak from a defective packing gland

25. a) the most likely cause is a defect in the auxiliary (micro) switch in the two-port valve causing the pump and boiler to receive a permanently live electrical connection

Chapter 8 – Electrical systems

Short answer questions

1. Electricity at Work Regulations; Building Regulations
2. Only competent personnel authorised by the electricity supplier (i.e. their own staff)
3. Residual current device
4. Circuit with permanently fixed appliances
5. Circuit feeding portable appliances
6. $8500 = 240 \times$ Amps, Amps $= 8500/240 = 35.4$A, nearest device usually 40A
7. Supplementary bonding
8. Heat-resistant cord
9. Trunking
10. MCB locking device

Multiple-choice test

1. c) BS 7671 Requirements for electrical installations
2. c) standard supply is 240V ac
3. c) these devices are contained in the consumer unit
4. d) the isolation switch is sited in the consumer unit
5. b) the standard rating for this application is 30mA
6. b) standard MCB rating for a central heating circuit directly connected to the consumer unit is 6A
7. b) the standard rating is 15A
8. b) 2.5mm twin and earth cable is normally used for this application
9. d) the standard size for this application is 10mm
10. a) the live conductor is brown
11. d) the final connection must be from an unswitched connection unit

12. b) a grommet (rubber bush) is used where a cable enters a metal box to prevent the box 'cutting' into the cable
13. b) only pull-cord switches of the double-pole type are suited to this application
14. c) a wiring centre is used for this application
15. b) an immersion heater must be supplied directly from the consumer unit
16. b) tight coils in cables result in resistance to the flow of electricity, which in turn results in heating
17. d) a strip connector is shown
18. b) a screw terminal is shown
19. c) an earth continuity test is used to establish this
20. b) a polarity test is used to establish this
21. c) the customer should be advised that the electricity supply is being tuned off
22. d) an approved voltage-indicating device should be used
23. c) when isolating at a fused spur the fuse and its holder (if possible) should be removed and retained in your pocket until the work is completed
24. d) isolation of this appliance must take place at the consumer unit; A and B are considered unsafe as the supply could simply be switched back on
25. a) a proving unit is used for this application

Chapter 9 – Above-ground discharge systems

Short answer questions

1. Building plans (drawings)
2. An electric drill and hole saw
3. Access pipe
4. Bird or wire cage
5. Drain connector
6. Danger of heavy falling objects
7. Usually by replacing the trap with a resealing trap or fitting ventilating pipework
8. momentum
9. Test plug or inflatable bag
10. Metal drive-in brackets

...ple-choice test

1. b) Part H Drainage and Waste Disposal
2. c) a job specification details the type of materials to be used
3. d) manufacturer instructions provide detailed guidance on the installation of plumbing components
4. b) enamelled pressed steel is the only option
5. c) wastes for baths are usually supplied as a kit containing rubber washers
6. a) a pressure-reducing valve is used
7. b) a modern alternative to the siphon is the drop valve
8. b) Water Regulations maximum flush volumes are 4 litre short flush and 6 litre long flush
9. a) the electrical connection in this type of location must only be made by an unswitched connection unit
10. a) unslotted wastes are used with appliances that do not have overflows
11. d) low-level bath trap
12. d) S-traps are particularly susceptible to trap seal loss by self-siphonage if not installed in line with regulation requirements
13. c) bottle traps because food matter can readily collect in them
14. c) 50mm, requirements for this changed with the 2002 version of Part H of the Building Regulations
15. c) 450mm is the minimum distance
16. b) this is a description of a primary ventilated stack system
17. c) it should rise to a height of 900mm
18. d) the component is a bird cage (vent terminal)
19. a) a smoke test should not be carried out on plastics as it can degrade them
20. c) the system is tested at 38mm water gauge for three minutes
21. b) as part of the test procedure all traps must be filled with water, the others are incorrect statements
22. a) checking and adjusting WC water levels is an essential check of the maintenance programme, the other points would not normally be a part of such a programme
23. a) manufacturer instructions will provide this detail

24. d) capping the pipe end with a bung should be the preferred option; newspaper may permit smells into the property
25. c) this is a description of a combined system
26. c) a trapped gulley is required with this type of system to prevent smells arising from the drainage system
27. a) this is an ogee gutter section
28. c) 1 in 600 is the usual recommended fall
29. d) a string line is used to lay gutter brackets in a straight line to the correct fall
30. d) this is a sign of the felt underlay disintegrating and not effectively directing the water into the gutter

Chapter 10 – Sheetlead work

Short answer questions

1. Lead Sheet Association
2. Local exhaust ventilation or breathing apparatus coupled with medical surveillance for staff
3. Lead dresser
4. Turn off the acetylene control first, then the oxygen control
5. Soaker length = gauge + lap + 25mm = 250 + 125 + 25 = 400mm
6. Soakers and step flashing to abutment with secret gutter
7. Code 3
8. Copper, tinned copper or stainless steel
9. Formula for circumference = $\pi \times D = 3.14 \times 200$ = 628 + 5mm = 633mm in length
10. Wind lift is the most likely cause of sheet lead movement on a roof

Multiple-choice test

1. d) this type of information will be provided in building plans
2. d) rolled sheet lead is manufactured to BS EN 12588
3. b) the recommended minimum code is code 4
4. c) code 5 is the minimum recommended code for bossing a front apron
5. b) sheet lead is used because of its malleability and the ease with which it can be formed to fit complex building shapes

6. b) nerve damage may be an outcome of lead poisoning
7. d) the tool is a chase wedge
8. a) continuous step flashings are set out and marked using a folding rule
9. c) oxygen bottles are colour-coded black
10. c) the gauges should be set at 0.14 bar
11. c) a carburising flame will be established, which is undesirable for lead welding
12. b) a butt joint is used for forming a back gutter
13. b) the recommended width of a sheet lead weld to code 4 is 10 mm
14. c) a copper clip can be used for this application
15. d) a valley gutter is not part of a chimney weathering set
16. d) a bossed front apron should be produced from a sheet lead roll 300mm in width as a minimum
17. a) LSA minimum recommendation is 150mm
18. b) the upstand should measure 100mm from the base of the gutter back rising up the back of the chimney
19. d) 175mm is the recommended minimum width – 75mm for the vertical upstand and 100 mm lap under the tiles
20. b) a storm collar is fitted to prevent water penetration into the property
21. c) the water line measurement is 65mm
22. c) LSA recommended spacing for wedges is 300–450mm
23. d) mastic is preferred as it permits some degree of movement
24. b) fatigue is caused by expansion/contraction movement of the sheet lead – it is made worse when sufficient room for thermal movement is not provided
25. a) lead and aluminium mixed in a salty environment leads to corrosion

Chapter 11 – Environmental awareness

Short answer questions

1. Standard Assessment Procedure
2. Boiler interlock
3. Solid fuel; Gas; Oil
4. Minimise the wastage of materials through inaccurate cutting and bending
5. That equipment is energy efficient
6. Cease working in the area of the material and report the matter to the employing company
7. Skip; Taking to an authorised waste disposal site
8. Sanitaryware
9. Body responsible for the drainage system local authority or water company
10. To provide proper instruction to the customer on the use of the boiler and leave the user instructions

Multiple-choice test

1. b) Building Regulations classifies them as controlled services
2. b) the pipework should be insulated up to 1.0m, or up to the point where it becomes concealed
3. c) a blowtorch is used to make capillary soldered fittings
4. c) solar power does not produce harmful emissions
5. d) the only acceptable method is to use a proprietary fitting
6. b) dead-legs reduce the efficiency of hot water systems
7. a) a waste-carrier's licence is required to transport waste materials for disposal
8. c) polystyrene will produce noxious fumes when burnt
9. a) the disposal of refrigerators is controlled by legislation owing to possible harmful emissions
10. a) the proper setting of controls is essential in reducing energy consumption

Chapter 12 – Customer care

Short answer questions

1. Clean and tidy workwear; Clean shoes – not dirtying carpets; Clean and tidy company vehicles
2. Answer based on an individual who has invited your company to undertake work in their property, often their home. The private customer will often have very little knowledge

of plumbing systems and will need explanation of what is happening as various parts of the job are progressed. The private customer will have a number of expectations of the work that you are doing

3. Verbal communication; Written communication

4. Written communication

5. Verbal communication

6. Answer based on – possibly not paying for the work, going to your company's competitors for work in the future or leaving potential customers with a bad impression of your company

7. Answer based on – not getting angry, in a low calm voice identifying the extent of the problem and then offering either a temporary or a permanent solution

8. Customer complaints procedure

9. Commissioning record (Benchmark Logbook)

10. Someone whose expectations of a job are well beyond the price they are prepared to pay; Someone who commissions work but has no intention of paying

Multiple-choice test

1. b) It should only be necessary to sheet the immediate work area when carrying out a standard service; if the boiler is very sooty for some reason, better protection may be necessary

2. a) an apology together with a good reason should be provided and the work should be re-scheduled if possible

3. b) the policy will include detail on customer complaint procedures

4. c) it is normal for the pump to be reported to the manufacturer for action, which may include providing a replacement, or a visit by a service engineer

5. a) the remaining items may be classed as commercially sensitive by the company

6. b) of the four options listed, responding to information requests promptly is likely to improve customer care, there is every possibility that the others could effect good customer care

7. a) a satisfaction sheet is used to check that the customer is satisfied with the work and adequate customer care has been provided

8. d) they should preferably be disposed of by the plumber unless otherwise agreed with the customer

9. b) a complaints procedure should be followed to ensure consistent application from complaint to complaint

10. b) effective staff training is more likely to result in the effective application of the customer-service policy

Chapter 13 – Advanced cold water systems

Short answer questions

1. Water Supply (Water Fittings) Regulations

2. Refuse consent; Grant consent; Grant consent with conditions

3. Compliance certificate

4. When the foundations were being built (laid)

5. Proprietary fitting, e.g. leadloc

6. Test for flow rate (using a weir gauge) and pressure (using a pressure gauge)

7. The system must be disinfected

8. Type AA air gap

9. Type AUK3 air gap

10. Pipework covered with waterproof insulation to 750mm depth below ground level; Mechanical protection to pipework to protect against knocks

Multiple-choice test

1. c) the Water Industry Approved Plumber Scheme

2. c) an Approved Contractor can issue a Water Regulations compliance certificate

3. b) bituminous materials are prohibited from the water supply

4. c) the minimum depth is 750mm

5. b) the BSI kitemark is shown

6. b) in a cold roof there should be no insulation under the base of the cistern in order to keep it warm

7. a) the cistern must be fully supported across its base, any chipboard surface under a cistern must be water-resistant material

8. d) hot and cold water pipework must not be ducted or chased into external wall surfaces to avoid frost

9. d) it must be routed around the chamber to avoid a possible contamination risk

10. a) a spherical plug valve is more likely to be used, owing to its suitability for high pressures and low cost

11. b) a temperature stabilisation period of 30 minutes must be allowed for before the test commences

12. c) pipework is tested to 1.5 times the maximum operating pressure

13. c) 30PPM, if less than this then the disinfection process must be repeated

14. d) unwholesome water with a high risk such as grey water recycling must be colour coded

15. a) a type AA air gap is shown

16. d) water in a bidet bowl is fluid category 5 – a serious health risk

17. b) fluid category 3 is a slight risk to health

18. b) a type ED double-check valve would be used, the others are either not suitable or uneconomic

19. c) it must be sited a minimum of 150mm above the urinal bowl

20. d) the plumber will usually require access to the commissioning manual

Chapter 14 – Advanced hot water systems

Short answer questions

1. 65°C

2. Building Regulations Approved Document L

3. Before the pipework is concealed

4. Fluid category 2

5. Check valve

6. Yes – unless the work is being carried out by an Approved Contractor

7. Pressure switch

8. 8 litres / 60 seconds = 0.13 l/s

9. 55°C

10. Cold water storage cistern

Multiple-choice test

1. d) the vent pipe is designed to prevent the hot water temperature from reaching 100°C at any time

2. c) a time clock is installed to control the operation of the pump (circulation in the system) during periods when hot water is not normally required in the building

3. a) system flushing should be carried out immediately prior to performance testing

4. b) the chlorine concentration should be 50PPM

5. c) a thermostatic mixing valve is used to control the temperature at hot water outlets

6. c) details will be found in the manufacturer installation instructions

7. c) as a minimum temperature and flow should be measured

8. a) an instantaneous water heater in which the temperature of water is directly linked to the flow rate from the appliance

9. d) it is not permissible to install an ascending spray bidet on a supply pipe

10. c) a shock arrestor may have to be fitted to protect against the pressure effects in the pipeline when the lever-operated taps are slammed shut

11. d) 12m is the maximum length of uninsulated draw-off for a 22mm pipe

12. a) a water governor provides a constant flow of water

13. c) an energy cut-out device (high-limit thermostat) provides protection against control thermostat failure

14. b) the minimum distance between the water level and the invert to the warning pipe is 25mm

15. d) the customer is likely to require to be advised that the system is not in operation due to commissioning

Chapter 15 – Unvented hot water systems

Short answer questions

1. Building Regulations – Parts G&L; Water Regulations

2. A hot water storage system incorporating a storage vessel that does not have an open vent to atmosphere
3. The expansion valve
4. Copper; Lined mild steel; Stainless steel
5. Cylinder air gap (bubble top); Expansion vessel
6. 500mm
7. Discharge via HEPvO valve to soil system
8. From the table the minimum pipe size that could be used with 11m pipe length is 35mm diameter, up to a maximum length of 18m (including fittings):
   - The reduction brought about by the elbows is 3 × 1.4 = 4.2m
   - The maximum pipe length including the elbows is 18m – 4.2m = 13.8m
     As the 13.8m permitted with the three elbows is greater than the actual length of 11m, the 35mm pipe size is suitable
9. Defective temperature-relief valve; Faults with the thermostats
10. Reinstating the cylinder air gap by partially draining the cylinder and refilling

Multiple-choice test

1. d) Component 9 is the tundish
2. c) Component 4 is the expansion valve
3. b) Component 2 is the control thermostat
4. b) Component 5 is the expansion vessel
5. c) Component 7 is the pressure-reducing valve
6. a) Component 1 is the high-limit thermostat
7. d) Component 8 is the line strainer
8. c) Component 6 is the check valve
9. b) Component 3 is the temperature-relief valve
10. a) the three-tier level of safety protection is provided by 1 – high-limit thermostat, 2 – control thermostat and 3 – temperature-relief valve
11. b) Part G – hygiene and Part L – energy conservation
12. d) 6 bar is a typical expansion valve setting
13. c) 80–85°C
14. d) the Building Regulations require control devices to prevent 100°C being reached
15. b) the system should be tested to 1.5 times the working pressure
16. c) the minimum distance should be 300mm

17. b) position would be found on installation drawings
18. d) a temperature relief valve has an integral test device
19. a) a hot tap should be opened to let air into the system to replace the water
20. c) a burst diaphragm on the expansion vessel could cause nuisance discharge of the expansion valve

Chapter 16 – Advanced above-ground discharge systems

Short answer questions

1. Fluid category 5
2. The dimensions (size) of the human body
3. Approved Document H
4. Installation drawings (building plans)
5. A ventilated branch discharge system will usually be chosen for this type of application in larger buildings
6. Long radius bend with a centre line radius of 200mm; 2 × 45° bends
7. To give access to any lengths of pipe that cannot be reached from any other part of the system
8. 1.7m
9. Air-admittance valve or resealing trap; Branch ventilating pipework to outside air; Branch ventilation pipework to ventilating stack
10. 6 litre long flush; 4 litre short flush

Multiple-choice test

1. d) BS EN 12056 details the requirements for sanitary pipework installation
2. c) in the primary ventilated stack system it is preferable for the appliances to be closely grouped around the main stack
3. c) the branch must be a minimum of 450mm above the invert level of the drain
4. a) the discharge unit method is used for pipe sizing purposes
5. d) two 80mm diameter WCs will require a 100mm discharge stack (one 80mm WC will only require 75mm)
6. b) the minimum dimension must be 200mm

7. b) a collar boss (soil manifold) overcomes the need to apply the minimum cross flow dimension

8. c) the bend radius should be a minimum of 25mm

9. b) pipework at too shallow a gradient may result in blockage occurring

10. b) the ventilating pipework must connect within 750mm of the trap

11. a) a 45° entry tee should be used to ensure that the basin waste is swept in the direction of the flow

12. c) the pipe must rise to a minimum height of 900mm above the opening if the outlet is within 3m of the opening

13. b) the valve contains a collapsible membrane

14. d) the maximum height is 2000mm to the highest sanitary appliance connection

15. b) a dripping float-operated valve in the WC may cause nuisance operation of the macerator unit

16. a) the protective tape must be removed before the installation work begins to check and make sure that the appliances are not damaged

17. b) a commissioning record may need to be completed to indicate the results of soundness and performance testing of the system

18. c) above-ground systems must be tested at a pressure of 38mm water gauge for three minutes

19. d) 25mm must be left in the trap seal

20. c) it is recommended that a performance test be carried out three times

Chapter 17 – Advanced central heating systems

Short answer questions

1. Minimum of 28mm diameter for gravity circulation

2. Negative pressure – positive pressure changes to negative at cold-feed pipe (the system configuration is undesirable)

3. Pump-overrun thermostat

4. Room thermostats or programmable room thermostats in all zones, or a room or programmable room thermostat in the main zone and individual TRVs on radiators in the other zones, or a combination of both of the above

5. 3 bar

6. Manifold; Spider

7. Neutral point

8. 1.5 times the maximum operating pressure

9. That it will satisfy the needs of the hot water system

10. Seasonal Efficiency of Domestic Boilers in the UK

Multiple-choice test

1. d) the Building Regulations contain details of hearth construction requirements

2. a) top, bottom, opposite end to promote better gravity circulation

3. b) minimum capacity is 100 litres

4. b) the minimum dimension is 25mm

5. d) interlock is an energy conservation requirement

6. b) a 3 amp fuse is used in a fused connection unit for a standard domestic central heating system

7. c) approximate temperature of 70°C

8. a) manufacturer instructions will detail the correct commissioning procedure

9. a) a type CA backflow preventer can be used, the others are unsuitable for a permanent connection

10. c) as a minimum a thermo-mechanical valve needs to be fitted

11. b) the vent pipe should rise to 450mm above the water level

12. b) 15 mm is the normal discharge pipe size

13. a) the minimum fall is 2.5°

14. c) excess flow of water is regulated by an automatic bypass valve

15. d) 10mm earthing cable is used for main bonding purposes

16. b) the gauge should be capable of reading 0 to 4 bar

17. a) a bicycle pump can be used to charge the pressure in an expansion vessel

18. b) kettling could be caused by insufficient water flow rate through the heat exchanger

19. c) the commissioning process includes balancing

20. b) system cleanser is added prior to treating with corrosion inhibitor

Chapter 18 – Gas supply systems

Short answer questions

1. Gas Safety (Installation & Use) Regulations; Building Regulations – Part J

2. No – pipework should be jointed with jointing paste or PTFE

3. Copper pipe coated by the manufacturer in a plastic sheath; Copper pipe wrapped with protective coating such as PVC tape

4. Visual inspection; Let-by test; Pipework only test; Complete installation test

5. $\dfrac{3600 \times 1040}{62} = 60{,}387$ btu/hr or

$60{,}387 / 3412 = 17.7$ kW

6. Carbon monoxide

7. Convert gross to net – 23 kW$/1.1 = 20.9$ kW
$20.9 - 7$ kW (adventitious ventilation) =
13.9 kW $\times 5$ cm² $= 69.5$ cm² (free area)

8. High level – 10 cm² $\times 23$ kW $= 230$ cm²
Low level – 20 cm² $\times 23$ kW $= 460$ cm²

9. Immediately dangerous

10. Slow ignition device

Multiple-choice test

1. d) a gas boiler in a rented property falls under the regulations, the rest are out of scope

2. a) the employer is directly responsible for ensuring that operatives are competent

3. a) the operative must not smoke or use any ignition source in such a manner as may lead to a risk of fire or explosion

4. b) any gas appliance must include a means of isolation such as a gas tap

5. c) a gas supplier must attend to the leak either by repair or cutting off within 12 hours

6. d) lead is excluded from use on a new pipework system

7. b) if leaving site, the pipe end must be sealed with an appropriate fitting

8. a) the handle must be parallel to the axis of the pipe when in the open position

9. c) a flued appliance must be connected by permanently fixed rigid pipework

10. a) under the regulations an installer must verify that the appliance is in a safe condition to use

11. b) a primary aim of the sleeve is to prevent gas escaping into the cavity

12. b) copper gas pipework must conform to BS EN 1057

13. b) 40mm minimum cover must be provided above buried pipework with pedestrian traffic

14. c) the maximum distance is 600mm

15. b) the recommended minimum distance is 25mm

16. b) the let-by test should be conducted for a period of 1 minute

17. a) no pressure drop is allowed to new or existing gas pipework

18. c) a gas escape can be traced using soap solution (leak-detection fluid)

19. a) the purge volume for an E6 meter is 0.010 m³

20. b) the maximum allowable pressure drop is 1 mbar

21. c) flame lift is occurring

22. b) $15.7 - 7 = 8.7$ kW $\times 5$ cm² $= 43.5$ cm²

23. d) an air vent through a cavity wall must be continually sleeved

24. c) the minimum distance to the first bend is 600 mm

25. b) the minimum distance is 25mm

26. d) single-skin vitreous enamel flue pipe is not suitable for external use

27. b) the minimum dimension should be 75mm

28. c) terminals less than 2m from ground level must be fitted with a terminal guard

29. b) the draught break should be at least 300mm above the insulation

30. d) a flue flow test is used to check on chimney suitability

31. c) a gas fire below 14 kW heat input must be fitted with an atmospheric sensing device

32. c) a slow ignition device minimises noisy ignition

33. b) a stability bracket is used to prevent overturning

34. d) an LPG boiler must not be sited in a basement

35. c) the appliance user instructions must be left with the customer as part of the handover procedure

Chapter 19 – Employment rights and responsibilities

Short answer questions

1. Race Relations Act

2. No employers are exempt

3. Statement of employment

4. Health and Safety at Work Act

5. There is no qualifying period for this

6. Direct; Indirect

7. 13 weeks' unpaid leave if in continuous employment for over 1 year

8. Doctor's certificate

9. Association of Plumbing and Heating Contractors

10. Unvented hot water systems; Water Regulations; Gas Accredited Certification Scheme (ACS)

Multiple-choice test

1. c) the regulations were introduced in 2003

2. d) apprentices under 19 are exempt from the National Minimum Wage

3. a) employers establish grievance procedures to deal with such disputes

4. b) access must be provided if employing more than five staff

5. d) the JIB for PMES sets the pay and conditions of plumbing operatives in England and Wales

6. a) an employee is entitled to holiday pay from the day s/he starts work

7. d) the statement of employment must be provided within two months of commencing work

8. b) a notice period of one week must be provided

9. c) four weeks is the minimum paid entitlement to holiday pay

10. d) an employment tribunal would hear a claim for unfair dismissal

Index